*Principles of* NUMERICAL TAXONOMY

A SERIES OF

BOOKS IN BIOLOGY

# PRINCIPLES OF
# NUMERICAL
# TAXONOMY

## ROBERT R. SOKAL

*The University of Kansas*

## PETER H. A. SNEATH

*Microbial Systematics Research Unit, University of
Leicester, England*

W. H. FREEMAN AND COMPANY

SAN FRANCISCO AND LONDON

261193

*We would stress the fact that, from the time of Linnaeus to our own,
a weak point in biological science has been the absence of any quantitative meaning in our classificatory terms. What is a Class, and
does Class A differ from Class B as much as Class C differs from
Class D? The question can be put for the other classificatory grades,
such as Order, Family, Genus, and Species. In no case can it be
answered fully, and in most cases it cannot be answered at all. . . .
Until some adequate reply can be given to such questions as these,
our classificatory schemes can never be satisfactory or "natural."
They can be little better than mnemonics—mere skeletons or frames
on which we hang somewhat disconnected fragments of knowledge.
Evolutionary doctrine, which has been at the back of all classificatory
systems of the last century, has provided no real answer to these difficulties. Geology has given a fragmentary answer here and there.
But to sketch the manner in which the various groups of living things
arose is a very different thing from ascribing any quantitative value
to those groups.*                                       *[Singer, 1959, p. 200.]*

# PREFACE

It is widely acknowledged that the science of taxonomy is one of the
most neglected disciplines in biology. Although new developments are
continually being made in techniques for studying living creatures, in
finding new characters, in describing new organisms, and in revising
the systematics of previously known organisms, little work has been
directed toward the conceptual basis of classification—that is, taxonomy
in the restricted sense of the theory of classification. Indeed, the taxonomy of today is but little advanced from that of a hundred, or even two
hundred, years ago. Biologists have amassed a wealth of material, both
of museum specimens and of new taxonomic characters, but they have
had little success in improving their power of digesting this material.
The practice of taxonomy has remained intuitive and commonly in-
articulate, an art rather than a science. And an uncritical attitude
toward some aspects of evolutionary theory has compounded the confusion.

In the last few years there has been increased awareness of the problems in the aims and practices of taxonomy. In particular, there has
been interest in the development of numerical methods in taxonomy as

an aid to making systematics a quantitative science, a step which comes in time to every scientific discipline.

Numerical taxonomy is the evaluation by numerical methods of the affinity or similarity between taxonomic units and the employment of these affinities in erecting a hierarchic order of taxa. The ideas on which numerical taxonomy rests go back to Adanson, a contemporary of Linnaeus, and have been repeatedly voiced. The present rapid development of these ideas is presumably a result of the development of computer techniques. Numerical taxonomy aims to develop methods which are objective and repeatable, both in evaluation of taxonomic affinity and in the erection of taxa. In addition, we believe that numerical methods may open up a wide field in the exact measurement of evolutionary rates and may provide a more critical approach to phylogenetic problems. It is worth noting that the success of the intuitive approach of the past lies in the ability of the mind to appreciate swiftly, though inexactly, overall similarity in morphological detail. This is not easy with data in tabular form, as with microbiological, chemical, or physiological data, which are now becoming so abundant; numerical methods are in these cases doubly necessary. The time now seems ripe to attempt a comprehensive treatment of these new advances.

It is the purpose of this book to present a firm theoretical basis for numerical taxonomy, to show why we believe numerical taxonomy has advantages over conventionally practiced taxonomy, to report on the various advances made in the field so far, and to furnish newcomers in the field with a detailed step-by-step description of the procedures employed in numerical taxonomy.

It is not our intention to treat at length all forms of numerical analysis which have been used in taxonomy for many special problems. There are numerous texts on the use of statistical and mathematical methods in biology, which can be consulted easily. We have therefore restricted the scope of this book to methods which are intended to demonstrate taxonomic relationships and to create taxonomic groupings, although some other techniques have been briefly treated for completeness. We have, however, attempted to make the treatment as broad as possible so as to be applicable to zoology, botany, microbiology, and paleontology, and other related sciences. This book is intended to serve practitioners in these sciences and will, we hope, invite them to look at their material in a new way. We hope also that students currently contemplating systematics as a career will wish to acquaint themselves with these methods and to evaluate their applicability to their own research.

In developing a theoretical foundation for numerical taxonomy we found it necessary to re-examine the theory of taxonomy as a whole, and we found much of the currently professed theory of phylogenetic systematics to be unsound and in need of critical re-evaluation. Of necessity, therefore, the book contains a critique of the methods and principles of phylogenetic systematics, in addition to a statement of our own views on numerical taxonomy.

Details on the use of this book are given in Chapter 1, "Introduction." The chapters dealing with the numerical methods will require a knowledge of statistics through correlation and regression. The rest of the book demands little or no mathematical background of the reader.

In preparing this book we have had the active assistance and encouragement of a number of colleagues. Professor Charles D. Michener of the University of Kansas has read and criticized the entire manuscript. He has been instrumental in much of the development of numerical taxonomy. Time and again he has pointed out weaknesses in our reasoning and has raised the problems of the practicing taxonomist relating to numerical taxonomy. Professor George W. Byers (University of Kansas) read the entire manuscript also and we are greatly indebted to him for his meticulous editorial care as well as his constructive criticism on many points. Portions of the book were read by Dr. W. T. Stearn (British Museum, Natural History), Dr. F. J. Rohlf (University of California, Santa Barbara), Professor Charles E. Leone (University of Kansas), and Professor H. Grüneberg, F.R.S., (University College, London). We are grateful for their valuable comments on their specialities.

An informal luncheon group of faculty and graduate students at the Entomology Department of the University of Kansas, "the Biosystematists," has had much to do with the origin of numerical taxonomy in America. The first ideas relating to this field were discussed by its members, and the manuscript for this book was read before this group and criticized by them. We are indebted to our colleagues and students in this group for many valuable suggestions and for helping us express our ideas more clearly than we might otherwise have done.

Preparation of this manuscript has involved the labors of many persons over a considerable period of time. Mr. Richard C. Rinkel and Mr. Anthony J. Boyce have helped in the preparation of the Appendix. A number of secretaries both in England and the United States have helped prepare the manuscript—our thanks go to Mrs. Elizabeth Ferrell, Mrs. Lois Harmon, Mrs. Maxine L. Howe, Miss Helen Lang-

Brown, Miss Barbara Mueller, Mrs. Dolores Vandermeer, and especially to Mrs. Betty Lou Deffley, who did the greatest part of the work. Mr. A. J. Lee of St. Albans, England, skillfully produced the figures from sketchy directions. Mr. Ivan Huber proofread the manuscript.

This book had its inception during the tenure of a Senior Postdoctoral Fellowship of the National Science Foundation (U.S.A.), which RRS spent at the Galton Laboratory, University College, London. Appreciation is expressed to Professor L. S. Penrose, F.R.S., head of the laboratory, for his cordial hospitality and encouragement.

The research leading to this book was financed by grants from the National Science Foundation (U.S.A.), the General Research Fund of the University of Kansas, and the Medical Research Council of Great Britain. We acknowledge gladly the encouragement of our work by our respective institutions, culminating in the preparation of this book. The authors, ordinarily domiciled on opposite sides of the Atlantic, were enabled to come together for completion of this work through a generous grant of the National Science Foundation.

We are indebted to Messrs. Abelard-Schuman Ltd., Publishers, for permission to cite a passage from C. Singer, *A History of Biology*. Other sources are acknowledged when used.

*Lawrence, Kansas*                         Robert R. Sokal
*March 1963*                            Peter H. A. Sneath

# CONTENTS

# A FLOW CHART OF NUMERICAL TAXONOMY

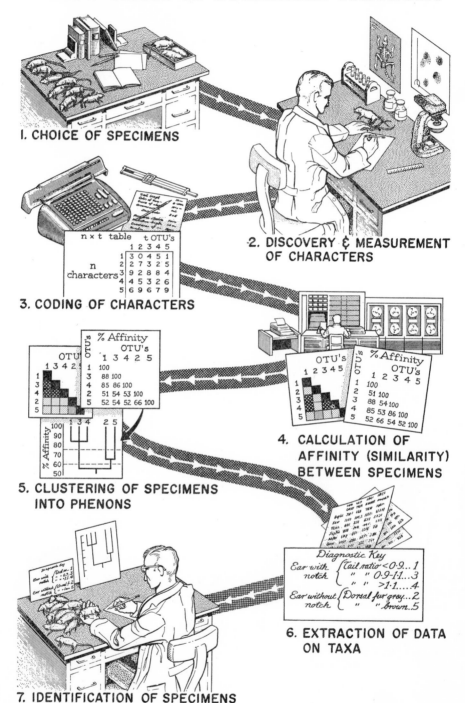

1. CHOICE OF SPECIMENS

2. DISCOVERY & MEASUREMENT OF CHARACTERS

3. CODING OF CHARACTERS

n × t table

|              |   | t OTU's |   |   |   |   |
|--------------|---|---------|---|---|---|---|
|              |   | 1       | 2 | 3 | 4 | 5 |
| n characters | 1 | 3       | 0 | 4 | 5 | 1 |
|              | 2 | 2       | 7 | 3 | 2 | 5 |
|              | 3 | 9       | 2 | 8 | 8 | 4 |
|              | 4 | 4       | 5 | 3 | 2 | 6 |
|              | 5 | 6       | 9 | 6 | 7 | 9 |

4. CALCULATION OF AFFINITY (SIMILARITY) BETWEEN SPECIMENS

% Affinity, OTU's

|   | 1 | 2 | 3 | 4 | 5 |
|---|---|---|---|---|---|
| 1 | 100 |   |   |   |   |
| 2 | 51 | 100 |   |   |   |
| 3 | 88 | 54 | 100 |   |   |
| 4 | 85 | 53 | 86 | 100 |   |
| 5 | 52 | 66 | 54 | 52 | 100 |

% Affinity, OTU's

|   | 1 | 3 | 4 | 2 | 5 |
|---|---|---|---|---|---|
| 1 | 100 |   |   |   |   |
| 3 | 88 | 100 |   |   |   |
| 4 | 85 | 86 | 100 |   |   |
| 2 | 51 | 54 | 53 | 100 |   |
| 5 | 52 | 54 | 52 | 66 | 100 |

5. CLUSTERING OF SPECIMENS INTO PHENONS

6. EXTRACTION OF DATA ON TAXA

Diagnostic Key

Ear with notch ⎰ Tail ratio < 0·9 ... 1
⎱ " " 0·9–1·1 ... 3
⎱ " " > 1·1 .... 4
Ear without notch ⎰ Dorsal fur grey ... 2
⎱ " " brown .. 5

7. IDENTIFICATION OF SPECIMENS

CHAPTER **1**

# Introduction

## 1.1. SUMMARY OF CONTENTS

The contents of this book fall into three main parts. The first part provides a background to the field of taxonomy in general and an introduction to numerical taxonomy in particular. In Chapter 2 we discuss in some detail the historical development of the conceptual basis of classification and our criticisms of current taxonomic practices. Chapter 3 treats various quantitative methods in taxonomy, other than those described in detail in subsequent chapters. This is followed in Chapter 4 by a discussion of the aims and principles of numerical taxonomy.

The central part of the book is arranged on a plan which closely reflects the successive steps followed by taxonomists, unconsciously for the most part, in performing the classificatory process. In Chapter 5 are discussed the choice of characters for numerical taxonomy, the coding of these characters for mathematical manipulation, and the selection of organisms for study. The estimation of taxonomic resemblance between organisms follows in Chapter 6. Chapter 7 considers the grouping of organisms into taxa on the basis of these resemblances.

The final part deals with the implications of numerical taxonomy for systematic research. We discuss the relation of numerical taxonomy to phylogeny and paleontology in Chapter 8 and to nomenclature and diagnostic keys in Chapter 9. Possible future developments and similar work in subjects other than the classification of living creatures are discussed in Chapter 10. An appendix has been added, in which details of the mathematical methods of numerical taxonomy are given, illustrated by elementary examples.

## 1.2. GUIDE TO THE USE OF THE BOOK

The summary of contents given above will itself serve as the most useful guide to the use of this book, but it may be well to emphasize a number of additional points. First, no critical systematist will employ a method of whose validity he is unconvinced. The justification for our standpoint is to be found particularly in Chapters 2 and 4; the former is mostly a criticism of current practices, and the latter is an attempt to construct logical alternatives to these. We would suggest that these chapters be read before embarking on the later ones; not only do they provide the justification for the methods, but there is also some danger in the unimaginative application of the procedures if the principles on which they are based have been imperfectly understood.

Second, the computational chapters will be most profitably read if reference is made to the pertinent examples in the Appendix, as indicated by the cross-references. The mathematical treatment has been made as simple as possible, and the examples should aid its painless assimilation. We have preferred to err on the side of prolixity in the interests of making the computations easily comprehensible, and only a slight knowledge of elementary mathematics and statistics is necessary.

Third, it should be emphasized that for any considerable body of data the assistance of computers is essential, not indeed because of the difficulty of the mathematical manipulations (for these can readily be performed with paper and pencil or desk calculators if only a few organisms are studied) but because with extensive data the analyses are too time-consuming to be practicable without computational aids. The Appendix therefore contains some notes on computer programs and the preparation of data for them.

## 1.3. DEFINITIONS OF CERTAIN TERMS

The adequate definition of taxonomic terms would almost require a book by itself. Many terms are used in so many different senses that we have had great difficulty in using them in a consistent and exact manner, and no doubt there are still a great many ambiguities which we have overlooked. The meanings of terms and symbols as they are used in this book can be looked up via the Index. There are, however, several which are employed so frequently that we have deemed it desirable to present them here at the outset.

Classification, systematics, and taxonomy are often used interchangeably. In recent years, especially in the United States, there has been a trend toward assigning separate meanings to these terms. In this sense they have been well defined by Simpson (1961) and we follow his usage here.

*Systematics.* ". . . *is the scientific study of the kinds and diversity of organisms and of any and all relationships among them*" (Simpson, 1961, p. 7). This definition uses systematics in its widest sense, concerning itself not only with the arrangement of organisms into taxa and with naming them, but also with the causes and origins of these arrangements.

*Classification.* We have adapted Simpson's definition (1961, p. 9), which restricted itself to zoological classification, to more general usage. *Classification is the ordering of organisms into groups (or sets) on the basis of their relationships, that is, of their associations by contiguity, similarity, or both.* We have restricted the definition above to organisms, since this book is primarily intended for the biological taxonomist. However, there are many methods of classification, including numerical taxonomy, which are equally applicable to concepts and entities other than organisms. Classification as defined above is the name of a process; however, it has also been used for the end product of this process. Thus the result of classification is a classification. The term classification has also been employed, mainly in fields outside biology, in the restricted sense of putting entities into distinct classes as opposed to arraying them in a continuous spectrum, cline, or other arrangement showing no distinct divisions. We have not restricted the term in this manner.

*Taxonomy.* ". . . *is the theoretical study of classification, including its bases, principles, procedures and rules*" (Simpson, 1961, p. 11). By this definition the bulk of the subject matter of our book is concerned with taxonomy, and for the same reason we have called our subject numerical taxonomy, rather than numerical systematics. Taxonomy, like classification, has also been used to designate the end products of the taxonomic process. Since this is a generally accepted usage, we will occasionally employ it in this sense.

There may be confusion over the term "relationship." This may imply relationship by ancestry (of which there are several kinds—see Section 8.1.2), or it may simply indicate the overall similarity as judged by the characters of the organisms without any implication as to their relationship by ancestry. For this meaning of overall similarity we have used the term "affinity," which was in common use in pre-Darwinian times. We may also distinguish this sort of relationship from relationship by ancestry by calling it *phenetic relationship*, employing the convenient term of H. K. Pusey as used by Cain and Harrison (1960b), to indicate that it is judged from the phenotype of the organism and not from its phylogeny.

We use the term *taxon* (plural *taxa*) as an abbreviation for taxonomic group of any nature or rank, as suggested by Lam (in Lanjouw, 1950) and Rickett (1958).

# CHAPTER 2

# A Critique of
# Current Taxonomy

## 2.1. THE ILLS OF MODERN TAXONOMY

Recent years have witnessed increasing dissatisfaction with the prin‚ ciples and practices of biological classification. New species are constantly being described and many new characters discovered in known species by modern studies in such fields as cytology, biochemistry, and behavior, as well as by more penetrating employment of traditional morphological methods. As our knowledge of the organic world increases there are continuing stresses and strains in the frame of the taxonomic system to accommodate these new discoveries, and the inadequacies of the present system become ever more apparent.

The thirties and forties of this century witnessed a considerable revision of our interpretation of evolutionary phenomena. Advances in genetics, cytology, and geographic variation had prepared the way for a "New Systematics," the advent of which might conveniently be dated with the appearance of Julian Huxley's book of the same name (1940). Considered *avant-garde* by taxonomists at first, this material slowly became assimilated, so that today terms such as cline, Rassenkreis, or gene pool are commonly used by most of them. However, a survey of the literature will soon make it apparent that most of the progress has been made at the species and infraspecies levels, and that there has in fact been little increase in our understanding of the nature and evolution of the higher categories. Books such as those by Rensch (1947), Schmalhausen (1949), and Simpson (1953) deal with this topic, but they contain little more than descriptive generalizations of it. The systematics of the higher categories, and indeed problems of classification in general, have not benefited particularly from the "New Systematics," which is in fact rather a poorly chosen term, since the subject concerns primarily infraspecific variation and mechanisms of speciation. A recent paper by Blackwelder (1962) discusses the failure of the "New Systematics" to provide an adequate basis for animal taxonomy.

During the last few years a number of publications have appeared which attempt a re-evaluation of the logical bases of taxonomy. This has involved a separation of the various functions which the science is trying to fulfill. Cain, in a series of papers (1956, 1958, 1959a,b,c; and see Cain and Harrison, 1960b), has performed this task admirably, and there have been similar independent contributions by Gilmour (1937, 1940, 1951, 1961b), Michener (1957), Michener and Sokal (1957), Sneath (1957a), Sokal (1960), and Sneath and Sokal (1962).

There is remarkable agreement among these various authors to the effect that the present system of taxonomy attempts to fulfill too many functions and as a consequence does none of them well. It attempts (1) to classify, (2) to name, (3) to indicate degree of resemblance (affinity), and (4) to show relationship by descent—all at the same time. We shall show in separate sections below that it is impossible not only in practice but also in theory for the current system to perform these tasks adequately. Section 2.2 will concern itself with the problems of the natural system; Section 2.3 will deal with the difficulties of assigning phylogenetic interpretations to expressions of phenetic resemblance.

It may be advantageous at this stage to outline an important logical fallacy underlying current taxonomic procedure. It is the self-reinforcing circular arguments used to establish categories, which on repeated application invest the latter with the appearance of possessing objective and definable reality. This type of reasoning is, of course, not restricted to taxonomy—but it is no less fallacious on that account. Let us illustrate this point. An investigator is faced with a group of similar species. He wishes to show relationships among the members of the group and is looking for characters which will subdivide it into several mutually exclusive taxa. A search for characters reveals that within a subgroup **A** certain characters appear constant, while varying in an uncorrelated manner in other subgroups. Hence a taxon **A** is described and defined on the basis of this character complex, say $X$. It is assumed that taxon **A** is a monophyletic or a "natural" taxon. Thus every member of **A** (both known and unknown forms) is expected to possess $X$; conversely, possession of the character complex $X$ defines **A**.

Henceforth group **A**, as defined by $X$, assumes a degree of permanence and reality quite out of keeping with the tentative basis on which it was established. Subsequently studied species are compared with **A** to establish their affinities; they may be within **A**, close to it, or far from it. It is quite possible that a species not showing $X$ would be excluded from **A**, although it was closer overall to most of the members of **A** than some were to each other. It may be said that such problems would arise only when **A** was an "artificial" group erected on the basis of "unsuitable" characters. However, except in long-established taxa or those separated by very wide gaps from their closest relatives, the effect of the last classification carried out with a limited number of characters is quite pervasive. The circular reasoning arises from the fact that new characters, instead of being evaluated on their own merits, are inevitably prejudiced by the prior erection of taxon **A** based on other characters ($X$). Such a prejudgment ignores the fact that the existence of **A** as a natural (or "monophyletic") group defined by character complex $X$ has been *assumed* but *not demonstrated*.

The taxonomist will recognize and define taxa on three kinds of evidence, which are not often clearly separated either in his mind or in publication. (1) Resemblance—those entities which phenetically resemble each other more than they do others form a taxon. (2) Homologous characters—a taxon is formed by entities sharing characters of common origin. (3) Common line of descent—membership in a common line of descent will define a taxon. Since (3) is rarely if ever known, it is usually inferred from (1) or (2). Conclusions on homologies (evidence of type 2) are often deduced from phylogenetic speculations (evidence of type 3). Thus taxonomists often reason facilely back and forth among these criteria without stopping to think how slender the evidence is on which their arguments are based. Their sound knowledge is usually restricted to an estimate of resemblance of a number of organisms without any knowledge of phylogeny and hence the common origin of their characters. Their estimates are usually based on few characters and thus do not reflect the overall similarity which could be obtained when more of the phenotype is considered. Once it is looked at critically, it becomes evident how much of taxonomic procedure is circular reasoning and extrapolation.

Phylogenetic interpretations of systematic relationships have remained in fashion ever since Haeckel. Modern emphasis on the "New Systematics" has attempted to embellish such conclusions with speculations on the evolutionary mechanisms likely to have brought about the supposed systematic relationships under study. The authors are familiar with practices in several university departments where "plain" taxonomic theses are not welcomed or recognized for the Ph.D. degree and where a discussion of phylogeny and evolutionary principles illustrated by the revised taxon is mandatory. In the absence of experimental and fossil evidence such accounts are usually purely speculative and involve much tortuous dialectic. It seems to us rather absurd to indulge in speculations of this sort when for most groups the basic facts of phenetic resemblance are still to be obtained. There is, of course, no harm in speculation per se. The points we wish to make are that phylogenetic speculations should not be involved in the classificatory process and that any such speculations should be based upon a sound phenetic classification.

It is current practice to employ only homologous characters in creating taxonomic groups (the word is used here in the sense of characters having a common ancestral origin). The aim of this practice is to create only phyletic groups, not phenetic ones, since phenetic resemblance is based on all characters, including convergent ones. We are therefore faced by the question of which kind of classification we wish to make. Whatever our wishes, a number of points are clear. First, at the infraspecific level it is often impossible to decide if a feature is homologous. For example, the independent occurrences of repeated albino mutations in a species, as in mice, are not homologous in the sense used above (though the *tendency for such mutations to occur* may be homologous if it is an inherited tendency of the species). Second, in major phyla there is seldom any doubt about whether most character complexes are homologous, taken as a whole. In the intermediate ranks these decisions are especially difficult to make. Third, it is doubtful if taxonomists are in practice prepared to make decisions on the homologies of the thousands of characters which the organisms possess. We may conclude that as a general principle restricting classification to using homologous characters only is not feasible even if it were always desirable. This is doubly true when we consider how confused the concept of homology has become (see Lam, 1959).

Giving different weight to different characters according to their presumed importance is still orthodox teaching today. We believe that such weighting is unsound, and it will be discussed at length in Section 5.7.

An undesirable procedure of taxonomy, amounting to improper weighting, is the way in which certain characters will be used to differentiate the species of one genus, while being ignored in the next genus.

This is not necessarily because the character has been found unsatisfactory. The resulting harm to taxonomy is far-reaching. Not only is the diagnostic value of the character diminished, but it carries the danger that such arbitrariness may yield arbitrary and artificial taxa. The practical need for simple methods of identification, generally by means of diagnostic keys, has also had an undesirable influence on methods of classification; prominent single characters are valuable for such keys, and hence they have commonly been unconsciously assumed to be very important for creating the taxa.

In discussing the ills of modern systematics, mention must be made of several other contributing factors. It is discouraging to see how fragmented the study of systematics has become. In many biological disciplines there is an unconscious arrogance which assumes that the methods and definitions of other disciplines are useless or misleading. Few zoologists discuss whether their systematic principles can be applied to botany, since for them taxonomy is zoological taxonomy, and if the zoological concepts do not fit plants this is of no interest. The reverse view is held by some botanists. The term species is employed almost exclusively for a genetic concept applicable only to sexually reproducing populations; its protagonists often seem to consider other creatures too aberrant to be worthy of serious taxonomic study. Very few writers have shown much appreciation of the scope of systematics, though some (for example Blackwelder and Boyden, 1952) have emphasized that it is a discipline central to all biology. In fact its basic concepts are not restricted to biology, for they are applicable to many other disciplines (see Section 10.6).

Contemporary taxonomy, while progressive in the establishment and revision of taxa, is decidedly conservative in its practices and philosophy. Published systematic work at the generic level and above is little different from that at the turn of the century. We have already examined one reason for this—the lack of a "new systematics" for the higher categories. A second, equally important cause, which for reasons of tact is rarely discussed, is the inadequate training and background of so many taxonomists. It is surely a reflection on the state of the science that the description and classification of organisms is today one of the few fields of biology to which amateurs without sound theoretical and practical training are still able to contribute. We do not wish to disparage the efforts of these amateurs, some of whom have made valuable contributions to biology in the past. Yet in taxonomy the bad work of both professional and amateur cannot be as readily ignored as it would be in other sci-

ences, because of the rules of priority and synonymy. As more sophisticated ideas and techniques percolate through systematics, amateurs not
trained in modern taxonomy will of necessity find their sphere of activity
progressively more circumscribed. It may be argued that amateurs
will still be needed for purely descriptive (so-called *alpha*) taxonomy.
However, as the methods of synthetic taxonomy become more elaborate
the proper collection of data will become more involved, whether the
trend of systematic research is in the biochemical or the biostatistical
direction.

Militating against progress in taxonomy is the deplorable fact that
success and prestige in biology seem to be largely associated with experimental work in fields such as genetics, biochemistry, or radiation biology.
Hence the best brains and the best facilities in biological institutions
(with a few exceptions) are not devoted to systematic work. This state
of affairs is reflected in the dearth of systematists in the most prestigious
academies. It may be that taxonomists are too overwhelmed with the
sheer bulk of the material confronting them that still requires description
and classification to have the time to work on a theory of taxonomy.
However, we hardly feel that this is a case where *tout comprendre, c'est
tout pardonner*. Without stopping to examine the cause-and-effect relationships involved, we may summarize this portion of our comments by
stating that taxonomy (at least of the higher categories) has become in
some ways a straggler in the progress of biological science.

Another deplorable feature of systematic research is the involvement
of personal feelings in nomenclatural procedures. While some subjective
bias of this sort is present in almost any science, taxonomy, alas, has
more than its proper share. The problems that exist in this connection
have been often discussed and are well known to systematists. Indeed,
some notable improvements in their attitudes concerning this matter
have taken place in recent years. Suffice it here to say that the prospects
of gaining fame or notoriety (of however illusory a nature) by the naming
or renaming of a category involve personal and subjective considerations which should be alien to scientific procedures.

One may ask how it is that taxonomists using such questionable methods have developed a body of knowledge which is admittedly useful and
in certain groups consistent to a high degree? While the facts of the case
are beyond dispute, its causes bear further examination.

The majority of taxa are definable because of the discontinuities arising in phyletic lines as by-products of the evolutionary process. (This
point is discussed in greater detail in Chapter 8.) Relationships are recog-

of monothetic groups is that they do not yield "natural" taxa, except by a lucky choice of the feature used for division. The advantage of monothetic groups is that keys and hierarchies are readily made.

A polythetic arrangement, on the other hand, places together organisms that have the greatest number of shared features, and no single feature is either essential to group membership or is sufficient to make an organism a member of the group. This concept was stated many years ago (for example, by Jevons, 1877, pp. 682–698). For its formal expression we cannot do better than to quote Beckner's definition (1959, p. 22):

> A class is ordinarily defined by reference to a set of properties which are both necessary and sufficient (by stipulation) for membership in the class. It is possible, however, to define a group $K$ in terms of a set $G$ of properties $f_1, f_2, \cdots, f_n$ in a different manner. Suppose we have an aggregation of individuals (we shall not as yet call them a class) such that:
>
> 1) Each one possesses a large (but unspecified) number of the properties in $G$.
> 2) Each $f$ in $G$ is possessed by large numbers of these individuals and
> 3) No $f$ in $G$ is possessed by every individual in the aggregate.
>
> By the terms of (3), no $f$ is necessary for membership in this aggregate; and nothing has been said to either warrant or rule out the possibility that some $f$ in $G$ is sufficient for membership in the aggregate.

He then goes on to say that a class is polythetic if the first two conditions are fulfilled and is fully polythetic if condition (3) is also fulfilled. He points out that taxonomic groups are polythetic classes, but that polythetic concepts are by no means restricted to taxonomy or even to biology, for Wittgenstein emphasized their importance in ordinary language and especially in philosophy—the concepts of "meaning," "referring," "description," and so on. There is a close parallel between Wittgenstein's "family resemblance" and taxonomic affinity. As we have noted above, natural taxa are usually not fully polythetic, since one can usually find some characters common to all members of a taxon. It is possible that they are never fully polythetic because there may be some characters (or genes) which are identical in all members of a given taxon; even if there are many alleles or pseudoalleles of a gene, there may well be parts of the gene which are identical in all members. Nevertheless, we must regard a taxon operationally as being possibly fully polythetic, since we cannot be sure that we have observed any characters that are common to all members.

Beckner points out also the importance of condition (2). If, for exam-

nized and organisms are more or less correctly classified because taxonomy, like other sciences, is self-correcting, proceeding in a manner analogous to iteration in numerical analysis. A wrong initial evaluation of a set of characters $A$ by taxonomist **X** is modified by further consideration of characters $B$ by taxonomist **Y**, followed by taxonomist **Z** studying characters $C$. In this manner, as a natural and logical consequence of the taxonomic procedure, more and more characters are being considered and a given single character or set of characters assumes progressively less importance. Consequently misevaluations and wrong classificatory judgments are amended by subsequent work. Time, expressed through the activities of successive taxonomists, becomes an equalizer of character weight. This self-correcting nature of taxonomy is an extremely important feature and justifies to a large degree the dependence of the worker in the field on prior studies.

However, taxonomic statements at a given time may be strongly biased by the last revision of the taxa concerned. Should the revision be carried out with less than usual care and competence, considerable confusion may pervade the system for a long period. Many times the results of a study cannot be confirmed independently because of the inaccessability of material or the lack of personnel or for both these reasons. Thus the baneful effect of poor taxonomic work may be protracted and far-reaching. It is for this reason that Michener and Sokal (1957) wrote:

> Taxonomy, more than most other sciences, is affected by subjective opinions of its practitioners. Except for the judgment of his colleagues there is virtually no defense against the poor taxonomist. Above the species level there are no experiments that can be repeated and shown invalid, no mathematical or symbolic reasoning that can be demonstrated to be in error.

It is the hope of numerical taxonomy to arrive at judgments of affinity based on multiple and unweighted characters without the time and controversy which seem necessary at present for the maturation of taxonomic judgments.

## 2.2. THE NATURAL SYSTEM

Great difficulties have always accompanied attempts at defining a natural system. Danser (1950) realizes the difficulty of defining natural groups but is not able to state any exact or scientific definition for them, ending with the hope that ". . . some day systematics will arrive at a more exact stage, but this does not alter the fact that already now we are entitled to face its problems, be it for the moment in a more intuitive but nevertheless scientific manner." Simpson (1961, p. 57) agrees that "in fact much of the theoretical discussion in the history of taxonomy has, beneath its impersonal language and objective façade, been an attempt to find some theoretical basis for these personal and subjective results."

The nature of a taxonomy depends on its purpose, as Gilmour (1937, 1940, 1951, 1961b) has emphasized. We could arrange living creatures in many ways, but we choose one way because we think it is best for some purpose. If the purpose is restricted, then the classification is a special classification, often called "arbitrary." Such a classification conveys less information than a general or "natural" one. For example, we can divide mammals into carnivores and herbivores for the purpose of ecology; then the designation "carnivore" only tells us the kind of food they eat. We hold the view with Gilmour that a "natural" taxonomy is a general arrangement intended for general use by all scientists.

The earliest attempt at systematics were based, as Cain (1958) has shown, on Aristotelian logic. This was the method used by early systematists such as Cesalpino and even largely by Linnaeus. The Aristotelian system as applied to taxonomy consisted in the attempt to discover and define the *essence* of a taxonomic group (what we may somewhat loosely think of as its "real nature" or "what makes the thing what it is"). In logic this essence gives rise to properties which are inevitable consequences: for example, the essence of a triangle on a plane surface is expressed by its definition as a figure bounded by three straight sides, and an inevitable consequence is that any two sides are together longer than the third. Such logical systems are known as systems of *analyzed entities*, and early systematists supposed that biological classifications could be of this kind. The terms *genus* and *species* had technical meanings in logic, and these were taken over into taxonomy. These points are well discussed by Thompson (1952) and Cain (1958, 1962). Aristotelian logic does not, however, lend itself to biological taxonomy, which is a system of *unanalyzed entities*, whose properties cannot be inferred from the definitions—at least not if the taxonomy is to be a natural one.

It is to the credit of John Ray and Caspar Bauhin that they were less bound by the iron fetters of Aristotelian logic than other early workers. They had a strong intuitive sense of what natural taxa were, although

they did not express themselves clearly. This is what de Candolle (1813, p. 66) aptly called "groping" (*tâtonnement*), though he only attributes this to later authors such as Magnol. According to de Candolle, Magnol claimed to have a clear idea of a natural family of plants even though he could not point to any one character which was diagnostic of the family.

This comment by Magnol and a similar comment by Ray (quoted by Cain, 1959c) were among the first admissions that it might not be possible to find *any* single diagnostic character for a natural taxonomic group. This is a point of the very greatest importance, which can scarcely be overemphasized. Michener (1957) supports this view for genera; others, among them Sneath (1957a), state that it is also true of natural taxa of *any* rank. While "artificial" or "arbitrary" taxa can indeed be defined by a single character, this is not necessarily true of natural taxa. Every systematist knows of instances where a character previously considered to be diagnostic of a taxon is lacking in a newly discovered organism which clearly belongs to the taxon. A striking example is the lack in some species of fish of red blood corpuscles (Ruud, 1954), hitherto considered to be an invariable attribute of all vertebrates. Fortunately, as Michener (1957) says, natural taxa generally do possess some distinctive characters in practice, although they need not do so in theory.

Biologists owe a debt of gratitude to Beckner (1959) for the first clear enunciation known to us of one important concept of natural taxa, a concept which Beckner calls "polytypic." Since this term and its converse, "monotypic," have meanings already well established in systematics, Sneath (1962) has suggested that "polythetic" and "monothetic" are better names (from *poly:* "many," *mono:* "one," *thetos:* "arrangement.") Simpson (1961, pp. 41–57) has given a discussion of the implications of these concepts in taxonomy.

The ruling idea of monothetic groups is that they are formed by rigid and successive logical divisions so that the possession of a unique set of features is both sufficient and necessary for membership in the group thus defined. They are called monothetic because the defining set of features is unique. Any monothetic system (such as that of Maccacaro, 1958, or in ecology that of Williams and Lambert, 1959) will always carry the risk of serious misclassification if we wish to make natural phenetic groups. This is because an organism which happens to be aberrant in the feature used to make the primary division will inevitably be moved to a category far from the required position, even if it is identical with its natural congeners in every other feature. The disadvantage

ple, the various $f$'s are found in only one individual of the aggregate, then each individual will possess a unique subset of the $f$'s and will share no $f$'s with any other individual. Such a situation does not yield a polythetic class: for example, individuals 1, 2, 3, and 4, with the respective $f$'s ABC, DEF, GHI, and JKL, do not form a polythetic class. If, however, individual 1 possesses ABC, individual 2 possesses BCD, individual 3 possesses ABD, and individual 4 possesses ACD, the class of $1 + 2 + 3 + 4$ is polythetic (and in this instance is also fully polythetic, since no one character is found in all the four individuals). This may be seen in an arrangement such as this one:

Individuals

| | 1 | 2 | 3 | 4 | 5 | 6 |
|---|---|---|---|---|---|---|
| | A | | A | A | | |
| | B | B | B | | | |
| | C | C | | C | | |
| Characters | | D | D | D | | |
| | | | | | F | F |
| | | | | | G | G |
| | | | | | H | H |

Individuals 5 and 6, however, form a monothetic group.

One of the difficulties of Beckner's definition is that in natural taxa we do commonly have $f$'s which are not possessed by large numbers of the class. Furthermore, we cannot test whether any given $f$ is possessed by large numbers of the class before we have made the class, and therefore we cannot decide whether to admit this $f$ into the set $G$. This difficulty can be avoided by defining class membership in terms of common (or shared) attributes. Polythetic groups can of course themselves be arranged polythetically to give higher polythetic groups, as is done in building a hierarchy in the natural system. The advantages of polythetic groups are that they are "natural," have a high content of information, and are useful for many purposes. Their disadvantages are that they may partly overlap one another (so that hierarchies and keys are less easy to make than with monothetic groups) and that they are not perfectly suited for any single purpose.

An important practical difference between "classification from below" (the grouping of species into genera, genera into tribes, tribes into families, and so on) and "classification from above" (the division of the kingdoms into phyla, phyla into classes, and so on) is that the latter

process is inevitably largely monothetic. Classification from above therefore carries the risk that the divisions do not give "natural" taxa, yet
it is necessary in practice in order to isolate a group of organisms of a
manageable size for study. The important point is that a group under
study may be incomplete or very heterogeneous; that is, some of its
closest relatives may have been omitted, either through ignorance or
because the forms have been misclassified.

A thorough early re-evaluation of systematics was made by Adanson
(1727–1806), a botanist of independent and original views. His experi-
ences in Senegal, where he found many new forms which would not fit
into the then current taxonomic system, led him to seek the true basis
of a natural classification. This he claimed to have found. He rejected
the a priori assumptions on the importance of different characters (which
were a consequence of Aristotelian logic); he correctly realized that
natural taxa are based on the concept of "affinity"—which is measured
by taking all characters into consideration—and that the taxa are separated from each other by means of correlated features (Adanson, 1763,
pp. clv, clxiv). The method he used was very cumbersome. He made a
number of separate classifications, each based on one character, and
examined them to find which classifications divided up the creatures in
the same way. These classifications he took as indicating the most natural
divisions, which were, of course, therefore based on the maximum correlations among the characters. The important corollary was that by treating every character in the same way he was in effect giving them equal
weight. His contemporaries attacked him on this very point (see de
Candolle, 1813, pp. 70–72), without realizing that their own beliefs on
the relative importance of various characters, far from being based on
a priori assumptions as they imagined, were in fact a posteriori deductions from intuitive taxonomies of precisely the kind Adanson was recommending (Sneath, 1957a; Cain, 1959a,b). This is an example of the
self-correcting nature of intuitive taxonomy (see Section 2.1). Adanson's
earliest work in this direction was on molluscs. In his treatment of this
group, in *Histoire naturelle du Sénégal*, he says that since the previous arbitrary systems are unsatisfactory he will use a different method, first
drawing up careful descriptions of all parts of the shell and of the body
of the mollusc. He then makes the following observation (1757, p. xi):

Je me contenterai de rapprocher les objets suivant le plus grand nombre
des degrés de leurs rapports & de leurs ressemblances . . . Ces objets
ainsi réunis, formeront plusiers petites familles que je réunirai encore

ensemble, afin d'en faire un tout dont les parties soient unies & liées intimement.

He gave a number of tables in which the molluscs were arranged according to a score or so of characters (Preface, pp. xxix–lxxxxviii), which foreshadowed the more elaborate tables in his botanical work of 1763. He was already aware that one could not choose diagnostic characters of genera while they were incompletely known, since new species might prove to be exceptional (Adanson, 1757, Pref., p. xx), a point which was also realized by Linnaeus. No other workers, except perhaps Vicq-d'Azyr (1792) and Whewell (1840) seem to have followed up Adanson's ideas until recently.

Vicq-d'Azyr clearly enunciates Adanson's principles (though without mentioning him) in the introduction to his work on comparative anatomy. He says that a natural class is the result of assembling species which have a greater number of resemblances to each other than they have to species in other classes, and continues ". . . d'où il résulte qu'il seroit possible qu'une class fût trés-naturelle, et qu'il n'y eût pas un seul caractère commun à toutes les espèces qui la composent." Whewell's idea of taxonomic affinity was evidently close to Adanson's, since he makes the point that natural classes must possess many correlated common features, although he repeats de Candolle's criticisms of equal weighting.

We may ask why Adanson's method, though excellent in theory, was a failure in practice. Stearn (1961) considers that the material available in Adanson's day was too limited to allow of success, and we may add that such methods were quite impracticable before the advent of computing machines. Nevertheless, as de Candolle admitted, Adanson's taxa were for the most part more natural than earlier arrangements.

In the pre-evolutionary days of systematics it had been found empirically that a nested, hierarchical system gave the most satisfactory and "natural" arrangement of the data. Such a system could generally be constructed on the basis of a few characters. The art of the practice lay in finding suitable characters, to prevent the classification from creating strange bedfellows, clearly incongruous as judged by their great differences in other characteristics. There was little attempt either to understand why this should happen or to discover the rational method of choosing the "right" characters. We discuss below the development of the understanding of what it is which makes taxonomic groups "natural" and how it is possible *after creating such natural taxa* to discover characters which are suitable for discriminating between them. Even at the time of Adanson the system must have been inadequate, since it did not provide for an effective evaluation of resemblance among the various forms. It is true that an approximate idea could be obtained from the classificatory scheme, since members of the same genus were more likely to resemble one another than were members of different genera. However, without an unmanageable proliferation of taxonomic categories, which were in any event of dubious validity at that time, the fine shades of difference and resemblance could not be shown.

Until the impact of the theory of evolution, the subsequent development of systematics took place largely in France (de Candolle, A. L. de Jussieu, Cuvier, and Lamarck) and was in the direction of greater sophistication on the theme of the coordination of characters into a harmonious whole. This was carried even to the point of implying that a whole animal could be reconstructed from one bone. One can, of course, identify a known animal from one bone, but to reconstruct from it a new animal with all its soft parts is a feat of a different order, as Simpson (1961, p. 44) points out.

The advent of the theory of evolution changed the practice of systematics very little, although the professed philosophical basis of systematics was radically altered. Natural classifications were considered to be those established on the basis of monophyletic taxa. (This whole question is discussed in detail in Section 2.3.)

The present century has witnessed a re-examination of the validity of the evolutionary basis of natural taxonomies. Empirical classifications have been proposed in several quarters. The conceptual basis of natural taxonomies was discussed from the standpoint of logic in a classic paper by Gilmour (1937) and expanded in later works (Gilmour, 1940, 1951, 1961b). He pointed out that logicians have long realized that the central idea underlying "natural" groupings is the great usefulness of a method which can group together entities in such a way that members of a group possess many attributes in common. Indeed, we maintain that the elusive property of naturalness is simply the degree to which this principle obtains. The idea of overall similarity follows from this and is a function of the proportion of attributes shared by two entities. As Gilmour points out, natural classifications are not restricted to biological ones (see Section 10.6). In addition, intermediate situations can occur between the highly natural (such as the class Mammalia) and the wholly artificial (such as creatures whose generic names begin with the letter "A"). An example of a partly natural group is the group which gardeners call "Alpines."

The reason for the great usefulness of natural classifications is that when the members of a group share many correlated attributes, the "implied information" or "content of information" (Sneath, 1957a) is high; this amounts to Gilmour's dictum, that a system of classification is the more natural the more propositions there are that can be made regarding its constituent classes. Remane (1956, p. 4) tries to show that the predictive value of taxonomic groups is only true of natural taxa, not of artificial ones. It is obvious that artificial groups established on a single character are of low predictive value. Nevertheless, such groups may by chance prove to be partly natural, since such a single character may be highly correlated with the other characters of the taxa in question. It would be possible to devise a measure of the extent to which this is true of any character in any given taxonomic system. The techniques of Rescigno and Maccacaro (1960) are steps in this direction. A natural classification can be used for a great variety of purposes, while an artificial one serves only the limited purpose for which it was constructed. As Sneath has emphasized (1958), natural or "general" classifications can never be perfect for all purposes, since this is a consequence of the way we make natural groupings. By putting together entities with the highest proportion of shared attributes, we debar ourselves from insisting that they shall share any particular attribute, as a very simple trial would show. This is the reason for emphasizing the historical importance of the realization that natural taxa do not necessarily possess any single specified feature. This spelled the doom of the Aristotelian concept of an *essence* of a taxon, for natural groups are in logic *unanalyzed entities* (see Cain, 1958). Simpson (1961) rejects as illogical the contention by Gilmour (1951) that a classification serving a large number of purposes will be more natural than one which is more specialized and that the most useful and generally applicable classification will be the most natural one. We feel that Gilmour's usage corresponds to the intuitive sense of naturalness which taxonomists have possessed since even before Darwin. Gilmour's dictum—that a system of classification is the more natural the more propositions there are that can be made regarding its constituent classes—admits of objective measurement and testing, in contradistinction to Simpson's natural system. Furthermore, Gilmour's system has powerful predictive properties; it is therefore to be recommended. We believe that it will eventually be shown that, with few exceptions, monophyletic taxa will also be most natural in the sense of Gilmour and that therefore the two concepts will emerge as substantially identical. If this is so, phylogenetic conclusions may eventually be drawn from a demonstration of naturalness, *sensu* Gilmour.

## 2.3. PHYLOGENETIC CONSIDERATIONS

We have seen in the previous section how the pre-Darwinian biologists interpreted a natural system. With the publication of the *Origin of Species*, however, the entire problem was viewed from a different perspective. Suddenly the reason for the existence of natural systematic categories became apparent: *their members were related because of descent from a common ancestor!* A taxon was now interpreted as a monophyletic array of related forms.

Science always receives a new impetus when a well-known and ordered body of facts can be given meaning by a new, consistent hypothesis. The present instance was no exception, and under the influence of the evolutionists, led by Haeckel, the fields of systematics and comparative morphology were reoriented phylogenetically. It has, however, been frequently pointed out (as by Bather, 1927, and Remane, 1956) that this change of philosophy did not bring with it a change in method. Taxonomy proceeded as before; only its terminology had changed. Remane (1956) quotes Naef (1919, pp. 35–36):

> . . . und was Haeckel und die Phylogenetiker zunächst getan haben, war nichts anderes als die Übersetzungen der speziellen Einsichten, die sich an diese Lehre früher geknüpft hatten, in eine Sprache durch Anwendung einer neuen Terminologie, ohne doch die Lehre selbst einer Vertiefung zuzuführen oder einer kritischen Betrachtung zu unterwerfen. Auch die—wenig abgeklärten—Grundbegriffe der alten Morphologie wurden von Haeckel einfach in die neue Sprache übersetzt, die dem Wesen nach eine genealogische war. Dabei wurde dann

| | |
|---|---|
| aus Systematik | Phylogenetik, |
| aus Formverwandtschaft | Blutsverwandtschaft, |
| aus Metamorphose | Stammesentwicklung, |
| aus systematischen Stufenreihen | Ahnenreihen, |
| aus Typus | Stammform, |
| aus typischen Zuständen | ursprüngliche, |
| aus atypischen | abgeänderte, |
| aus niederen Tieren | primitive, |
| aus atypischer Ähnlichkeit | Konvergenz, |
| aus Ableitung | Abstammung usw. usw. |

It is also noteworthy that T. H. Huxley, writing at the height of his protagonism of Darwin's evolutionary theory, was perceptive enough to avoid confusing phylogeny with classification (Huxley, 1869).

The difficulty with the use of a phylogenetic approach in systematics emerged after the first wave of enthusiasm for it had subsided and has remained apparent to perceptive observers ever since. *We cannot make use of phylogeny for classification, since in the vast majority of cases phylogenies are unknown.* This is one of the statements most commonly heard at meetings of taxonomists, yet it is most consistently ignored. Let us restate it in other words for emphasis. The theoretical principle of descent with modification—phylogenetics—is clearly responsible for the existence and structure of a natural system of classification; we may even agree with Tschulok (1922) that the natural system can be considered as proof of the theory of evolution. However, since we have only an infinitesimal portion of phylogenetic history in the fossil record, it is almost impossible to establish natural taxa on a phylogenetic basis. Conversely, it is unsound to derive a definitive phylogeny from a tentative natural classification. We have described this fallacy of circular reasoning earlier.

In recent years three comprehensive analytical studies of systematic principles have been published in books by Hennig (1950), Remane (1956), and Simpson (1961). It is especially regrettable that the earlier two books, published in German, have been almost entirely ignored in the English and American literature. Hennig's book presents the issues with particular clarity and objectivity, and there is considerable truth in Kiriakoff's (1959) statement that a number of controversies of the last decade published in the United States are in a sense outdated and could have been guided into more productive channels if Hennig's thoughts had been available to the disputants.

All three authors mentioned above are fully aware of the dilemma of circular reasoning inherent in systematic procedure. They are not satisfied with solutions based on "groping." Simpson (1961) thinks that taxonomy is an evolutionary science, and he attempts to outline a series of phylogenetic principles on the basis of which taxonomic evidence should be examined to yield evolutionary interpretations and classifications. We shall examine these principles in detail later in Chapter 8. However, Simpson nowhere in his book is able to present a logical and consistent defense for the circularity of reasoning inherent in such procedures. By calling the process of classification an art, rather than a science, he defines the problem out of existence.

Hennig (1950) describes the dilemma in even greater detail. He defends the circularity of reasoning by the "method of reciprocal illumination." By this he means that some light is thrown from one source of logical illumination onto a natural situation, kindling another, brighter light in the latter, which in turn will throw added illumination onto the first source. Thus, in a self-reinforcing, positive feedback type of analysis, the relationships under study are eventually clarified. Hennig feels that phylogenetic relationships are the entity of systematics whose parts consist of morphological, ecological, physiological, and zoogeographic similarities. Each of these parts mirrors phylogenetic relationships, which are to be investigated by the method of reciprocal illumination. But we cannot see how the principle of reciprocal illumination differs from the much-condemned vertical construction of hypothesis upon hypothesis.

Remane (1956), in spite of his fundamentally phylogenetic orientation, has also realized that phylogenetic reasoning cannot serve as the basis for erecting a natural system. He similarly rejects affinity (based on few characters) as the basis of a natural system. He considers that while both of these approaches enter on occasion into the techniques practiced by "good systematists," the exclusive application of only one of them is likely to lead to misclassification. Affinity or resemblance when based on one or few characters can lead the systematist astray, Remane claims, as he would be too easily deceived by chance convergences resulting from poor sampling of the characters. Remane attempts escape from the *circulus vitiosus* by basing his taxonomy on nonphylogenetic criteria of homology.

In spite of the differences in fundamental outlook among these three authors, their actual approach to classification is quite similar and is akin to that employed by the majority of competent taxonomists today (or 100 years ago, for that matter). The procedure is difficult to define and delineate; attempts to do so of necessity illuminate the faults of the system. The method will often lead to roughly correct (that is, reasonable) results because of happily correct intuition or the self-correcting features of the classificatory process already discussed.

The basis of the classical method of establishing taxa is commonly held to be the recognition of homologies. Similarly, the recognition of analogies will serve to separate artificial taxa. Success in distinguishing homologies from analogies will therefore reflect success in systematics. In determining which characters are homologous (of common descent) and which have been independently evolved, the systematist has to express a judgment on the relative probability of the independent origin of different character complexes. Sometimes, as in color patterns, knowledge of the genetics of the character in the forms (or in related forms) may be invoked. More often the worker has to weigh independently the relative improbabilities of various phenetic rearrangements in order to arrive at a working hypothesis. Thus, indigo (as a glycoside) must be of independent origin in such widely scattered families of plants as Leguminosae, Cruciferae, Acanthaceae, Orchidaceae, and Polygonaceae. This seems overwhelmingly more probable than that these taxa together form a natural phenetic and monophyletic taxon—the family "Indigoaceae." Luminescence has presumably arisen repeatedly and independently in algae, bacteria, fungi, crustacea, insects, myriapods, tunicates, coelenterates, annelids, molluscs, and fishes, with apparently very similar biochemical mechanisms in each case so far examined. Chlorophyll in bacteria has presumably arisen independently of chlorophyll in higher plants, and hemoglobin has arisen in annelids, molluscs, crustacea, and insects as well as in vertebrates. Entomologists have decided that social organization arose independently in the termites, bees, wasps, and ants, and evidence is accumulating that it arose independently several times in the bees. Social parasitism in bees and slave-making in ants appear to have arisen independently a number of times. But the occurrence of symbiotic flagellates in the guts of termites and the roach *Cryptocercus* appears to be traceable to an ancestor carrying such flagellates. Even judgments of this kind rely heavily on estimates of similarity between the organisms or structures concerned.

Classifications are only as good as the homologies of the characters on which they are based. Furthermore, decisions on homologies of certain characters are based upon the validity of the classification of the groups involved in the argument; this classification in turn is based upon homologies of other characters used to establish the classification *ab initio*. When the circular arguments are interrupted we are left with much uncertainty. We feel therefore that the operational homology of Adansonian taxonomy involving fewer assumptions (see Section 5.3.4) is to be preferred to the classical methods.

Further difficulties are presented by cases of convergence—that is, by the resemblances of certain subordinate taxonomic groups in *different* higher taxa. If no account is taken of this convergence and the classification is based on descent alone, the biologist inspecting the nomenclature or a family tree of the group will have no idea of the phenetic closeness of the taxa concerned. Such resemblance, while considered "superficial" by the phylogeneticist, should not be lightly dismissed. It does represent important genetic changes and presumably important physiological and ecological similarity. But if the resemblance of the two groups is considered in establishing the classification, erroneous conclusions may be reached about common ancestry or recency of separation of the stems.

As soon as phylogenetic considerations were added to systematics, three new questions arose. What are the phylogenetic relationships, or which stem branched off where? When in geological or relative evolutionary time did a given branching take place? How rapid was the evolutionary rate of a given line in a given time period? Classificatory theory and procedure, already inadequate, could not simultaneously accommodate these differing aspects of the problem.

The first of the new questions raised was emphasized the most. Undoubtedly more utter rubbish has been written since the time of Haeckel on supposed phylogenies than on any other biological topic. The fact is that we have a reasonably correct picture of the phylogenies of only a very few taxa and these entirely on the basis of paleontological evidence. Even in paleontology the proportion of fact to speculation is not too high. We quote a recent critic in this field (Challinor, 1959): "Works which refer to the fossil evidence of evolution usually cite a few of the well-known cases of evolutionary series as if they were merely representatives of a host that might have been quoted, instead of stressing the fact that records of such cases are rare."

Speculation on phyletic relationships based on neontological evidence is very questionable indeed. Sporne (1956) has discussed this in detail in the case of plant phylogeny, particularly the pitfalls in interpreting continuous series of characters. The well-known law of recapitulation, by which the successive embryonic states of an animal are said to mirror its phylogeny, is now realized to be open to similar misinterpretations, since there is no way of being certain which embryonic features do and which do not reflect the actual phylogeny (see George, 1933). Similar difficulties apply to other laws, such as Dollo's law, and to chromosomal karyotypes (Simpson, 1953, pp. 245–259, 310; Stebbins, 1950, pp. 442–475, 498). While both positive and negative statements of a very general nature can be made with a reasonable probability of correctness—as that vertebrates did *not* descend from spiderlike ancestors, that mammals evolved from reptilelike ancestors—detailed establishment of relationships by descent are likely to be quite fanciful. What evidence on the development of piston engines would be yielded by a present-day comparative study of such varying machines as an airplane engine, a diesel engine, and a car motor? Would we be able to reason back to the early steam engines? It may be argued that "living fossils," which are often transitional forms, help us in establishing a possible reconstruction of the chain of events. In the analogy employed by us, these living fossils would be old steam and other engines found in abandoned mine shafts or still working in primitive regions of the world. Such evidence would surely help in raising the confidence which we could place in any given evolutionary construct. However, the improvement brought about by living fossils is essentially one of degree. Thus an unusual number of relict forms would have to occur before we could establish our hypothesis with certainty. We would first have to assure ourselves that these were indeed relicts: it is no easy matter to recognize a living fossil before any fossils are known. Even then it is unlikely that we would understand the detailed derivation of every form.

Hennig (1950), aware of the above criticisms of the phylogenetic approach to taxonomy, justifies such a procedure on the basis of three main arguments. The first is that the phylogenetic system is the most meaningful of all possible systems because all other types of classifications, such as ecological, zoogeographic, or morphological, can be derived and explained through the phylogenetic system. In a sense this argument is analogous to that of Gilmour, who states that a natural system is the one of most general application. Indeed, none of the special classifications could occupy such a central and all-explanatory position as does a phylogenetic system. The theory of evolution is the most adequate, most unitary, and indeed simplest hypothesis to which a great variety of biological phenomena—geographic distribution, physiological adaptation, morphological similarity, or biocoenotic complexity—can be related. Phylogeny can thus be seen as the central cause of much biology, yet it cannot be used for an explanatory concept, as it is not known in the vast majority of instances. Hence an empirical classification, although it may not be able to explain the above-mentioned biological phenomena, is at least a self-sufficient, factual procedure and may in most cases be the best classification that we can get.

Hennig's second reason for preferring a phylogenetic taxonomy has been negated by the development of numerical taxonomy. He thought that phylogenetic relationships are at least in principle measurable, but that similarities are not. The very opposite opinion is held today.

Third, Hennig claims that there is no exact correspondence between morphological similarity and phylogenetic relationship and that convergence may mask phylogenetic relationships. He feels that of the two relationships the second is the more important. It remains to be demonstrated which of the two relationships would be more pertinent to the taxonomist (in this connection, see Sneath and Sokal, 1962). In any case this is a field unexplored in theory or practice. Until it can be shown through plausible models to what degree phylogenetic relationship can differ from morphological (phenetic) relationship or until a case of known phyletic history can be used to explore quantitatively the correspondence of morphological with phylogenetic relationships, judgments on such issues should be suspended in favor of research upon them.

Careful thought must also be expended on the meaning of rate of evolution (or of divergence). An overall rate of divergence based on some multivariate summary or abstraction of the phenotype can be given, if the time elapsed to achieve this divergence is known. In many cases divergence may be very rapid but may only involve a single organ or organ system. The overall divergence of the descendent forms from the ancestral stocks may not be impressive; yet the actual rate of change for the organ system concerned may be very high. Such situations can very easily give rise to errors of estimate regarding times of branching. As judged by its feathers, *Archaeopteryx* was a bird; as judged by its skeleton, it was still a reptile. Evolution of new food preferences or color adaptations to different backgrounds may be in this category.

Difficulties arise often when organisms exist in phenetically different life forms. These could be immature forms and adults (as in many insects), males and females (many birds), or different morphotypes occurring in alternation of generations (aphids, Sporozoa, plants) or through social differentiation (termites, ants). Sometimes a satisfactory classification can be based on one of these forms but not on the other. More disturbing are cases where separate classifications are possible but do not match. Such examples are conventionally explained away by bad choice of characters and by nonrecognition of homologies (Remane, 1956). In view of the unreliability of classifications based on few characters, it seems to us surprising that more such incongruences, as Weismann termed the phenomenon, do not occur.

Customary procedure in dealing with incongruences is objectionable: the taxonomy of the later described stage is constantly compared with the earlier classified one. Thus almost inevitably the earlier classification will influence the later one. A thorough investigation of this phenomenon has yet to be made, but it is our belief, defended in Chapter 5, that similar classifications would result from an analysis of sufficient numbers of characters in different life forms of identical taxa, at least as a rule.

If it is the aim of systematics to structure the organic world phenetically and phyletically, then we must regretfully conclude that no currently available taxonomic method can achieve this simultaneously. Michener and Sokal (1957) have said that classification cannot describe both affinity and descent in a single scheme, and this point must be re-emphasized.

Verbal or written descriptions of relations among organisms have proved quite inadequate. For this reason a variety of mnemonic and didactic aids have been developed, most of them graphic. These are largely different forms of trees of relationships (or phylogenetic trees). Mayr, Linsley, and Usinger (1953) have called these drawings *dendrograms*, which seems a suitable term without any implication about the nature of the relationship.

A dendritic description of the taxonomic system has much to recommend it and seems in many ways to be the "natural" way of illustrating relationships and descent. Other schemes of presentation have been tried repeatedly but unsuccessfully (Remane, 1956). A vague, general agreement on the interpretation of diagrams of relationship exists among taxonomists, yet when a given diagram is subjected to detailed, critical scrutiny we rarely find consistency of meaning within it. The interpretation of the basic facts which a diagram offers is likely to be based on varying degrees of certainty in different parts of the tree. No generally accepted conventions for constructing such diagrams exist; hence, seemingly similar diagrams may have quite different meanings, which are often not clearly enunciated by the author of the tree. Cain and Harrison (1960b) have shown in an illuminating discussion on the different components that can be included in phylogenetic relationships, that often an author has not himself a clear idea of the meaning of a diagram of relationships presented by him.

The following symbolisms have been used most frequently.

(1) The vertical axis (or radius in circular dendrograms)—to indicate time, either in absolute units or in relative evolutionary ones (most frequently unspecified).

(2) Furcations—to indicate branches in the phyletic sequence in order to indicate the relationships between the forms based on the lineages alone (not considering their phenetic similarities); that is, the *cladistic* affinity (Cain and Harrison, 1960b).

(3) Location and relative position of tips of branches with respect to each other—to indicate (phenetic) relationships.

(4) Location of furcation along a vertical axis (which now designates resemblance)—to indicate closeness of relationships between taxa represented by stems issuing from the furcation. Symbolisms (3) and (4) are often used in combination to indicate what part of the relationships is due to convergence and what part is due to inheritance of characters of a common ancestor (*patristic* affinity, Cain and Harrison, 1960b).

(5) Levels of tips along a vertical axis (or along the radius of a circular dendrogram)—to indicate whether the forms are recent or extinct, and also to give some estimate of the time scale of the extinction.

(6) Levels of tips along a vertical axis (or along the radius of a circular dendrogram)—to indicate degree of perfection or complexity of form. This convention, related to the *scala naturae* of an earlier day, is largely out of fashion, although some of its ideas and its vocabulary are still employed occasionally. Thus Rensch (1947) uses the term *Höherentwicklung*.

(7) The angle between stems—to represent velocity of (phenetic?) differentiation.

(8) Thickness of stems—to represent abundance at a given point in time. Abundance is usually measured by the number of species or taxa contained within the stem, but occasionally represents the number of organisms supposedly extant.

It is easily seen that (1), (2), and (5) can be combined into a single diagram. Unless the rate of evolution has been constant, (4) cannot also be included. It is generally impossible to represent phenetic relationships on a two-dimensional graph; hence (3) is bound to be a distorted representation. The use of the angle to indicate velocity of evolutionary change (7) is never very successful except in the simplest diagrams. Abundance (8) can usually be added to most diagrams, although the results are often not very esthetic. The basic difficulty is the graphic representation of phenetic resemblances and phenetic change. These are multidimensional relationships and cannot satisfactorily be compressed into a two-dimensional diagram. An interesting contribution by Hayata (1921, 1931), discussed at some length by Du Rietz (1930), emphasizes the multidimensional nature of taxonomic resemblance, with the added implication that evolution may be much more reticulate than is commonly thought. The only possible way of transmitting the various types of information listed in points (1) through (8) is by three separate graphs for (a) time and branches (cladistic relationships), possibly combining symbolisms 1, 2, 5, 7, and 8; (b) phenetic relationships between junctions of stems only, as customarily employed in dendrograms in numerical taxonomy—symbolism (4); (c) complexity of form or organization —symbolism (6). Phenetic relationships among tips of branches (symbolism 3) can usually not be represented in a two- or three-dimensional space. Proper representation would require two-dimensional cross sections through the hyperspace which is necessary to represent such relations properly (see Section 6.2.3). We shall consider the mechanics of such a presentation in greater detail in Section 7.4.

As regards aspect (2)—phyletic sequence—it is obvious that a diagram can be constructed only if phylogenetic evidence can be obtained from fossils or in some other reliable fashion. We have already pointed out the dangers of deductive reasoning in tracing phylogenies. The sequences in phyletic lines are often much more uncertain than authors wish to admit. Some authors indicate probable descent by dotted lines. If there are many such dotted sections, the chances of the diagram's being substantially and seriously misleading may be very high indeed. Unfortunately there seems to be no study on this point to tell how misleading earlier phylogenies have been when compared with later detailed and convincing fossil evidence. Such a study might be illuminating. It is true that many authors, quite properly, disavow any phylogenetic significance of their diagrams and caution readers against considering them to be in any way reflections of evolutionary history. We ourselves follow conventional practice in arranging taxa by a system of hierarchic, nested categories which roughly give an indication of point (4). These can easily be represented by a table (such as Table 1 in Michener and Sokal, 1957); a dendrogram is another acceptable form and has been used by Michener and Sokal (1957, Figures 5 through 8; Figures 12 through 15 in the same paper do not fall into this category, being attempts at phyletic interpretations). The form of dendrograms, together with the intellectual traditions of present-day zoologists, makes it very difficult to view them without some evolutionary interpretations.

The criticisms of phylogenetic taxonomy enumerated above (and many more) have been voiced repeatedly and by a large number of writers during the past hundred years. An adequate summary of them would require a volume thicker than the present one. In return, these criticisms have prompted defenses of the phylogenetic approach, among the most recent being those by Hennig (1950, 1957) in Germany and by Simpson (1961) in the United States. One might expect that after a subject has been discussed for so long a period of time some agreement would have been reached on the relative merits of the various points of view put forward. This does not appear to be the case, however. In our view, a major difficulty in which the critics of the phylogenetic method have found themselves in the past is that though being able to criticize the position of the phylogeneticist on valid grounds, they have been unable to suggest a consistent and workable alternative procedure. Such a goal is now within reach, as we hope to demonstrate in the chapters that follow. For this reason we have kept our criticism of current, largely phylogenetic principles of taxonomy relatively brief and shall fill the greater part of this book with a positive statement of our views, in the belief that the inherent faults of the phylogenetic method will thereby be most clearly shown. Further discussion of phylogenetic aspects of systematics can be found in Sections 4.6, 4.7, and 5.5 and in Chapter 8.

## 2.4. PROBLEMS OF TAXONOMIC RANK

### 2.4.1. Criteria for taxonomic rank

Phenetic as well as genetic criteria for taxonomic rank are commonly used. At and below the level of biological species they may be in conflict. If a genetic criterion is used to define species, there may be a variable species whose members interbreed freely; yet an adjacent group of equal variability may be split by genetic isolating mechanisms into several distinct biological species of much smaller internal variability (for example, sibling species). The phenetic ranks of the species are very different in the two groups. In the absence of data on breeding and in all apomictic groups (which include the great majority of practical applications in systematics), the species are based on the phenetic similarity between the individuals and on phenotypic gaps. These are assumed to be good indices of the genetic position, although they need not be. The rank of higher categories must perforce depend on phenetic and not genetic criteria. The intrusion of an entirely different criterion for taxonomic rank in those few situations where genetic or phyletic relations are known with certainty, seems to us to be a needless source of confusion. Alternative terminologies have been suggested for genetic and also ecological entities (especially in botany, where these problems are most acute); these terms have not been widely used, possibly because of the prestige attached to the term "species" (compare Gilmour and Gregor, 1939; Camp and Gilly, 1943; Gilmour and Heslop-Harrison, 1954). For reasons of clarity it is desirable that the meaning in which taxonomic rank is used should be specified. In this book it will be used in the sense of phenetic rank, unless otherwise indicated. We have not attempted to define and distinguish different usages of the term species; where it is germane to our argument we have qualified the term to avoid confusion.

It is undesirable for the rank of a group to be affected by the number of contained subgroups. There is a modern tendency to make each family contain only a few genera and each genus only a few species; in some works most genera are monotypic. The rank should be based on affinity alone. In our view it is better to introduce new rank categories (such as subfamily or superclass) than to use the number of contained subgroups as an arbiter of rank.

There has indeed been a great elaboration of such new categories of rank, largely independent of the cycles of "lumping" and "splitting" which Simpson (1945) has commented upon. This practice has not always been justifiable, for although the traditional categories of phylum, class, order, family, genus, species may be inadequate, it seems labored to use forty or fifty new categories without any numerical justification; such new categories have contributed little other than being handy containers for speculative views on minutiae. Although careless creation of new categories of rank is undesirable, we believe that when they are necessary numerical taxonomy will afford good evidence on which to base them.

### 2.4.2. Limits of taxa

Limits of taxonomic groups can be considered from two points of view. One can trace the change of taxa with time, looking at the phylogenetic tree in its entirety. This is what Simpson (1945) has called vertical classification. One can also look at a cross section of the tree and obtain the relationships among taxa at a given point in time (horizontal classification, Simpson, 1945). We shall first consider the problems in vertical classification, which can only be practiced on fossil material.

It is obvious that when one phyletic lineage evolves into a new form there can be no sharp division between the ancestral and the descendant species, other than an arbitrary one, except in the case of allopolyploids and other forms of hybrid origins. This has been well treated by Bather (1927), who discusses the various ways in which the division can be made. It is inevitable that the accidents of discovery of fossil forms should affect classificatory decisions, since the divisions will at first be placed where there are gaps in the fossil record. As the gaps are closed by new discoveries, the most common practice is to choose for the dividing line some prominent, but commonly arbitrary, evolutionary step—for example, the change in jaw structure in the evolution of reptiles into mammals. So long as the arbitrariness is clearly realized, these methods are unobjectionable and are matters of convenience. The choice of such an arbitrary step is not without some danger, however, for it may lead to incongruous situations.

Yet a better plan, commonly advocated in paleontology when a relatively full fossil record is known, is to place the divisions at places where abrupt changes in the rate or direction of evolution make for rational and convenient groups or where phyletic lines branch. The demerit of this course is that the divisions are then through parts of the lineages which are of special interest for students of evolution. Nevertheless, the bulk of the total material will be grouped in a convenient way, and it is standard practice in analogous situations to make the divisions on the same principle (such as where a small amount of hybridization occurs between living species, even if it is the hybrids which are of most interest to us). An acceptable nomenclature for the borderline forms, such as X-Y intermediate forms, or X-Y hybrids, is then the main problem.

As is discussed later (Section 8.2.1), the development of numerical taxonomy may allow us to find in the fossil record the points of abrupt evolutionary change and diminish this dependence on arbitrary evolutionary steps. Yet in practice there are few fossil series of such completeness that they warrant altering the rather simple treatment mentioned above.

To turn to horizontal classification, much of the difficulty lies in the definitions which we adopt or in the kinds of grouping we recognize. A phenetic taxonomic group may not always be identical with a phyletic group. For example, the appearance of a sterility barrier will at once divide a normal genetic species into two sibling species. Yet for many generations (until the two sibling species have accumulated sufficient genetic differences in the course of their independent evolution) they may remain one single phenetic group because the differences which cause the sterility barrier (plus the few other accumulated differences) will be insignificant in comparison with the many variable attributes of other kinds which the two sibling species will share. It may be unwise to call this phenetic group a single taxon without qualifying this latter term, but it will certainly be a single phenetic taxon, and it is also a single natural taxon, where the word "natural" has the restricted meaning discussed in Section 2.2. Without the use of a more precise definition of the term species, the situation is certain to become confused. Such situations are evidently not uncommon; closely similar species may overlap in all observed features, as suggested by investigations such as those of Ehrlich (1961c) on butterflies and Lack (1947, pp. 82–86, 88–89) on Darwin's finches in the Galapagos Islands. It is notorious that many birds are classified almost only upon their skins, and the acknowledged success of the taxonomist is, as Lack points out, in large measure because the species recognition marks, which enable the birds to recognize mates from their own species, are usually visual features which the taxonomist also uses to distinguish these species; where visual marks are absent (as in some warblers which recognize one another by song) the classification is more difficult (Lack, 1947, pp. 16–54).

If a difficulty in assigning limits to taxa can occur when the facts are not in dispute, it is no wonder that confusion is common when the facts are uncertain. Numerical taxonomy may not solve the genetic problems, but by making precise the phenetic groupings it will help their solution.

One of the more obvious principles of delimiting taxa is that we place divisions at places in the taxonomic scheme which are empty—that is, where there are no known creatures. This is a corollary of the concepts underlying natural taxonomies, for it is these gaps in the universe of possible character combinations which give us the correlations between features on which the natural taxonomic groupings are based. But this itself creates its own difficulties. As Michener (1957) has emphasized, the gaps may only be gaps in our knowledge of living or extinct forms, and no consistent treatment has been developed to deal with this problem.

It is widely acknowledged that it is unwise to recognize taxa which are only differentiated on one or two features, though in some branches of biology systematists find this temptation hard to resist. Even if it is practicable to name endless varieties of this sort, the fact that they are usually established on a few features raises the suspicion that they are quite arbitrary taxonomic groups. How many geographical races, color variants, or other forms in mammals, birds, and butterflies can stand critical examination in this regard? This is the substance behind the criticism of Wilson and Brown (1953), and most of the current systematics of bacteria and yeasts is unsound for the same reason.

Low taxonomic ranks may be difficult to define and to arrange hierarchically. Such groups would appear in a numerical taxonomic study as contiguous and indistinct clusters of individuals. Methods for best dividing the organisms into clusters have only recently been considered, and at present there is no consistent practice among taxonomists. Procedures such as "the 75% rule" are often ambiguous (Pimentel, 1959), since different results may be obtained using different features. If a single variable feature is employed the divisions are, in general, not natural taxa, and the divisions may not correspond at all to phenetic clusters.

### 2.4.3. The hierarchy of characters

One fallacious argument, happily now on its way out, is the theory of the hierarchy of characters. By this is meant the claim that one can lay down a priori rules as to which sorts of characters separate species, which sorts separate genera, which sorts separate families, and so on. This is the antithesis of the a posteriori method of discovery. The latter *finds* those features which do in fact separate the previously recognized natural taxa. It is, we maintain, the correct procedure. The hierarchic claim is another form of the theory of unequal and a priori weighting. It is very old; in fact, as Cain (1958) has shown, it springs from the Aristotelian theory of "essences." He cites Cesalpino, who stated that nutrition was of paramount importance to plants, and hence, a priori, the form of root was the first subdividing feature for plants, yielding the major division of herbs and trees. De Candolle (1813, pp. 73–89) called it the principle of subordination of characters, attributing it to Bernard de Jussieu, and listed the importance of botanical characters in the following order: those of the embryo, those of the stamens and pistil, those of the envelopes of the embryo, and those of accessory floral structures. However, he qualified these rules with so many exceptions that their validity is very doubtful on his own showing, and it is clear that in practice it is the correlation among various characters which is the real basis of his theories.

We believe that no such hierarchies can be made a priori, and it is well known that in practice quite different hierarchies of characters are used for different taxonomic groups. Characters which separate the species of one genus usually do not do so in the next genus; where they do appear to do so, the taxonomies are commonly arbitrary and unnatural. Many systematists have believed that certain classes of characters will separate species within genera (for example, physiological characters) while other classes (such as morphological characters) separate genera within each family. It is easy to find exceptions in most natural classifications, and in practice some physiological and some morphological characters are found both to separate species and to separate genera. The difficulty is to decide which physiological characters and which morphological characters are those obeying the rule and which are the exceptions; in any event, many of them can be plausibly regarded as both morphological and physiological. Similar objections apply to all classes of characters and to all taxonomic ranks. It would indeed be curious if evolution, which is responsible for the natural hierarchy, should be so obliging as to operate only on certain classes of characters at specified taxonomic ranks. Again, it is clear that in practice it is correlations among characters, whatever their nature, which decide the issue, for otherwise it is impossible to explain why diametrically opposite views are held by different systematists of undoubted competence. Frequently the problem of classes of characters arises because taxonomists are aiming at two mutually incompatible purposes, as when, for example, adaptive features are used to estimate the degree of evolutionary convergence, while nonadaptive features are used to estimate phylogenetic relations; discrepancies between the schemes are then inevitable.

### 2.4.4. Adaptive characters

Overemphasis on adaptiveness of characters is another fault of modern systematics. Some taxonomists prefer to base their classification on what they suppose to be nonadaptive characters. However, modern genetics is showing us that few if any characters can be considered nonadaptive. The converse view—that taxa should be based on adaptive characters (Inger, 1958)—is quite impracticable, as has been shown by Sokal (1959).

## 2.5. NOMENCLATURE

It is not our intention to enter upon an extensive discussion and criticism of present-day practices in nomenclature. First of all, such an undertaking would require considerable space to do it justice; more important, however, we have no constructive revision to offer in connection with our proposals for numerical taxonomy. An excellent discussion of the problems of nomenclature is that of Simpson (1961, pp. 28–34). The phenon system of nomenclature which we do propose (in Section 9.1.1) is not suggested as a substitute for the existing system of nomenclature but is designed to be used alongside it.

An ideal system of nomenclature would contain within it information serving to distinguish at least symbolically its lowest units, presumably species. It would also contain information linking a given species to other species and give some idea of its affinity with its neighbors. A third requirement of an ideal nomenclatural system would be to locate the lowest unit correctly within the hierarchy of taxa in nature; that is, the name should inform about the phylum, class, order, family, and any other necessary taxon to which the organism belongs. A fourth requisite of such a system would be that it serve as a ready and internationally accepted handle for recognizing and dealing with the species.

Systematists have from time to time attempted to make binominal nomenclature serve all these functions. It is of course easily recognized that it can do none of them at all well. Since the time of Linnaeus no attempt has been made to summarize species differences in a single word. There are by now so many genera that most generic names are quite unfamiliar to all but a few specialists, and generic names in different categories convey different ideas of affinity to persons working with them. Since no familial or other information of higher category is contained in the binomen, it cannot serve as a marker of the species' place in the system of nature; finally, instability of nomenclature has restricted much of the usefulness of the binomen as a handle or label.

# CHAPTER 3

# New Methods in Taxonomy

In this chapter we shall briefly review a number of methods recently introduced into taxonomy. This will include a short section on early developments related to numerical taxonomy.

Some techniques, such as comparative serology, may be regarded as quantitative techniques which yield measures of overall taxonomic similarity. Other techniques which yield many characters in a single technical procedure are here called *polyphenic* methods. These do not themselves yield measures of affinity directly, but they can be made to do so by appropriate mathematical methods such as those described in Chapters 5 and 6. Finally, brief mention is made of newer or less usual characters which may be employed in systematics.

We believe that the results obtained by these methods should be incorporated into the body of taxonomic knowledge; they should, whenever feasible, be included with other more usual characters, such as morphological ones, in analyses for the estimation of affinity by numerical methods. Indeed, their advent makes the use of modern computing techniques a necessity for taxonomy in the future. Just as the problem in Linnaeus' time was the flood of new organisms which were being discovered, so one problem of today is the flood of new characters now available which must be handled in some fashion (Cain, 1959c).

## 3.1. THE DEVELOPMENT OF NUMERICAL METHODS IN TAXONOMY

The earliest attempts to apply numerical methods to taxonomy date from the rise of biometrics in the last century. As early as 1898 Heincke used a measure of phenetic distance to distinguish between races of the herring. It was early realized that biometrics could be applied to systematics, but the only important eventual development was that of discriminant functions (Fisher, 1936), which is useful in only one specialized problem of taxonomy.

One of the earliest statistics of interest to systematists was the "Coefficient of Racial Likeness" (Pearson, 1926). It was extensively applied in physical anthropology but does not seem to have been taken up by taxonomists. The C.R.L. was close to being a coefficient of taxonomic similarity, and was subsequently developed by Mahalanobis in the form of the "Generalized Distance" statistic, which is also formally a coefficient of this kind (see Rao, 1948). Anderson and Whitaker (1934) and Anderson and Abbe (1934) employed a similar statistic, which was also equivalent to a diagonal in a multidimensional Euclidean space, and which they called the "General Index." These statistics, though mathematically adequate, did not lead to notable advances for two reasons: (1) they were developed as discriminant functions to aid in the allocation of individuals to existing taxa and not as methods for creating taxa; and (2) as a consequence of (1) these workers selected principally those characters which gave the best discrimination between the taxa, and—since it is usually only necessary to employ a small number of such characters, once they have been found—these methods were in practice based on few rather than many characters. Some of the characters were selected on a priori grounds, and their small number led to instability on repeating the work with other characters. These techniques, with others developed later, have been very widely and successfully used for the study of certain limited taxonomic problems. We may, for example, cite the elegant work of Blackith (1957) on sexual and phase variation in locusts.

Some studies with aims similar to those of numerical taxonomy today should be mentioned. Smirnov (1925) established types on a quantitative basis. His work has been discussed and evaluated from different points of view by Hennig (1950) and Sokal (1962b). Haltenorth (1937) in a study of similarities among eight species of large cats developed a coefficient similar to that of Cain and Harrison (1958). At about the same time Zarapkin (1939) developed a rather elaborate technique called *Divergenzanalyse*, arriving at a quantity analogous to taxonomic distance. The *Affinitätsrechnung* by Schilder and Schilder (1951) is also a computation of taxonomic distance. We believe that these methods did not succeed at the time they were developed because of the entrenched nature of phylogenetic systematics and since for any substantial number of characters or taxa the methods advocated by these authors presented computational difficulties insurmountable at the time.

Other early methods, but ones specifically intended for taxonomy, are those of Forbes (1933), Anderson and Owenbey (1939), Sturtevant (1939, 1942), Boeke (1942), James (1953), Stallings and Turner (1957), Hudson, Lanzillotti, and Edwards (1959), and Chillcott (1960), based on variations of matching coefficients. These authors did not develop their methods sufficiently to meet the main needs of numerical taxonomy and hesitated to give equal weight to every feature or to employ large numbers of characters. Similar trends can also be seen in the history of bacterial classification, where the earlier reliance on a few morphological or physiological characters has given place to attempts at classification in the Adansonian tradition (see Sneath, 1962).

We believe that one of the main conceptual difficulties which retarded progress in numerical taxonomy was the problem of weighting, even if this was to some extent an illusory one, and the liberating effect of accepting equal weighting can scarcely be overemphasized. The use of many characters is also a prerequisite. In addition, the use of methods of cluster analysis in building the taxonomic hierarchy has been a major advance. It is in these three points that numerical taxonomy chiefly differs from the earlier ideas and methods. No comprehensive review of numerical taxonomy has yet appeared, but we list here some of the literature which discusses or reviews specific topics and methods in this field.

General articles are those of Sokal (1960), Rogers (1961), Sneath (1961, 1962), Sneath and Sokal (1962), Sokal (1964), and a number of reports of meetings—for example, Gilmour (1961a), Williams and Lambert (1961c), and papers in a recent issue of *Systematic Zoology* (Ehrlich, 1961b, c; Russell, 1961; Daly, 1961; Jahn, 1961). The following reviews are restricted to bacteriology: Sneath (1958), Cowan (1959), Silvestri (1960), Brisbane and Rovira (1961), and Floodgate (1962); these have recently been summarized by Sneath (1962).

Below are listed some papers discussing certain topics in numerical taxonomy. Despite a good deal of overlap in subject matter, they can be roughly divided into theoretical and methodological papers. Mainly theoretical discussions are those of Michener and Sokal (1957), Sneath (1957a), Michener (1957), Cain and Harrison (1958), Ehrlich (1958), Sneath (1961), and Sokal (1962b). Papers discussing mainly methods are those of Sneath (1957b), Sokal and Michener (1958), Sokal (1958),

Rogers and Tanimoto (1960), Sokal (1961), Rohlf and Sokal (1962), Sneath (1962), and Sokal and Rohlf (1962).

A comprehensive listing of applications of numerical taxonomy to various systematic groups since 1957 is given in Section 10.1.1.

## 3.2.  COMPARATIVE SEROLOGY

Comparative serology yields measures of taxonomic relations just as numerical taxonomy does. It grew out of medical immunology, from the pioneering work of Nuttall (1901, 1904). It has been greatly expanded by Boyden and his colleagues, and the reviews of Erhardt (1931) and Boyden (1942, 1953, 1958) and on comparative serology of plants by Chester (1937) are valuable. The symposium on Taxonomic Biochemistry, Physiology, and Serology (Leone, 1963) contains much recent material on this field and on other methods discussed in this chapter.

The basic principle, that the proteins of one organism will react strongly with antibodies to the proteins of a very similar organism, but less so in the case of a dissimilar organism, has been shown to have a very wide application. It is being used, despite certain pitfalls, as a court of appeal in doubtful taxonomic cases. The precise meaning of the resemblance shown by this immunological technique will inevitably be somewhat obscure until a great deal more is known about the nature of antigen-antibody reactions. However, it is likely that serological resemblance can best be expressed as an overall similarity of the structure of the relevant proteins, in which a very large number of small differences and resemblances (due to amino acid sequences and perhaps also to folding of the polypeptide chain) are reflected in the reactions with the antisera. This seems more than plausible, since those relatively rare examples in which serology indicates a relationship clearly discordant with accepted taxonomy are commonly due to the close similarity of those widely distributed cell components which give the cross-reaction. Usually carbohydrates and not proteins are responsible for the unexpected serological findings. It is not surprising that two creatures which both produce large amounts of, say, a polymer of glucuronic acid, could show a strong serological cross-reaction because of this.

The many small differences and resemblances in the proteins may perhaps be validly thought of as a large sample of the features of the organism. Modern genetic theory suggests that this is so, since the protein structure is considered to be determined by the fine structure of the genes. In this context we may cite the comments of Crick (1958) on the application to taxonomy of the details of protein structure.

> Biologists should realize that before long we shall have a subject which might be called "protein taxonomy"—the study of the amino acid sequences of the proteins of an organism and the comparison of them between different species. It can be argued that these sequences are the most delicate expression possible of the phenotype of an organism and that vast amounts of evolutionary information may be hidden away within them.

We may add to this the comment that such studies will allow an evaluation of immunological relationships and that in addition the use of techniques of numerical taxonomy will be essential to the interpretation and analysis of the amino acid sequences. Information on the sequences in the small protein molecules of different species is already becoming available (see Anfinsen, 1959, pp. 142–162), though the data are insufficient to warrant numerical analysis at present. That different proteins of the same animal usually do not cross-react serologically (see Cinader, 1957) suggests that they do not possess extensive common amino acid sequences, and therefore they are presumably the products of separate genes.

When we turn to comparison between organisms, it is probably only a small part of the protein molecule whose structure is fixed because of the functional requirements of the protein; the remainder of the molecule, perhaps the major part, could then vary extensively without greatly affecting the function of the molecule and could therefore reflect intraorganismic diversity as well as the genetic differences between different kinds of organisms. In this connection the relation between serological and genetic characters shown by the work of Irwin and his colleagues (Irwin, 1959) is of interest. Whether these differences in protein structure can be considered a reasonably random sample of the genetic differences of the whole organism is a problem to which no clear answer can yet be given. There is the serious danger that if we study serologically only a single protein (which is desirable for other reasons) we may in effect be studying the fine structure of only one gene, and we have as yet no knowledge of whether the fine structure will be representative of the differences in structure of the other genes. For example, if there had been no evolution of the fine structure of such a gene during the radiating evolution of a group of organisms, the serological studies would show a disproportionate similarity—even identity—between the evolved taxa. If all birds had retained the same serum proteins that their reptilian ancestor possessed, then avian serum serology would be uniformly uninteresting. And conversely, rapid evolution in such a gene would yield a disproportionate dissimilarity between the descendant forms. Therefore, the value of serology (and of other techniques which study fine chemical structure) does not depend on the "conservatism" of the proteins; extreme conservatism and precociousness are alike fatal. Most usefully, the evolution in protein structure should be generally proportionate to that in other characters. We have no strong reasons to expect that individual genes controlling protein structure will not accumulate changes proportionate to the changes in other genes; if one did find a protein which was aberrant in this respect, it seems unlikely that other proteins would also be aberrant. The use of several proteins would greatly add confidence to the conclusions of comparative serology, so that this might well repay the extra labor involved.

The decoding of fine protein and fine genetic structure in the next few decades will help us to answer whether evolution in protein structure is proportionate to that in other characters, and there are many signs that differences in protein structure do in general parallel other differences. The well-known correspondence between orthodox taxonomy and serology is one piece of evidence. Internal evidence points in the same direction: Boyden, DeFalco, and Gemeroy (1951) showed that there is a very close parallel between the serological resemblances based on serum albumins and those based on serum globulins; recent work on other proteins such as those of egg white, hemoglobins, and red cell antigens shows close agreement with earlier comparative serology and among themselves (Mainardi, 1958a, b; Sibley, 1960); there is high serological similarity between proteins in different stages of the life cycle (Wilhelmi, 1940; Spiegel, 1960).

If the assumption is true—that in general the fine structure of one or two proteins is an adequate and random sample of features—we would expect that each feature of fine structure would in practice contribute equal weight to the serological results. Though our knowledge is scanty on this point, it seems likely that single amino acid differences will generally have approximately equal effects on the serology. Therefore it is not implausible that comparative serology is a quantitative taxonomic method which will generally yield the same conclusions as numerical taxonomy. One might speak of it as a method for estimating affinity in which the immunized animal acts as the computing machine when it produces the specific antibodies.

There are pitfalls in the use of serology, which Boyden (1942, 1958) has discussed in detail. In brief, one may obtain misleading results because of: (1) the apparently fortuitous occurrence in distant taxa of very similar substances, usually carbohydrates, which dominate the serological reactions; (2) the poor antigenicity of some substances and the variation in discrimination and antibody response given by different animals used for immunization; and (3) distortions due to the use of uncontrolled mixtures of antigens or unsuitable techniques. Despite these, the method is very valuable and can profitably be used not only in deciding difficult cases but also in making exploratory studies. It yields measures of affinity which are formally quite independent from phylogeny, though not all its practitioners have made this distinction in their published work. There is also the need, not appreciated by systematic serologists, for cluster analysis of the serological affinities themselves in order to yield taxonomic groupings, as discussed in Chapter 7.

Several measures of serological similarity have been devised. In the early work of Nuttall (1904) a rough indication of the similarity between two taxa was given by listing the percentage of cross-reactions of a certain strength obtained by serological comparison of a number of species of the two taxa. Boyden (1932) expressed the similarity between two samples as the arithmetic mean of the two reciprocal heterologous titrations after the titers had been first expressed as percentages of the homologous titers; he converted this index $M$ into a measure of serological distance by subtracting it from 100. Chu, Andrewes, and Gledhill (1950) and Mainardi (1958a, 1959b) employed the geometric mean instead of the arithmetic mean, and Mainardi calls this the immunological distance, $I.D.$:

$$I.D. = \sqrt{\frac{Ho_a}{He_a} \times \frac{Ho_b}{He_b}},$$

where $Ho$ and $He$ stand for the homologous and heterologous titers respectively with the antisera $a$ and $b$ (note that the titers are properly the dilutions of serum giving the end point, not the concentrations). This is an improvement on Boyden's $100 - M$ index, but it suffers from the defect that immunological identity corresponds to an immunological distance of 1; it is also unduly sensitive to fluctuations in the end point of the titrations, which are seldom accurate to within one doubling dilution. *I.D.* is better expressed in a logarithmic scale, and with doubling dilutions the appropriate statistic would be $\log_2 I.D.$

This statistic is still inefficient in that each reaction is obtained from the end point only, and a scoring system which makes use of the results with each dilution is better (see Dömök, Szafir, and Farkas, 1954; Race and Sanger, 1950, p. 166). If a score of 1 is given for each maximal reaction and a fractional value for a lesser reaction, the sum of the scores for a titration is equivalent to a logarithmic measure, and with doubling dilutions, $\log_2 I.D.$ will be equivalent to $\frac{1}{2}$ (sum of homologous scores) $- \frac{1}{2}$ (sum of heterologous scores).

The quantitative precipitation reaction has been used extensively since the introduction of nephelometry (measuring turbidity of suspensions). The importance of studying the reaction at successive dilutions is stressed by Bolton, Leone, and Boyden (1948) and Boyden (1942). The usual way of expressing the serological similarity seems to be reasonably adequate. This is to plot the curve of the amount of precipitate obtained at the various dilutions, to calculate the area under the curve, and then to express this area as a percentage of the area obtained from the homologous titration.

Since serology measures so many features at once, it might be argued that it should be given great weight in a taxonomic study. One cannot convert a serological cross-reaction into a single character to be incorporated, with other observed features, into a numerical analysis. The serological results are already a matrix of similarity coefficients. This matrix is not symmetrical, for the reaction—for example, of anti-horse with cow serum, and anti-cow with horse serum—may not be the same in degree. It is possible to break down serological data to give antigenic formulas for the different reacting antigenic factors. This is not simple, but where it can be done these factors can be included like other characters in numerical taxonomic analyses.

Since, for the reasons given above, we have no way yet of knowing what weight should logically be given to a coefficient of serological cross-reaction compared with the weight of an affinity value obtained by numerical analysis, it would be difficult to combine the two coefficients. Comparisons between the two methods are thus of some importance and should be encouraged.

Some less well-known forms of comparative serology may be mentioned. The technique can be applied equally well to many sorts of protein: serum proteins, red corpuscle antigens, egg-white proteins,

proteins of seeds, insect proteins, and so on (see Mainardi, 1958a, b, 1959a, b; Dujarric de la Rivière, Saint-Paul, and Eyquem, 1953; Leone, 1947). Even allergic reactions in man may reflect the taxonomic relationships between the organisms which produce the offending substances (Perlman, 1961). One of the technical difficulties in the past has been the use of mixed antigens such as crude serum; another has been that in microbiology the cell-surface antigens may entirely dominate the serology. Both of these difficulties may be overcome by developments in gel precipitation methods, which should in any event be a valuable adjunct to the usual methods (for example, Gell, Hawkes, and Wright, 1960; and see Ouchterlony, 1958, 1962, and Crowle, 1960). Particularly valuable would be a critical re-examination of the serological relations between plants described by Mez and his colleagues and summarized in the *Königsberger Stammbaum* (Mez and Ziegenspeck, 1926), for, as Chester (1937) points out, their findings have been generally ignored despite the fact that no convincing criticism has been made of much of their work.

## 3.3. POLYPHENIC METHODS

### 3.3.1. Chromatography

The use of chromatography, especially two-way paper chromatography, is a relatively new technique in taxonomy, pioneered by Proom and Woiwod (1949) and Micks and Ellis (1952). Like serology, it can be applied to a wide range of tissue fluids and tissue extracts, and a variety of classes of chemical substances may be detected and estimated in a semiquantitative fashion. Wright (1959) and Buzzati-Traverso (1960) have reviewed these methods in zoology, mentioning for example work on insects, fish, molluscs, and echinoderms, and the use of tissue fluids, muscle squashes, and mucus, which were examined for amino acids, pigments, and fluorescent substances. Mainardi (1958a) has studied tissue extracts of birds, and there have been many examples in botany, such as the works by Turner and Alston (1959) and by Pecket (1959); other work has been reviewed by Thompson et al. (1959). In bacteriology it has been used by Cummins and Harris (1956, 1958) to study the relation of the cell-wall composition to taxonomy; Mattick, Cheeseman, Berridge, and Bottazzi (1956) have employed extracts of bacteria, and Proom and Woiwod (1949) have used changes in the culture media for taxonomic purposes.

Unlike serology, the result of these examinations is not a similarity index but is instead a set of data on the occurrence of individual chemical substances, which are perfectly good characters for taxonomic use. The data should obviously be handled by numerical taxonomic methods, and Cheeseman and Berridge (1959) have given an example using the bacterial genus *Lactobacillus*.

It is probably seldom that the number of compounds in the chromatograms will be numerous enough and of a sufficiently wide genetic origin to give an adequate sample of the characters of the organism; therefore, these methods should be used as an adjunct to others. They may be particularly useful for the identification of taxa (as contrasted with their classification).

### 3.3.2. Electrophoresis

A similar technique for separating and identifying chemical constituents of organisms is electrophoresis on paper or in gels. The principles and difficulties found in chromatography prevail also in this technique. Electrophoresis has been applied to the proteins of insect hemolymph (Brezner and Enns, 1958; van Sande and Karcher, 1960) and to hemoglobin in birds (Mainardi, 1958a; Conterio and Mainardi, 1959). The elegant work of Sibley (1960) on the proteins of egg white of birds is a notable example of this method. Sibley's findings have been of the greatest interest and generally correlate well with other estimates of taxonomic affinity. Electrophoretic patterns should be subjected to numerical analysis; at present the interpretations of the electrophoretic curves have been largely made by eye, and the estimates of similarity may be highly subjective.

### 3.3.3. Infrared spectroscopy

Another new technique is that of infrared spectroscopy. The pattern of absorption of infrared light by tissues or biological products depends on their chemical composition and can therefore yield many features useful in taxonomy. This technique seems to have been applied mainly to microorganisms, starting with the work of Randall et al. (1951) and Stevenson and Bolduan (1952), although Micks and Benedict (1953) applied it to mosquitoes.

The subject has been excellently reviewed by Norris (1959). While mainly used for identification of bacteria, there is no reason why it should not also be employed for the creation of taxonomic groups and the assessment of affinity. The development of automatic analyses and comparisons between spectra (Rogoff, 1957) could yield similarity coefficients based on many chemical attributes. As in other methods discussed above, care must be taken that an excess of some single chemical compound does not dominate the spectrum to such an extent as to give patently false estimates of affinity.

## 3.4. OTHER METHODS

Almost every new technique in biology gives new characters which can be employed in systematics. A few of the more outstanding recent examples are mentioned here. These new characters must be incorporated into the existing body of taxonomic knowledge, and it is our belief that only numerical taxonomy can adequately do this.

Much information on chromosomes is now available from the intensive cytotaxonomic work of the past few decades. It has been the disposition of cytotaxonomists to give this information a very heavy weight (Löve and Löve, 1961), and the equal disposition of others to give it very little—at least when it does not fit previous systematic schemes, as is often the case (see Frahm-Leliveld, 1958). There seems to us to be no warrant for either practice. Clearly, a large number of features can be obtained from cytology, and these can be legitimately included in numerical analyses with the same weight as any other features.

Chemistry is now giving the systematists many new characters, both in plants and animals (see Bate-Smith, 1959, and Florkin, 1949) and even in paleontological material (Abelson, 1957). Newer cytological methods, especially the use of the electron microscope, behavioral studies, ecology, histology (as in Andrew, 1959), and parasitology can all yield a wealth of new material, which we should use as it becomes available. There seems to be no likelihood that any of these newer methods will prove to be an adequate sole basis for taxonomy; to qualify as such, a method would have to reflect accurately the entire genotype. A step in this direction has been taken by estimating the degree to which samples of single-strand DNA from two organisms can form hybrid double-strand DNA (Doty, Marmur, Eigner, and Schildkraut, 1960; Schildkraut, Marmur, and Doty, 1961). This depends on the degree to which the two forms of DNA are similar chemically and are homologous in a genetic sense. Such homology itself depends on the base composition, which can also be a guide to genetic similarity (Lee, Wahl, and Barbu, 1956; Sueoka, 1961).

CHAPTER **4**

# The Aims and Principles of Numerical Taxonomy

## 4.1. DEFINITION OF NUMERICAL TAXONOMY

Having shown what we (and many other critics) believe to be the faults of classificatory methods as currently practiced, we shall state in the present chapter the aims and principles of numerical taxonomy. This will be done in a relatively brief manner in order to provide the reader with a summary of our position. A detailed justification of our assumptions and techniques can be found in Chapters 5 through 9.

Before proceeding, it is necessary that we clearly define our use of the term "numerical taxonomy." We mean by it *the numerical evaluation of the affinity or similarity between taxonomic units and the ordering of these units into taxa on the basis of their affinities*. The term may include the drawing of phylogenetic inferences from the data by statistical or other mathematical methods to the extent to which this should prove possible. These methods will almost always involve the conversion of information about taxonomic entities into numerical quantities. We have preferred the term "numerical" to the term "quantitative," since the latter would include other methods (such as serology or paper chromatography) which we do not discuss in detail here but which have been briefly contrasted in Chapter 3. These latter methods, in a purely formal sense, bear a relation to numerical taxonomy similar to that of analog to digital computation.

We do not wish to widen the term "numerical taxonomy" to include every application of statistical or other numerical methods in systematic research. Our approach consists of a variety of multivariate techniques; but such techniques when not applied to problems of classification are not included in numerical taxonomy. Similarly, classificatory studies based on single or few characters are not included since they do not meet the conditions we feel necessary for a valid taxonomy.

The practice of numerical taxonomy involves a number of fundamental assumptions and philosophical attitudes toward taxonomic work, which we shall discuss and defend in detail in the sections that follow. We have already shown that none of the attitudes and assumptions is new. They, as well as isolated attempts at a numerical treatment of taxonomic relationships, date back over 200 years. However, we would prefer to limit numerical taxonomy to the integrated approach of recent years, which deliberately set out to revise taxonomic theory and practice.

## 4.2. THE AIMS OF NUMERICAL TAXONOMY

Numerical taxonomy would have no claim to the serious attention of biologists unless it could overcome some of the faults found in conventional taxonomic procedure. While we feel that the methods to be discussed below have a number of ancillary advantages, to which we shall draw attention at the appropriate places, the outstanding aims of numerical taxonomy are *repeatability* and *objectivity*.

Although we cannot expect scientists always to agree on interpretations of facts, it is the aim of scientific methodology to reach agreement on the facts themselves through the repeatability of observations. It is in this direction that numerical taxonomy aims. We hope by numerical methods to approach the goal where different scientists working independently will obtain accurate and identical estimates of the resemblance between two forms of organisms, given the same characters on which to base their judgment. Classification must be freed from the inevitable individual biases of the conventional practitioner of taxonomy.

Closely tied up with repeatability is the notion of objectivity. It would hardly seem necessary to stress that, like most rules of scientific methodology, objectivity is a relative concept, seldom fully realized. Yet misunderstandings have arisen on this score (Inger, 1958; Sokal, 1959). By including many characters without previous arbitrary selection or elimination, and by providing standard methods of processing the data and evaluating the results, we reduce subjective bias and hence increase objectivity. Objective and repeatable procedures should together lead to very stable taxonomies, which are unlikely to be overthrown by later discoveries.

## 4.3. THE BASIC POSITIONS

Numerical taxonomy is based on the ideas first put forward by Adanson. They may be called Adansonian and are described concisely by the following axioms (modified from Sneath, 1958).

(1) The ideal taxonomy is that in which the taxa have the greatest content of information and which is based on as many characters as possible.

(2) A priori, every character is of equal weight in creating natural taxa.

(3) Overall similarity (or affinity) between any two entities is a function of the similarity of the many characters in which they are being compared.

(4) Distinct taxa can be constructed because of diverse character correlations in the groups under study.

(5) Taxonomy as conceived by us is therefore a strictly empirical science.

(6) Affinity is estimated independently of phylogenetic considerations.

Axioms (1) through (3) are discussed in Section 4.4, "The Estimation of Resemblance"; axiom (4) is treated in Section 4.5, "The Construction of Natural Taxa"; axioms (5) and (6) are dealt with in Section 4.6, "Empirical versus Phylogenetic Taxonomy."

## 4.4. THE ESTIMATION OF RESEMBLANCE

This is the most important and fundamental step in numerical taxonomy. It commences with the collection of information about characters in the taxonomic group to be studied. This information may already exist and merely require extraction from the literature, or it may have to be discovered entirely or partly de novo. In most cases both of these procedures will need to be applied. For the method to be reliable, many characters are needed. At least sixty seem desirable, and less than forty should never be used. All kinds of characters are equally desirable: morphological, physiological, ethological, and sometimes even distributional ones. We must guard only against introducing bias into our choice of characters and against characters which are not an accurate expression of the properties of the organisms.

We assume characters to be equivalent since we believe that there are no special groups of genes related to single morphological regions but that a random sample of the genotype is best obtained by sampling many and various characters. The general occurrence of pleiotropism, as well as the fact that a given character is usually responsive to more than one locus, confirms us in our position.

From our assertion of the equal taxonomic value of every character (see Sections 5.2 and 5.3 for our definition of a character) it is only a small step to the Adansonian practice of equal weight for every character when using it to evaluate taxonomic relationships. This is a point in direct conflict with traditional taxonomic practice and over which much controversy has raged. We propose to discuss this issue in some detail in the next chapter and would like to mention here only that, granted the desirability of the separation of the measure of resemblance from a study of phylogeny, equal weighting is an almost self-evident logical consequence. We feel reassured in that at least three independent researchers working along somewhat different lines and from different assumptions have all reached the identical conclusion.

The actual computation of a measure of affinity can be done in a variety of ways (Chapter 6). Most methods result in coefficients of similarity ranging between unity and zero, the former for perfect agreement, the latter for none whatever. Except in unusual cases the calculations are likely to be rather tedious, and electronic computation will be needed for any but very minor studies.

The similarity coefficients are then tabulated in matrix form with one coefficient for every pair of taxonomic entities (see Appendix, Table A-6). If a symmetrical (mirror image) matrix is to be tabulated for $t$ entities, a $t \times t$ matrix will result with unity in the principal diagonal (often represented by X in the diagonal; see Appendix, Table A-14). This matrix can be represented geometrically by points in a space (see Figure 6-2 in Chapter 6). A maximum of $t - 1$ dimensions is needed for a correct representation of the $t$ points (taxonomic entities) in the space. The distances between the points are related to taxonomic distances.

## 4.5. THE CONSTRUCTION OF NATURAL TAXA

It is our belief (expounded in detail in Chapter 7) that when taxa are established on the basis of an adequate representation of characters, the resulting classification will be natural, in the sense of Gilmour.

Classification in numerical taxonomy is based on a matrix of resemblances, and it consists of various techniques designed to disclose and summarize the structure of the matrix. A rough, graphical representation of the structure can be obtained by differential shading of the elements of the matrix (see Figure 7-3). In this manner the structure of the assemblage of taxonomic entities becomes immediately apparent if they have previously been roughly grouped so that supposedly similar forms are near each other. If, as is methodologically preferable, the entities are placed in the matrix without predetermined order, visual grouping is not easily accomplished without rearrangement. The various computational methods for clustering will process the data equally efficiently whether they are ordered or not. Since computational methods simultaneously provide some numerical evaluation of the taxonomic relationships, they are to be preferred.

These numerical methods, familiar in psychometrics for many years, are collectively called cluster analysis (see Section 7.3.2). By way of a general description, they may be recognized as more or less automatic methods for establishing and defining clusters of mutually high similarity coefficients among the entities in the resemblance matrix. These clusters may be likened to hills and peaks on a topographic chart, and the criteria for establishing the clusters are analogous to the contour lines of such a map. Rigid criteria correspond to high elevation lines which surround isolated high peaks—for example, species groups in a matrix of resemblances between species. As the criteria become more relaxed the clusters grow and become interrelated in the same way that isolated peaks acquire broader bases and become connected to form mountain complexes and eventually chains, with progress from higher to lower level contour lines. It should be emphasized again that the clusters are based on phenetic resemblances only and have no necessary phyletic connotations.

Differences in methods of clustering refer mainly to definition of the cluster, whether by lowest or highest or average resemblance. Of particular importance are the principles upon which the relationships among the relatively higher categories are to be based. What weight is to be given to isolated single entities when their resemblance to a group containing several other entities is to be evaluated? Are resemblances among the higher units to be based on averages of the resemblances of individual entities or are they to be computed in some other manner? Various approaches have been taken so far; their relative merits are discussed in Section 7.3.2.6. The differences among them are, however, largely matters of technical detail.

The important common aspect of all these methods is that they permit the delimitation of taxonomic groups in an entirely objective manner, providing that the coefficients of relationship have been properly based on many characters chosen without bias and correctly computed. This is best illustrated by using a diagram of relationships of the type shown in Figure 7-10. Horizontal transects at any level will include in a taxon all those entities branching off a single stem crossed by the transect. If this is the first (and finest) grouping, there will be no upper limit to the closeness of the relationships within a taxon, but the transect will constitute the lower limit of affinity. Thus objectively definable and— what is even more important—exactly comparable limits can be drawn for all taxonomic groups within a particular study. Similar transects at progressively lower levels of affinity will create taxa of higher and higher taxonomic rank.

The number and position of transects should follow some prearranged system. Clearly they will depend on the size of the matrix: too many transects would provide too fine a classification; too few would leave much structure unrevealed. The aims of the investigator, conventions in the particular group, and questions of convenience and esthetics would all affect the placing of the transects. While Mayr, Linsley, and Usinger (1953) would permit considerations of convenience to affect both the number and size of taxa of a given rank, we consider the number of taxa to be established at any rank a relatively unimportant and arbitrary detail. But once a transect has been established, the structure within a taxon (and hence the number of lower ranked taxa contained therein) depends entirely on the resemblance values of entities and stems and is not subject to the manipulations of the investigator. In other words, *the position and number of transects is arbitrary, but they must be straight and horizontal lines.* Thus within one study the criteria for one taxonomic level must be identical.

We view monotypic taxa or very numerous ones with equanimity. Their occurrence does not lead us, respectively, into lumping or splitting. In taking such a position we are motivated by an effort to supply taxa with some objective and definable criteria. While conventional systematics purports that its taxonomic ranks represent affinity levels as well as monophyletic groups, they are in reality dubious vehicles for either concept. Numerical taxonomy restricts its criteria to phenetic affinity only but attempts to apply its criteria with consistency. In erecting taxa, some criterion for intragroup cohesion has to be established. This will largely depend on the method of cluster formation (Section 7.3.2.).

Biologists who use the results of taxonomic research are much concerned with the stability of a classification. The stability of a scheme based on numerical taxonomy may be affected in two ways.

(1) More information (in the form of new characters) may accumulate. If the initial evaluation of resemblances has been based on an adequate sample of characters it is our contention that their (relative) values would change very little on the addition of further characters (Section 5.6).

(2) New taxonomic entities may be included in subsequent studies. Although this will not change resemblance values among the old entities, application of the previous criteria for levels and number of transects may result in new and different taxa. Agreement will have to be reached by practitioners of numerical taxonomy on whether the established system should be rearranged to suit the new results or whether the new data should be judged by standards of relationship already established—that is, whether the transects should be continued at the level at which they were drawn in the first study. The pros and cons of this issue are discussed in Section 7.8.

In establishing a series of nested categories, the question of naming them inevitably arises. What level in the hierarchy are we to call a subgenus, a genus, a family? Have these terms any significance of their own other than as indications of the relative levels of the transects? It is generally accepted in conventional systematics that genera (and other categories) in such diverse groups as insects, birds, and flowering plants do not represent taxa of equivalent affinity values. Is it possible for numerical taxonomy to set up such equivalent categories, although these would be based on entirely different groups of characters (discussion in Section 7.5)? It would appear preferable to employ a new series of terms for the hierarchic system established by numerical taxonomy, which would include in the terms a quantitative estimate of the affinity of the group. The term 80-phenon (or 60-phenon) is suggested to connote groups affiliated at levels no lower than 80% (or 60%) of the scale used in the analysis (see Section 9.1.1). Though the use of unfamiliar terms has some disadvantages, it would obviate the use of the imprecise older terms with their semantic and emotional encumbrances.

Mention should be made of alternative ways of obtaining structure from a matrix of resemblances. Sokal has suggested the use of multiple factor analysis for matrices based on correlation coefficients (Sokal, 1958; Rohlf and Sokal, 1962). This method is also described in Section 7.3.3.

## 4.6. EMPIRICAL VERSUS PHYLOGENETIC TAXONOMY

It should by now be apparent that the taxonomic procedures proposed above are of a strictly empirical nature. As such they are related to procedures used by some typologists in the past. This, however, is not an automatic disqualification of our views (as Simpson, 1961, would imply), since there are certain typological viewpoints which are more defensible than the corresponding phylogenetic views (Sokal, 1962b). The fundamental test of the validity of empiricism in taxonomy must be whether it can be used as a consequential and consistent method for arranging organized nature. We hope to convince the reader that it can be so used and that it is the only reasonable approach.

A basic (and very controversial) attitude of the proponents of numerical taxonomy is the strict separation of phylogenetic speculation from taxonomic procedure. Taxonomic relationships between taxa are to be evaluated purely on the basis of the resemblances existing *now* in the material at hand. The relationships are thus *static* (Michener, 1957) or *phenetic*, as we now prefer to call them. They do not take into account the mode of origin of the resemblances found nor the rate at which resemblances may have increased or decreased in the past. This attitude is taken for two distinct reasons.

(1) Until and unless methods are developed for objectively assessing and quantifying the phylogenetic significance of character differences or affinities, the consideration of such information is incompatible with our stated aim of objectivity and repeatability for the taxonomic process.

(2) We have mentioned in Section 2.3 that we do not at the moment possess (nor can we currently conceive of) a classificatory scheme, graphic or otherwise, able simultaneously to yield information on degree of resemblance, descent, and rate of evolutionary progress. Any scheme attempting to combine these approaches must of necessity involve

compromises and inconsistencies, to which any observer of our present-day *systema naturae* must testify. We therefore treat these aspects of taxonomy separately, establishing the phenetic resemblances of taxonomic entities and basing our classification on this information alone. Any phylogenetic deductions are then made on the basis of the phenetic classification but are not involved in the classificatory process.

The separation of phenetic and phyletic considerations in taxonomy is a very drastic step, to which we have not come lightly. Unavoidably, misunderstandings with our colleagues are frequent. It is difficult for all of us to abandon patterns of thought acquired with our early training. Numerical taxonomy is accused of being anti-evolutionary and of dragging taxonomy back into its typological, pre-evolutionary period. The practitioners of the new methods are lumped with the few surviving true anti-evolutionists because the latter also propose classification of organisms on the basis of their visible characters and without phylogenetic considerations. As it happens, all the proponents of numerical taxonomy are evolutionary biologists in their own right. They are firmly convinced that phylogeny is responsible for the existence and structure of the natural system. They are criticizing not evolution or the study of phylogeny but speculation passed off as fact. We believe that numerical taxonomy offers new opportunities for measuring and studying evolution in quantitative terms, as discussed in Chapter 8.

Not only do we insist on the separation of phenetic from phyletic considerations in taxonomic procedure, but we also feel that only phenetic evidence can be used to establish a satisfactory classification. We hold this belief for two reasons.

(1) The available fossil record is so fragmentary that the phylogeny of the vast majority of taxa is unknown; taxonomy as a subject can scarcely be restricted to a few favored groups simply to satisfy the dogma that to be natural a classification must be phylogenetic.

(2) Even when fossil evidence is available, this evidence itself must first be interpreted in a strictly phenetic manner—with the exception that a time scale is given in addition, which may restrict certain choices of interpretation of the phylogeny—since the criteria for choosing the ancestral forms in a phylogeny are phenetic criteria and are based on the phenetic relationship between putative ancestor and descendant. Any attempt to decide the phylogeny on one set of characters, in particular those believed to be homologous (derived from a common

ancestor, by the common definition of the term), or to decide the lines of descent without resorting to phenetic criteria, or to decide a priori which characters are important or are reliable guides to the phylogeny, soon leads to a tangle of circular arguments from which there is no escape. Even Simpson (1961), who strongly supports a phylogenetically based taxonomy, is aware of and points out the *circulus vitiosus* of this procedure.

To ignore phylogenetic considerations while evaluating taxonomic relationships is not an easy mental task for a biologist of this day and age. For almost a century there has been an intimate conceptual association between taxonomic and phylogenetic reasoning, so that terms such as "specialized," "primitive," "homologous," and many others have assumed double meanings whose distinction is rarely attempted. We ourselves find difficulty in keeping apart phyletic and phenetic implications of the terms we use. We have, however, made every effort to do so in this book.

## 4.7. THE RECOGNITION OF PHYLETIC RELATIONSHIPS

Much of our discussion of phylogeny has been destructive criticism, unavoidably so since it is useless to build classifications upon phylogenetic speculations. Our present aim is to make classificatorily stable phenetic groups. Nevertheless, we believe that numerical taxonomy offers constructive suggestions for the study of evolution (Chapter 8). We believe that quantified measures of phenetic affinity between organisms of different periods will afford the phylogeneticist with objective information. Such information may serve several purposes. It may indicate which of a number of forms is most likely to have been the ancestor or the descendant of a given organism, thus assisting in the construction of phylogenetic trees. It may indicate the rates and direction of evolution, or it may assist in the solution of some stratigraphic problems.

Even when organisms from only one period of time are studied, their phenetic relations may be of phylogenetic interest. At the very least they will serve as a sounder basis for phylogenetic speculation than has hitherto been available. Much useful information may also be obtained for studies of speciation by comparing phenetic differences with genetic or geographical data.

## 4.8.  IDENTIFICATION OF SPECIMENS

One of the tasks of the taxonomist revising a group is to set up a scheme for the simple and rapid identification of undetermined specimens by persons not necessarily familiar with the group in question. This is usually accomplished by the preparation of a taxonomic key (for a recent discussion see Metcalf, 1954). Such a key may be based as much as possible on the natural system of classification, so that following the various dichotomies in sequence one traces along the branches of the dendrogram from high-ranking taxa, through intermediate ones, to the ultimate entities of the system. Other keys are entirely artificial and utilitarian, their arrangement ensuring the simplest possible discrimination of the forms and having no relation to the taxonomic structure of the entities. For purposes of identification alone, both types of keys may be equally suitable. What aid, if any, can numerical taxonomy give in the construction of taxonomic keys?

All the various methods of estimating resemblances in numerical taxonomy abstract or summarize information based on many characters. They thus submerge the very data used by taxonomists in making keys. This does not mean, however, that practitioners of numerical taxonomy will be unable to construct keys. The basic information on the characters and their states in each taxonomic entity which is fed into computers is eminently well suited for the construction of keys. The various machines available in the average computation laboratory are able—better and faster than the most practiced taxonomist—to sift through the mass of information available.

## 4.9.  NOMENCLATURE

It does not seem to us that numerical taxonomy is likely to cause very great changes in the present system of nomenclature (see Chapter 9). The increased differentiation in phenetic affinities will mean that finer differences in rank can be distinguished. To take advantage of this we have suggested the phenon system of nomenclature. This seems to us preferable to attempting on every occasion to force categories of rank upon the affinity scale. Such a terminology would, we think, assist the stability of the present nomenclature. However, if a numerical study showed considerable changes from the orthodox nomenclature, the author has no choice but to alter the classification and to make such changes of name as are then required. We must do this if we are to provide other biologists with the benefits of improved classifications.

The present dependence of the system of nomenclature upon types may be somewhat changed by the advent of numerical taxonomy, for it will be in principle possible to determine the limits of taxonomic groups, which up to the present has been a matter of individual opinion. Numerical nomenclatures for intermediate forms, whether phenotypic or phyletic, may also prove of some use. New nomenclatural types may also be chosen from numerical taxonomies. All of these developments would be best coordinated with recent methods of handling data by modern data-processing machinery.

# CHAPTER 5

# Taxonomic Evidence:
# Characters and Taxa

We now proceed to a detailed discussion of the data necessary for obtaining estimates of affinity between taxa. This leads us first into a consideration of the nature of taxonomic characters, to a discussion of problems in character evaluation, such as convergence and weighting, and eventually to an account of the fundamental taxonomic units to be employed in numerical taxonomy.

## 5.1. PRELIMINARY CHOICE OF SPECIMENS

There is no sharp distinction between the selection of specimens and the selection of characters, since these generally proceed *pari passu*. Both of these are discussed in some detail here and in Section 5.4. Nevertheless, one must first make a preliminary selection of specimens in order to restrict one's study to a manageable taxonomic group. This group is selected by "classification from above," and selection is therefore necessarily based on rather few characters.

A point of some importance is to guard against the exclusion of pertinent material because it does not strictly fulfill all the criteria for the working definition of the taxon to be studied. The danger is that aberrant forms or descriptions of aberrant taxa in the literature may be excluded because they do not possess some character of the taxon which the systematist considers essential or diagnostic. Gross mistakes are unlikely: penguins will not be excluded from a study on birds because they cannot fly, nor will bats be included because they do fly. Yet less extreme cases may well occur, especially in poorly known taxa. We have seen from the discussion of natural classification in Section 2.2 that it is not possible to be certain that all members of a taxon will possess any given character. It is therefore advisable to spread one's net widely rather than to risk excluding forms because of some aberrance. The inclusion of a small amount of possibly atypical or unsatisfactory material, which may have to be excluded in the final analysis, is a worthwhile insurance against an unrepresentative study. Very similar considerations will apply to material which has been extracted from the literature, though the danger of mistakes is naturally greater.

There is no need to belabor the point, now very well understood, of choosing adequate numbers of specimens for establishing taxa. These could be individuals for establishing species, or species for erecting higher taxa. To some degree the exemplar method proposed in the next chapter (Section 6.4) is in contradiction to this admonition, since by that method only single representatives of given taxa are used in the studies. However, it is clear that such exemplars are only reference points and do not indicate the limits of the taxa which they represent. The special problems attendant on material of different ages, different stages of the life cycle, and fragmentary material are discussed in Sections 5.3.7 and 6.5.

## 5.2. DEFINITION OF TAXONOMIC CHARACTERS

Procedure in taxonomy, orthodox or numerical, is based on taxonomic characters. The term character has been employed in at least two distinct senses by systematists. Its commonest usage is as a distinguishing feature of taxa—a characteristic (or feature) of one kind of organism which will distinguish it from another kind. Thus, serrated leaves may distinguish one species of plant from another and hence are called a character; similarly, punctate elytra may differentiate between two species of beetles, or resistance to phenol separate two strains of bacteria. This appears to be the sense in which Mayr, Linsley, and Usinger (1953) define a taxonomic character, as "any attribute of an organism or of a group of organisms by which it differs from an organism belonging to a different taxonomic category or resembles an organism belonging to the same category." Unfortunately such definitions point out again the circular reasoning which may infiltrate taxonomic procedure: if the term character is restricted to differences between *taxa*, the taxa themselves cannot be recognized without the characters themselves being first known.

Another frequent meaning of the term character, which has been espoused by numerical taxonomists as being the more useful one in their work, is that a character is a property or "feature which varies from one kind of organism to another" (Michener and Sokal, 1957) or "anything that can be considered as a variable independent of any other thing considered at the same time" (Cain and Harrison, 1958; we assume the independence referred to is logical rather than functional or mathematical). Thus, referring to the previous examples, the nature of the margins of the leaves becomes the character, while entire, serrated, undulating, or any other types of margin become different *states* of the character (Michener and Sokal, 1957). Cain and Harrison (1958) would call these the *values* of a character. We prefer the earlier term, since it does not imply a quantitative expression and is thus more suitable in cases of qualitative difference. The word "state" may imply qualitative rather than quantitative subdivision, but in the absence of a more suitable term we employ it to cover both. In the sense in which these terms will be used in this book, the condition with respect to punctation of the elytral surface and the property of phenol resistance would be characters, while smooth or punctate and resistant or susceptible, respectively, would be character states.

No objection should be raised to defining a character as a feature which varies from one organism to another. However, if we say that it varies between kinds of organisms (or species) then we are ourselves in the same sort of dilemma as a systematist attempting to apply the definition of character in the first paragraph of this section—that is, defining characters on the basis of predefined taxa. Thus we would first have to define our species before we could define the characters. To be extremely critical, therefore, we would have to define characters entirely on the basis of the differences between individuals. Specific characters are, of course, nothing but summaries or abstractions of the characteristics of a large number of individuals.

Sneath (1957b), partly to make his data conform to his methodology, but largely because of the peculiar nature of taxonomic characters in the bacteria, established characters (which he called "features") of two states (which he called positive and negative features or values). In the interest of generality we shall also use the character-state terminology for this type of data.

The general definition of characters established above cannot, however, give much aid to the practicing taxonomist in the process of recognizing and describing individual characters. We shall go into this problem in the next section, from both the theoretical and practical points of view.

## 5.3. UNIT CHARACTERS

### 5.3.1. Theoretical considerations

The person embarking on work in numerical taxonomy is apt to be puzzled by the task of recognizing the basic units of information for the study. We have called these the *unit characters*. Cain and Harrison (1958) have called them "single characters." In trying to define these characters we must first ask ourselves what properties we wish to recognize. Do we wish to recognize genes, or a unit element in selection, or a logical construct? If, as is now clear, genes are themselves complex entities, shall we subdivide them? And if so, to what extent?

Most definitions of a unit character have been too restricted; defining a unit character in terms of morphology, chemistry, genetics or evolution does not allow the broad treatment needed for a general theory of systematics. For this we need to define unit characters in terms of information theory, for in every instance it is information which the characters convey to the taxonomist; this idea is closely linked to the concept of natural taxa as groups with high content of information (see Section 2.2). We may also plausibly interpret the general theory in terms of modern genetic theory. An attempt to introduce the concept of information has been made (Sneath, 1957b), and a unit character (there called a "feature") was defined as an attribute possessed by an organism about which one statement can be made, thus yielding a single piece of information. These attributes are formally logical constructs, since they will change if the technique of observation changes; the definition is therefore an operational one. Where a character can vary continuously, such as the length of an organ, this character of length is broken down into as many steps as the observational method will allow with good reliability. Either each step is counted as a feature, or at least the minimum number of features necessary to account for the existing variation is postulated.

This approach may be carried to its logical conclusion, where each unit character or feature represents an alternative which can be answered as "Yes" or "No," "Possessed" or "Not Possessed"; the information content can then be measured as "bits," as is usual in information theory.

(A "bit" in information theory is a single piece of information conveyed, for example, by one electrical impulse; it can be represented by a binary digit.) Each feature is one bit: a character with $x$ states is composed of no more than $x$ bits. In practice we sometimes have to use a third category "Not Known" or "Uncertain if Possessed," but in principle this is not needed.

Clearly even the most simple organisms contain a great many bits of information. We may plausibly relate this number to the genome in the following way. On the current hypothesis of genetic structure, the genome consists of a series of nucleotides which are paired one-to-one in a double helix of deoxyribonucleic acid (DNA). On the Watson-Crick model of DNA each adenine residue is paired to a thymine residue and vice versa, and each cytosine residue is paired to a guanine residue and vice versa. The genetic information is then postulated to reside in the sequence of the different nucleotides and may be thought of as a code message written in an alphabet of four letters, each letter representing one of the four alternative nucleotides—those containing thymine, cytosine, adenine, or guanine. The genetic code message is then believed to be translated into other codes determining the amino acid sequence of proteins and the structure of other molecules in the cell, and these in turn determine the physiological and morphological properties of the organism (this is excellently discussed by Anfinsen, 1959). We may tentatively identify our taxonomic bits with the genetic code, and since it is believed that all or at least the great bulk of the DNA is functional, we can calculate on this hypothesis the number of nucleotide pairs and the number of taxonomic bits per genome (each nucleotide pair is equivalent to two bits, since there are four alternatives). The weight of a nucleotide pair is about $10^{-21}$ g and a diploid mammalian nucleus contains on the order of $5 \times 10^{-12}$ g of DNA, or about $5 \times 10^9$ nucleotide pairs; a haploid chromosome set will contain half this. This figure of $2.5 \times 10^9$ pairs will comprise $5 \times 10^9$ bits, which will mean that there will be $2^{5,000,000,000}$ possible alternative combinations of nucleotide pairs in the haploid genome. Dobzhansky (1959) and Sneath (1964) list some figures for the nucleotide pairs in various organisms, from which we may choose a few examples. The number of bits of information in a haploid set of chromosomes of man and of the horse is about $6 \times 10^9$, of an *Amphiuma* about $1.7 \times 10^{11}$, of a crab about $3 \times 10^9$, and of a sponge about $1 \times 10^8$. Some other examples of the number of bits in the haploid state (calculated from data cited by Jacob and Wollman, 1958; Ogur et al., 1951; Frisch-Niggemeyer, 1956; Pontecorvo and Roper,

1956; and Allison and Burke, 1962) are: lily, $1 \times 10^{11}$; *Drosophila*, $1.5 \times 10^{8}$; *Aspergillus*, $8 \times 10^{7}$; the bacterium *Escherichia coli*, $2 \times 10^{7}$; $T_2$ bacteriophage, $4 \times 10^{5}$; most DNA viruses, $3.6 \times 10^{5}$; and some RNA viruses, $1.2 \times 10^{4}$. The number of functional genes is of course much smaller, since each gene is made up of many bits. These figures are only speculative, and do not include any non-chromosomal genetic information or environmental effects, but it is clear that the content of information is much smaller in microorganisms than in higher organisms. The scale of the potential store of information in a nucleus may be judged from the estimate that the Library of Congress contains between $10^{13}$ and $10^{14}$ bits (see Good, 1958). It is interesting to note that Elsasser (1958, pp. 100–104) estimated from morphological considerations that the information in man was at least $10^{7}$ bits. It should be noted that the bits are a measure of the potential information content, not of the number of alternative permutations of the information. The latter is $2^{x}$ when the number of bits is $x$, as shown in the example above.

### 5.3.2. Working definition

Except in those few and simple organisms whose fine chemical structure is gradually being unraveled, the above considerations are premature. A workable definition which the practicing taxonomist can use is needed. We may define a unit character as *a taxonomic character of two or more states, which within the study at hand cannot be subdivided logically, except for subdivision brought about by changes in the method of coding.*

Since we cannot in most cases make genetic inferences from phenetic studies of characters, we shall generally have to use phenotypic characters as our basic information, defining these as narrowly as possible. Our failure to make *logical* subdivisions may rest on ignorance of the finer structure or the causation of a character. Thus presence or absence of a bristle in an insect may be a unit character, if we know nothing of its finer structure and have no way of subdividing it. Even if the general morphogenesis of the structure is known from a representative form, unless morphogenetic differences can be established which can serve as taxonomic characters within the group studied, the presence or absence of the bristle remains the unit character. To consider another character, the same insect may possess or lack DDT-dehydrogenase, which character we are again unable to subdivide further in view of our present knowledge. Thus, the organizational levels of unit characters may differ considerably from character to character and with advances in our knowledge. The ruling idea is that each character state should contribute one new item of information.

### 5.3.3. Inadmissible characters

The proper selection of characters is clearly a critical point in the application of numerical taxonomy, as it is in other taxonomies, and misunderstandings have arisen on this score. Full discussion of this subject is intentionally delayed until Section 5.4.4, when more of our general viewpoint will have been presented. There are, however, certain kinds of characters whose nature clearly disqualifies them from employment in a numerical taxonomic study. These are listed in the present section as inadmissible characters.

#### 5.3.3.1. Meaningless characters

It is undesirable to use attributes which are not a reflection of the genotypes of the organisms themselves. For this reason taxonomists do not include the names or numbers given to specimens, nor do they employ characters whose response to the environment is so variable that it is not possible to decide what is environmentally and what is genetically determined. The number of leaves on a branch of a tree may be an example of the latter, though if acceptable evidence is forthcoming that this number is relatively constant in a species it might be admissible. This is a matter of scientific judgment, not simply of taxonomic method, and each case must be treated on its merits.

#### 5.3.3.2. Logically correlated characters

We must exclude as redundant any property which is a logical consequence of another. We cannot use both hemoglobin and redness of blood if the latter is defined as possession of hemoglobin. Mathematical manipulations which constitute logical consequences should be avoided: for example, we could not employ both the length and half the length of an organ, or the radius and the circumference of a circular structure. Similarly, characters which are tautological—those which are true by definition and those which are based on properties known to be obligatory—should not be included. An example of tautology is to score both length and height of a man. An example of a character which is true by definition is to score "presence of calcium in raphides" after having scored "raphides composed of calcium oxalate"; by definition, this substance contains calcium. To score in this instance "raphides insoluble in acetic acid" would be scoring a character which is a known and invariable property of calcium oxalate, though it is not part of the definition of that compound; if this is known, the property must be omitted. In making these qualifications for admissibility we are fully aware that many or most of the "inadmissible" characters would be inadmissible on more than one count. Thus, if we use two tautological characters, we would find on examining our data after they had been prepared for machine computation that the two characters are perfectly correlated. According to our rules on empirical correlations (see Section 5.3.3.6) there would be much suspicion about using both of these characters. It is quite likely that we would therefore reject one of them by the empirical correlation criterion.

### 5.3.3.3. *Partial logical correlations*

Many cases will arise where the dependence of one character upon another is not total but only partial. Cain and Harrison (1958) illustrate this by an example.

> Degree of melanization of the skin in mg./sq. cm. must not be used together with skin colour estimated by some colorimetric method, if the melanin is making a contribution, which is some function of its own density, to the skin colour, unless this contribution can be subtracted from the measurement of skin colour.

We would recommend the following procedure in cases of partial logical correlations. When a character **B** depends in part upon another character **A**, the decision whether to employ **B** as well as **A** will depend on the nature of the factors other than **A** that affect **B**. If, to the best of our knowledge, these factors reflect heritable variations, we would include **B**. But if these factors represent experimental or technical error or are otherwise unaccountable, we would not use character **B**.

### 5.3.3.4. *Invariant characters*

We would exclude characters which do not vary within the entire sample of organisms or taxa. To include them would not add any information about affinities within the sample. Employment of invariant characters would simply raise the magnitude of all the coefficients of similarity uniformly and would thus diminish the differences among the coefficients; these differences, however, are the very facts which we would like to bring out and study. There may be instances, notably in bacteriology, where established techniques prescribe a list of tests to be performed. It may be argued that from the point of view of obtaining standardized results all tests should be included in the computation; however, since all coefficients obtained are only relative quantities, we would recommend that invariant characters not be included.

### 5.3.3.5. *Experimental error*

One should guard against subdivision of characters on grounds subject to experimental error. Thus, it would not be proper to divide hemoglobin content of mammalian blood into classes 1% wide, since the customary method of determination is not accurate to this figure.

### 5.3.3.6. *Empirical correlations*

How should we decide if two characters not logically related, but highly correlated empirically, are to be counted as separate unit characters? It is possible to give extreme examples which are absurd. Thus it is observationally true to say that certain avian characters are invariably associated, and likewise certain mammalian characters. Should we attribute this effect to a single character in which birds and mammals differ—a gene, perhaps, which if it mutated would turn a bird into a mammal at one jump? Clearly, we would here prefer to postulate many independent genes, and we would treat these features as independent despite the strictest correlation. In still other instances we would not assume independence so easily. The close correlation between pink eyes and white skin of total albinos in most vertebrates would be counted as a single character, since the total absence of pigment implies lack of retinal pigment.

Yet it remains true that we often need to postulate independent characters even in cases such as the albinos, for occasional albinos do have some retinal pigment. The same is true of most other apparently dependent associations. Any exception will suffice to prove that more than one character is involved. Even strictly functional associations are not as dependent as they seem at first sight: the need for the teeth to meet is only true for a species as a whole; aberrant individuals can and do occur. The fact that selection keeps two characters (the position of the top teeth and the position of the bottom teeth) in close correspondence does not necessarily imply unitary causation of these characters. In coding such a species for analysis we would employ two characters in spite of their stringent empirical correlation in the material at hand.

In serially homologous structures such as segments of an annelid or appendages of an arthropod, or in generally homologous structures such as hairs on the body surface, a character affecting equally all the members of the series could be subdivided into separate characters for each member. However, no new information would be brought about by such a procedure. In such a case we would employ only one character.

In summary, when we have evidence that more than one factor affects two correlated characters within a study, regardless of whether this evidence comes from within the study or from outside, we would include both characters; otherwise we would employ only one. Our position is that we assume at least some independent sources of variation in any empirical correlation, unless we have reason to believe otherwise. This would err in the direction of redundancy, but it would be counter-balanced by the likelihood of obtaining new information.

### 5.3.4. Operational homology

When scoring the characters of the organisms for comparison, we must decide what is the "same" character and the "same" state in two forms. In many instances there will be no problem. In others, especially if taxa are distantly related, we will be uncertain, and it is tempting to appeal to homology to answer our question. We have seen in Section 2.3 that it is in many cases difficult, if not impossible, to decide if two characters are homologous by the criterion of common descent (or by being traceable to a common ancestral organ or structure). By this criterion the characters are the "same" only in the restricted sense of having the same evolutionary origin, of which we may have little evidence. For example, is the amino acid methionine homologous by descent in bacteria, birds, and begonias? In order to cut this Gordian knot we prefer to call two character states the "same" whenever they are indistinguishable. Similarly, if the abstraction or idea of two characters cannot be distinguished in the taxa, then again we would consider them to be the "same." In practice the worker will divide his organisms into major structures or other such divisions (for example, head, limbs, leaves), and he must first decide whether these are the "same." Then he can proceed to look for differences in their properties which may be used as the bases for setting up the characters and their states. Within each major structure he again looks for subsidiary structures and repeats these procedures. Characters in this sense are synthesized from the states.

For example, consider two species of insects that are both black, while others in the same genus are red. If we had no way of distinguishing the two kinds of black, we would consider them to have the same character state, "black." Similarly, we would consider "redness" and "blackness" to be states of the same character, "body color," unless we had reason to believe that this color was of a different nature in some of these insects than in others. If, for instance, we found colors due to pigments as well as colors due to optical interference phenomena (such as iridescence) occurring in the group of insects under consideration, we would then subdivide our former character "body color" into two: "pigmental body color" and "structural (interference) body color."

By way of another example, leaves on a given series of plants may be long or short. We first have to decide what a leaf is and whether the structures seen on the separate specimens are in fact leaves—that is, are the "same"—or perhaps are other structures such as modified stems. Having decided that they are leaves, we also have to agree on what we shall call a short leaf—perhaps one of less than 3 cm; if so, we shall call a long leaf one that is longer than 3 cm. In this sense all leaves shorter than 3 cm are homologously short leaves, those longer than that are homologously long. The character will now be called "length of leaf," with two states, "short" and "long." Clearly it could have had more states had one wished to construct it in such a manner. In each leaf other characters, such as the venation, pubescence, and similar properties, could be coded as characters.

We call this approach "operational homology." Our position is largely that of common sense; when we say that two characters are operationally homologous we imply that they are very much alike in general and in particular. If the characters are "not quite the same," then more than one character is involved, and they should be broken into several independent ones; some of these independent characters will then be indistinguishable and will be scored as "the same" character in the two organisms.

Special problems in defining homology arise in the case of rudimentary or degenerate characters. In such cases it would often be impossible to surmise supposed lines of descent, without intermediate forms represented by developmental stages or by fossils. The actual establishment of the homology even in such cases remains on morphological grounds—by comparison of adjacent stages in each ontogenetic or fossil sequence. The procedures involved are therefore not especially different from those of operational homology. When fossil evidence is lacking, homologies of rudimentary organs are frequently established on the basis of a comparative series of recent forms, showing varying expression of the structure in question. Here again a comparative morphological approach is used between adjacent recent forms, and the evolutionary sequence is then inferred. While a phylogenetic theme underlies all such comparisons, taxonomists are in fact establishing homologies only on phenetic evidence in these cases, just as the vast majority of taxonomic work is based on phenetic classifications, notwithstanding phylogenetic protestations to the contrary. A phylogenetic concept of homology, while simple to define and satisfying to contemplate, is not susceptible to direct proof but only to proof-by-inference. Zangerl (1948) has pointed out quite correctly that any phylogenetic definition of homology robs the concept of its only possible function, namely as a tool, since we do not and cannot know anything a priori about the causality of a given structural relationship between parts of *different* organisms.

Despite this superficial air of simplicity, operational homology does present considerable logical difficulties which have seldom been discussed. We should first mention that this was close to the original meaning of the term "homology" as employed by Richard Owen (see Simpson, 1961, p. 79). Owen used it to mean the "same" organ in two organisms, as opposed to analogy, which was "different" organs fulfilling the same function. Whether an organ was "the same" was judged by its morphology and the correspondence of its parts. Woodger (1945) has discussed this in some detail and has shown the close connection between homology in the sense of morphological correspondence and a common structural plan or *Bauplan*. He points out that in making such morphological correspondences we pair the different parts of the structure in two organisms, with the aim of obtaining the greatest number of one-to-one pairings. For example, if we pair head of cat with head of dog we find numerous subsidiary pairings within this major pairing—for example, eye with eye, brain with brain; further pairings occur within the latter structures—lens with lens, retina with retina, cerebellum with cerebellum, and so on, down to histological levels and farther. A similar comparison between head and leg would show few such correspondences. Woodger illustrates his arguments by the example of the pentadactyl limb. He shows that the pairing of the "same" bone in two forms—as humerus with humerus, radius with radius, and so on—depends on the spatial relations of the bones. For example, the humerus is proximal to the other bones, the radius and ulna are both immediately distal to the the humerus, the ulna being postaxial to the radius, and so on. In a newly studied creature we call a bone the radius if we find that it bears these relations to the other bones, and if they in turn bear their own proper relations to each other. Such matching sets of bones he calls *isomorphic;* such sets form a *Bauplan.* He also discusses the difficulties which arise if some bones are atrophied or if their articulations are abnormal, when it may be difficult to recognize which bone corresponds to which.

Woodger correctly says that morphologists pair off organs one with the other intuitively so as to make the greatest number of one-to-one correspondences. We may add that this process is closely analogous to classification of organisms themselves. The aim is to make pairs within which are further pairs, and ultimately to group structures so that there is the greatest number of common properties in the "organ taxa" so set up. This is evident from a consideration of why we pair an eye with another eye and not with an ear. In both alternatives there are some shared properties (both organs are carried on the cranium, both are special sense organs) and some differences (no eye is identical with any other eye), but there is no single property which we can satisfactorily postulate a priori as being essential to the definition of an eye or an ear (since we may be sure that some morphologist will soon find an exception to our rule). Therefore the concept of morphological correspondence is polythetic (see Section 2.2), just as natural taxonomic groups are; hence morphological correspondence can, like natural taxa, only be defined as arrangements by which the groups so formed possess the greatest possible number of common properties. Such reasoning leads us to the threshold of an empirical "numerical homology"—that is, a numerical taxonomy of organic structure.

It is somewhat embarrassing to find that within the concept of natural taxonomic groups there are similar concepts of natural organ groups, and we may question whether there are not yet other concepts (such as natural gene groups) concealed within these, like a nest of Chinese boxes. There must, however, be some limit to this process, even if the limit lies at the fine structure of the genes.

The presence of an enzyme such as $\beta$-galactosidase in both an insect and a vertebrate raises an interesting point. Could the enzymatically active area of the enzyme in both animals be derived virtually unchanged from a common ancestor? This might happen if any change in this area led to loss of activity; such change would then be selected against. The rest of the enzyme might become different in the two forms because of the accumulation of changes in the molecule which were advantageous because they assisted the action of the enzyme in the particular conditions prevailing in the two lineages. We can infer that this has happened to some extent, since we know from serological and biochemical evidence that the same enzymes in closely related genera are usually markedly different in some properties, and yet they are most probably derived from a common ancestor (see, for instance, the work of Vithayathil et al., 1961). We do not know how far we may plausibly trace back the homology. Nevertheless, there does seem to be a possibility of the re-evolution of an enzyme if it has, by an extensive genetic deletion, been totally lost. The sporadic occurrence of enzymes unusual in animals, such as the carbohydrate-splitting enzymes of the snail, argues in favor of the possibility of evolution de novo, for it would be difficult to believe that these enzymes in snails are derived from their remote protistan ancestry. It seems very likely, however, that when such re-evolution does occur it is due to reduplication of a gene controlling the production of a similar enzyme followed by change in the enzymatic properties of one of the duplicate enzymes. It would otherwise be difficult to understand how the functional enzyme could be selected for during the period when presumably inactive protein molecules were being synthesized, under the control of the evolving but useless gene. The genetic information required seems to be much too great to be acquired by a single chance mutation, since the probability of a random sequence of amino acids being enzymically active must be exceedingly small. A further possibility is the transfer of genes from very dissimilar organisms. In the bacteria we know of mechanisms by which large amounts of genetic information (equivalent to complete genes and to complex biosynthetic pathways and their enzymes) can be transferred from one bacterium to another without direct cell contact. This can occur by the transfer of DNA either by a bacteriophage or else directly by solution in the medium, and in principle there seems to be no reason why genes should not sometimes be transferred to distantly related bacteria. If animal and plant viruses can in the same way carry genes derived from their hosts, or if direct DNA transfer can occur with successful incorporation into the genome of the recipient organism, we can envisage how a gene might be transferred to distantly related plants or animals. It is therefore not beyond the bounds of possibility that some unusual features of higher organisms are derived by gene transfer from very dissimilar forms of life.

So far as numerical taxonomy is concerned, the position on homology is no worse than that in conventional systematics: in both we have to decide as best we can what characters are "the same" in different organisms, and in the end this entails the application of uniform criteria to individual specimens; what is not distinguishable on these criteria must be considered as "the same" in these respects. Lest it be objected that one must first achieve a "numerical homology" before proceeding to numerical taxonomy, we may point out that it is possible to formulate a list of characters and their states so that they do not presuppose a prior knowledge of homologies. Such an approach has been successful in constructing phenetic classifications in bacteriology. There is no reason why it should not succeed with other organisms.

### 5.3.5. Two-state versus multistate characters

*Characters of two states (or all-or-none characters)* may be recorded as + and − or as 1 and 0. Provision must also be made for entries which cannot be scored, either because the characters are missing, unscorable, or inapplicable. For example, the data may be unknown, or the specimen damaged, or there may be a "logical bar" which prevents scoring of the entry. Such entries have been scored by Sneath (1957b) as NC (standing for "no comparison is to be made with this entry"); a special symbol may be convenient for use with computers, where a blank space may be ambiguous. This straightforward method of coding is referred to by Sneath (1957b) as method *A* and by Beers and Lockhart (1962) and Beers, Fisher, Megraw, and Lockhart (1962) as method 1.

It is usual to record positive characters (or attributes marked as present) as + (or as 1) and negative characters (or attributes marked as absent) as − (or as 0), but in most applications it is immaterial whether characters are scored as + or −. For ease in comprehension, however, it is usual to follow the convention above, in particular where an organ is missing, since the negative sign is a clearer indication that attributes belonging to that organ must be scored NC.

When only two alternatives present themselves to the observer, there is no choice. However, two kinds of multistate characters can occur. The states of *quantitative multistate characters* can each be expressed by a single numerical value; that is, they can be arranged in order of magnitude along a one-dimensional axis. Examples are the amount of a chemical produced by a bacterial strain, length of an animal, or amount of pubescence on a leaf. Characters such as this can almost always be conveniently coded into a number of states (1, 2, 3, $\cdots$) corresponding to their range of variation.

Often problems of scale will arise. If the amount of some substance produced is 1, 10, 100, and 10,000 units, respectively, in four taxa, one can code these 0, 1, 2, and 4, using a logarithmic transformation. This indeed is desirable rather than scoring it in its original scale, since the untransformed variable would exert excessive weight in most coefficients of similarity even if the characters were standardized. Transformations of this type are, of course, standard in statistical procedure. We should emphasize here that no character must be allowed to assume excessive weight; to permit this would make nonsense of our attempt to choose a wide and numerous sample of characters. It is far better to reduce the weight on such a character by transformation or standardization than to run the risk of its swamping the measures of affinity.

Should quantitative multistate characters be turned into several two-state characters, as shown by Sneath (1957b)? There is no practical necessity for this step when the method of similarity estimation is by correlation or distance analysis. These methods allow for a quantitative distinction between dissimilarities arising from two taxa possessing adjacent character states and those arising from taxa exhibiting states near the opposite ends of the scale. However, when association coefficients are to be computed, most of which require two-state characters, we have the choice of recoding the character in some fashion into several two-state characters or arbitrarily dividing the scale into two (not necessarily equally long) parts. The first course has much to recommend it. Quantitative multistate characters are very likely to be caused by more than one genetic factor and several two-state characters may thus be more appropriate. But since we do not in fact know whether one or several factors (genes?) are behind the expression of even two-state characters, use of the second option may be more conservative, while undoubtedly losing some information.

*Qualitative multistate characters* are those in which the several states cannot be arrayed in some obvious order but still refer to a unit character on logical grounds. An example would be sculpture patterns on the surface of an organism or alternative color patterns of a given structure. Here, ordering of states along a scale has been defended by some more or less hypothetical evolutionary sequence in which the supposedly primitive state is placed at one end of the scale in instances of linear sequences, or toward the middle of the scale in instances of V-shaped evolutionary sequences. The dangers inherent in such a procedure have been stressed in Chapter 2. Ordering of states along a scale might be followed in cases of other sequences: metabolic chains, ecological (successional) stages, and others.

If the investigator wishes—and also in cases where no reliable sequence can be established—an alternative course may be followed. This converts the qualitative multistate character into several new characters. This step is frequently not an easy task since the recoding has to be done in such a way that a positive score on one of the new characters does not automatically bring about negative scores on all other such characters derived from the same qualitative character. This is the problem of avoiding logically correlated characters, which is discussed from a more general point of view in Section 5.3.5.2.

A detailed exposition of techniques for recoding multistate characters into two-state characters is given in Section 5.3.6, below. The general reader who is not faced with this particular problem can, however, skip that section without losing the continuity of the argument. The problem of coding characters which are variable within the fundamental taxonomic units is discussed further in Section 6.4.

### 5.3.6. Recoding multistate characters into two-state characters

Persons wishing to employ association coefficients (see Section 6.2.1) may need to convert multistate characters into two-state characters. This procedure is also of interest if the characters are to be handled by information theory techniques as bits. Such recoding can be done in a number of ways, but it presents some logical difficulties, since one must decide whether the attributes comprising a multistate character should be treated as additive or nonadditive.

*Additive coding.* By this method the multiple character states are scored as a series of + signs. Thus a character with five states could be coded as follows:

|  |  | Two-state characters | | | |
|---|---|---|---|---|---|
|  |  | 1 | 2 | 3 | 4 |
| Multiple states | 0 | — | — | — | — |
|  | 1 | + | — | — | — |
|  | 2 | + | + | — | — |
|  | 3 | + | + | + | — |
|  | 4 | + | + | + | + |

In this way a multistate character of $x$ states is turned into $x - 1$ two-state characters. The scoring is termed additive since the state *3*, for instance, is expressed as the sum of the effects of the positive states of the two-state characters **1**, **2**, and **3**.

As with all-or-none characters this convention (few + signs for low quantitative values and many + signs for high quantitative values) is followed for two reasons: it is easier to understand and one must follow one convention consistently to be able to recognize overall size in characters where one can properly talk of size.

Additive scoring may exaggerate dissimilarities due to differences in overall size, although this effect is in general not pronounced, as might be thought. It has the merit of retaining the information on the magnitude of difference in the characters. It does, however, involve some logical redundancy. If, for example, an organism is marked — on character **1**, it is by definition also — on characters **2**, **3**, and **4**, and if it is marked + on character **4**, it is by definition also + on characters **1**, **2**, and **3**.

*Nonadditive coding.* Suppose we do not wish to assume that the effect on the phenotype of several small genetic changes is additive. We may then set up the following model. Two organisms **B** and **C**, sharing a multistate character but differing in state, may be regarded as being similar in one respect, $X$ (in possessing a detectable value for the character) but also different in one respect, $Y$ (in having a different value for the character). The magnitude of this difference is not considered. Their similarity on this character is therefore $\frac{1}{2}$. If they possess the same state they are similar in both respects with similarity $\frac{2}{2}$. However, an organism **A** in which the character is not detectable (has the value zero) differs in the first respect $X$ from **B** and **C**, but since it could not by definition manifest any positive value of the character, it is not comparable with respect to $Y$ or any subdivision of $Y$. All states other than $X$ must therefore be scored NC.

The coding scheme will therefore be as follows:

| Organism | Multistate character | Two-state characters | | | |
| --- | --- | --- | --- | --- | --- |
| | | $X$ | $Y_1$ | $Y_2$ | $Y_3$ |
| A | State 0 (character undetectable) | — | NC | NC | NC |
| B | State 1 (weak positive) | + | + | — | — |
| C | State 2 (moderate positive) | + | NC | + | — |
| D | State 3 (strong positive) | + | NC | NC | + |

This scheme is that referred to by Sneath (1957b) as method $C$ and by Beers and Lockhart (1962) and Beers, Fisher, Megraw, and Lockhart (1962) as method 2. It has been used chiefly in bacteriology.

The details of the scoring system suggested by Sneath (1957b) seem in retrospect to be unnecessarily complicated. They dealt at some length with the logic of coding, since it was felt that with the small number of characters usually available in microorganisms it was important to make the best use of them. We may omit as redundant any character which is invariant in all the OTU's (operational taxonomic units; Section 5.8), and we can therefore dispense with the scoring system there labeled $B$, as Beers and Lockhart (1962) and Beers, Fisher, Megraw, and Lockhart (1962) have suggested. When many characters are employed the different methods will usually give very similar results, and additive coding appears simple and adequate.

The different coding methods above give somewhat different average weights to each multistate character. When each state of the character is equally frequent among the OTU's and the number of such states is large, the mean similarity between all possible pairs of OTU's (expressed as matches out of the total number of comparisons, and including two minus values as a match) approaches $\frac{2}{3}$ with additive scoring, but $\frac{1}{3}$ on nonadditive scoring. If negative matches are not included, the mean similarities are $\frac{1}{2}$ in both instances.

*Binary coding.* An interesting alternative which can claim some logical basis is to code characters by employing the binary equivalent of the numerical value of the character state. For example, the binary equivalent of 6 is 110 (or $++-$ in the plus and minus convention) while that of 5 is 101 (or $+-+$). One here uses the convention that the right-hand binary place indicates the "unit" (which determines its odd or even value), the next indicates the "twos," the next indicates the "fours," and so on, in the same way that in decimal notation the right-hand place indicates the "units," the next place the "tens," the next the "hundreds." One may postulate that as a general rule it is permissible to assume that a multistate character is controlled by a number of attributes, assumed to be genetic, which control the size of the character in a similar way. For example, the state 6 is regarded as being the result of the action of genetic attributes $a$ and $b$ but not $c$, while state 5 is the result of genetic attributes $a$ and $c$ but not $b$. Each successive attribute then determines a doubling in the size (when expressed as the number of the character state). It must be emphasized that we do not know if this is true for any character, but we do know that a minimum number of attributes is needed to allow expression of a given number of character states, and this minimum number is the number of binary digits in this convention. It is also the most economical hypothesis: it uses the fewest attributes and the simplest relation between the attributes, the relation of doubling.

We would expect that when large numbers of features are employed this convention will give satisfactory results. It also has the merit of avoiding the difficulty of overall size. The problem of the size factor arises because in additive scoring the presence of some attributes necessarily involves the presence of many others; for example, in the example on additive coding the presence of two-state character 4 necessarily involves the presence of two-state characters 1, 2, and 3. This is not so with nonadditive scoring, which gives an expected similarity value of $\frac{1}{2}$ between two entities, however great the observed degree of difference is (that is, for entities differing in state, and ignoring negative matches and the complication of the completely negative score). Binary coding strikes a mean between these extremes. The relationship between entities in binary coding is, however, arbitrary in one respect. The difference between 7 and 8 (0111 and 1000) is greater than that between 6 and 7 (0110 and 0111). This, in effect, allocates weights at random to the underlying genetic determinants. When the number of character states is large and all states are equal in frequency among OTU's, the mean value for similarity including negative matches is $\frac{1}{2}$.

### 5.3.7. Age, growth, and allometry

In much numerical taxonomic work, particularly with fully adult individuals, the absolute size of a quantitative character (or the ratio between it and some standard measure, such as length or weight) can be employed directly by suitable scaling and coding. This may on occasion be an unsafe procedure, since the size of the character may be dependent on factors other than age—for example, the state of nutrition or, in bacteriology, the temperature of growth. The problem is particularly acute with fossil material, where one has no direct knowledge of the age of the individuals at death, and commonly too few specimens are available for an indirect answer to this question. In addition, it is generally found that the ratio of the size of the character to some standard character also varies with age. Therefore another way of expressing the character is desirable, and this may be done by means of one or the other of the allometry formulas. The reader is referred to Huxley (1932) and Medawar (1945) for a general treatment of this subject.

In most cases it is found that a straight line is obtained if the logarithm of the size of a character is plotted against the logarithm of age (or the logarithm of a standard character, such as total body length). This relation will prove adequate for most numerical taxonomic work, particularly if, as we advise, an effort is made to restrict the study to comparable stages of the life cycle. More complex relations, which are discussed in the works cited above, can be handled on the same principles. The usual allometry formula is

$$\log y = \log a + b \log x,$$

where $y$ is age (or some other standard measure), $x$ is the size of the character under study, and $a$ and $b$ are constants describing, respectively, the value of $y$ when $x = 1$ and the slope of the line. We have adopted the customary symbolism of the regression equation rather than the converse one often applied to the allometry equation, in order to promote uniformity in statistical symbols.

The constants of this formula are normally obtained by plotting a scatter diagram of values of $\log y$ against $\log x$ and fitting the line by the least squares method, employing the usual formulas for the regression of $\log y$ on $\log x$. It is, of course, first necessary to be sure that the scatter diagram does approximate a straight line, failing which some other allometric transformation is required. It is also necessary to be sure that the population is homogeneous and does not, for example, consist of individuals of several different species. These points will commonly be evident from the scatter diagram on inspection, and standard statistical techniques can be used to test them. It is probable that electronic computing techniques will be essential in any large-scale work of this kind, both to obtain the regression lines and to check their significance.

Once obtained, the constants $a$ and $b$ can be regarded as characters themselves, since they express the genetic factors which relate the size of the character under study with the standard character. These two constants can then be scaled and coded in the usual way. The operational taxonomic units will now be the populations and not individuals. The standard character will most commonly be overall length, age, or weight, but more sophisticated parameters (such as the geometric mean of length, breadth, and thickness) may prove to be useful. An additional constant, $s_{y \cdot x}$, expressing the scatter about the regression line, may also be employed, since it may be regarded as an additional attribute of the population, but it may not always be clear how much of it is due to errors of measurement, heterogeneity of the sample, environmental effects on the phenotype, and similar factors. Caution is advised here.

Allometry is a problem related to the effect of environment on characters (age, amount of available nutrition, and others) and to the problem of redundancy and empirical correlation; (that is, the crude measures may depend on a small number of underlying causes). The orthodox systematist faced with this problem chooses specimens of equal age or size for comparison, intuitively judging these as equivalent. Cases occur, however, where choosing equivalent specimens is exceptionally difficult. For example, if an amphibian larva suffers a delayed metamorphosis it may not be comparable either in age or size to any stage of another amphibian, and where delayed metamorphosis is the rule, as in the axolotl, *Ambystoma mexicanum*, this may be a considerable problem. In such cases it may be necessary to restrict the characters to those which do not show pronounced allometric changes, as is of course the practice in orthodox taxonomy in these cases. As explained in another section, we would expect, if the nonspecificity hypothesis is true, that the resulting taxonomy will be generally satisfactory.

D'Arcy Thompson (1917) pointed out that many organic shapes could

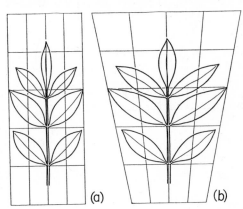

FIGURE 5-1

*Transformation grid (after D'Arcy Thompson) applied by us to a hypothetical leaf, showing a regular expansion of the distal part of leaf b as compared with leaf a.*

be expressed as simple mathematical transformations of other shapes (further discussed by Woodger, 1945). Raup (1961) has applied this idea to the shape of shells of molluscs. He shows that the shape of many gastropod shells can be specified by the profile of the whorl at one point together with a function expressing the rate at which the whorl increases in size at each complete turn of the helix. Clearly, these two characters— the profile and the rate of increase per turn—would express the morphometrics of the shell more economically than measuring a large number of dimensions of the shell at random.

The simpler of the transformation grids given by D'Arcy Thompson (see Figure 5-1) can be treated in the same way. If there is a straightforward expansion of one part of the grid, this is the only pertinent difference between the forms as represented there; all the other differences in measurements are a consequence of it. One would prefer to use

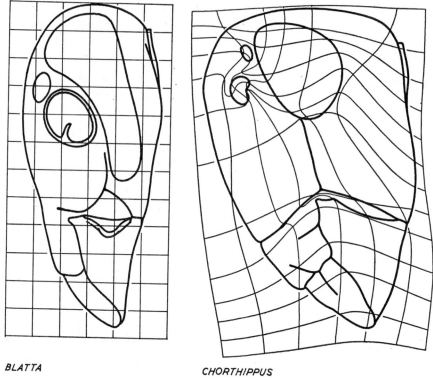

BLATTA                          CHORTHIPPUS

FIGURE 5-2

*Transformation grids of complex forms.* **Above:** *two orthopteran heads.* [*Drawn from nature, with the grids added by Mr. A. J. Lee.*] **Facing page:** *the transformation between two marsupial skulls.* [*After Parker and Haswell, and Cuvier.*]

for numerical taxonomy a single figure that described this expansion rather than many independent measurements. The latter would indicate a much greater difference than would seem justified; moreover, many of the characters would be redundant, since their values would be logical consequences of the expansion function.

Here again we meet the problem of empirical correlation. The simplest hypothesis is that mentioned above, but it is also possible that the expansion is due to a number of genetic changes, each controlling the expansion of one portion of the body. If we have no evidence bearing on this, we would prefer the simplest hypothesis.

No general and simple methods seem yet to have been developed for extracting the factors responsible for such transformations. While it may be easy to recognize that a figure such as Figure 5-1 is due to a regular

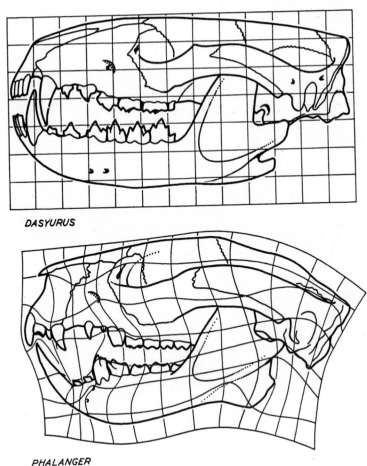

DASYURUS

PHALANGER

expansion, it is not easy to see how many separate factors are needed to express more complicated examples, such as the marsupial skulls and insect heads shown in Figure 5-2. Not only are the grid lines deformed in several ways, but the deformation is different in different parts of the skull.

What would be useful would be a way of extracting the minimum number of factors that would account for the difference in form; then these could be employed as characters. It may be that automatic methods can be developed for electronic computers so that diagrams could be compared and these factors extracted mechanically. It would probably be at first necessary to mark operationally homologous points on the diagrams before feeding them into the computer. This would involve superimposing a rectangular grid on one figure and marking on the other figure the points corresponding to the grid line intersections. Alternatively, the grid coordinates could be recorded for a number of operationally homologous points in the two diagrams.

A related method is that of Smirnov (1927), who resolved the shapes of the elytra of coccinellid beetles into a number of components by a method based on Fourier series.

## 5.4. KINDS OF CHARACTERS AND HOW TO CHOOSE THEM

Given agreement on what to call a unit character, we next turn to the problem of what kinds of characters to employ as the basic data for a numerical taxonomic study and how to choose these characters. Before we can enter upon a profitable discussion of these points we need to state and amplify two pertinent fundamental hypotheses.

### 5.4.1. The nexus hypothesis

This assumes that every taxonomic character is likely to be affected by more than one genetic factor and that, conversely, most genes affect more than one character. The result is a complicated nexus of cause and effect. Since numerical taxonomy cannot base its judgments on direct knowledge of genetic factors, it has to rely on information gained from (phenetic) taxonomic characters (as is, of course, done even in genetic research). Any character should give information about several genes. It should be possible in general to pick up the effect of a given gene through any one of several characters.

A detailed justification of the nexus hypothesis would require a long and thorough examination of much genetic evidence, which would be out of place here. We may cite in its support that the multifactorial nature of most characters is well known (Lerner, 1958; Falconer, 1960), and the common occurrence of pleiotropy is even better established (Waddington, 1957). Pleiotropic gene action often involves several organ systems and can be investigated by a number of approaches. Even when a unifying developmental process seems responsible for the pleiotropy, as in the well-known case of cartilage hypertrophy in the rat (Grüneberg, 1938) or in the more recent example of Danforth's short tail in the mouse (Grüneberg, 1958), the characters resulting as intermediate and end products of these processes are quite heterogeneous. While pleiotropic effects have not yet been described for a large number of mutations, this is probably due to failure to search for them. Even when, as in the ABO blood groups in man, it would appear that the antigens produced are reasonably close to being primary gene products, recent work on their adaptive significance tends to suggest some pleiotropic action (see Sheppard, 1959).

### 5.4.2. The hypothesis of nonspecificity

Here we assume that there are no distinct large *classes* of genes affecting exclusively one class of characters such as morphological, physiological, or ethological, or affecting special regions of the organism such as head, skeleton, leaves. The emphasis in this statement is on "classes of genes." Although a given gene may have a main effect on one region or kind of character, it is likely to have side effects or chain-reaction effects on other regions and characters.

If this assumption is warranted, then obtaining a disproportionately large number of characters from one body region or of one special kind would not restrict our information to a special class of genes. Furthermore, we would have to conclude that there are no a priori grounds for favoring one character over another. That all kinds of characters, such as bionomic, physiological, morphological, and the like, are of equal taxonomic merit has been quite generally accepted in recent years (Mayr, Linsley, and Usinger, 1953; Michener, 1953). However, certain body regions and organs still hold a considerable mystique for taxonomists as classificatory tools, while others are neglected.

Like the nexus hypothesis, the nonspecificity hypothesis may only hold in part. There may be some genes which affect the characters of one organ only. If such classes of genes are few in number, the nonspecificity hypothesis will still be substantially correct.

### 5.4.3. The evidence for nonspecificity: taxonomic congruence

Tests of the hypothesis of nonspecificity may be made at a variety of organizational levels in a classification. For instance, we may look for nonspecificity in connection with organs or regions of the body. Thus, if the hypothesis holds strictly, identical classifications should result from characters of the brain and from characters of the intestinal tract; from characters of the epithelium and from those of the connective tissue, or from head versus body or wing characters. All such tests would involve different portions of the same individuals. Yet there may be dimorphic or polymorphic manifestations of the gene pool of a species. These would lead to tests of congruence between taxonomic systems based on females or males, or based on diverse life history stages, such as insect larvae, pupae, and adults, or on different castes in social insects, or even on different adult forms in cyclomorphic organisms such as aphids. Considered a priori, the hypothesis of nonspecificity would seem more reasonable when applied to organs than to sexual or life history forms. Hennig (1950, p. 151) concurs in this.

What evidence is there for or against the hypothesis of nonspecificity? We may start our discussion with some general observations: it is obvious that the hypothesis must be generally true; on the whole, classifications based on separate sets of characters, be these from organs or life history stages, agree well with each other. It is well known that revisions of established groups based on morphological evidence from a newly investigated organ system frequently confirm previous classifications. If there were no relation at all between classifications established on the basis of larvae or adults, or males or females, or on muscles versus bones, this would have emerged before now. But perfect congruence between such systems has not been shown in the few instances where this has been investigated with any precision.

One must have many characters for measuring congruence. Admittedly, when a life history stage shows very few observable characters, one might be misled. We believe this to be so because the known characters are so few. Should serious incongruences between life history stages occur in a given study, it would raise the question of whether the classification of either stage is reliable. It would be difficult on theoretical grounds to justify any decisions between taxonomies based on one stage and those based on another stage. Where possible, one should choose characters from all stages of the life cycle when performing a numerical analysis.

That the hypothesis of nonspecificity on the whole must hold is shown in vertebrate paleontology and in much of vertebrate systematics where classifications are based on skeletons or even portions of skeletons. Yet consistent classifications can be established from such material. This means that other characters clearly are correlated with the skeletal characters. Thus, in a general way (and for the higher categories), the hypothesis of nonspecificity is supported by paleontology. We are not aware of any studies specifically and quantitatively testing this point.

An argument against the hypothesis rests on cytological evidence that certain genes appear to be active only at specific times in the life history of an organism (see Clever, 1961). If that is indeed so, then there would be separate classes of genes (at least as regards ontogenetic stages) leading to incongruence between life history stages.

Might the hypothesis of nonspecificity be entirely invalid? If we assumed that each character is affected by one gene only and that any gene affected only one character, then the absurdity of the extreme version of such a belief should be quite evident from the virtually infinite number of possible characters *vis-à-vis* the finite number of genes in an organism, and also from the existence of character correlations within freely interbreeding groups. Furthermore, if separate classifications could be set up by dividing taxonomic characters into logical sets—such as between sexes, between life history stages, head versus body, outside versus inside, nervous system versus circulatory system, and others—the large if not infinite number of independent classifications which could be set up in that way speaks equally for the absurdity of such a view.

It would therefore seem that incongruence is not an all-or-nothing phenomenon but that in different taxonomic groups varying amounts of incongruence will be shown by various sets of characters. It will be one of the tasks of numerical taxonomists in the next few years to investigate quantitatively the extent of such incongruences. Hennig (1950), writing before the development of numerical taxonomy, has clearly seen this problem, although to him the congruence of two classifications based on separate sets of characters proves the phylogenetic validity of the established system. Since he knew of no satisfactory way of quantitatively describing the similarity of two organisms, he felt that incongruences could not be quantitatively evaluated. We hope, however, to have shown in our present work that such comparisons are feasible and legitimate. Hennig (1950) and Remane (1956) both discuss the problem of nonspecificity in some detail, citing the work of Thienemann (1924, 1936) and Thienemann and Krüger (1937) on species and genera of chironomids. Thienemann, aiming at phylogenetic classifications, came to the disturbing conclusion that concordant classifications of larvae, pupae, and adults are impossible to achieve. Remane believes that he can order Thienemann's data into a proper phylogenetic scheme, while Hennig points out that genetic and phylogenetic criteria are necessary to establish species, and consequently the phenetic incongruencies are inconsequential. From our point of view such cases are interesting and challenging for numerical taxonomy to investigate; yet we cannot place much reliance on such data because rarely are they established on known phylogeny or on the basis of adequate numbers of characters studied by acceptable (quantitative) methods of phenetic comparison. Our confidence in phyletic relationships increases somewhat as we deal with higher categories; however, in these circumstances the hypothesis of nonspecificity is also less likely to be violated. Thus agreements between phenetic and phyletic classifications are more likely at the higher levels, and evidence from such cases would not be critical for taxa at the level investigated by Thienemann.

We think that sex differences will seldom prove troublesome in taxonomy. It seems certain that if one compared within one species all the features of a male with all the features of a female, the overall resemblance in most instances will be very high; the great majority of features will not be appreciably affected by sex. Such strong resemblance may not hold in some highly differentiated groups such as those showing much sexual dimorphism. Good examples would be some birds (ducks, pheasants, birds of paradise), fig insects (*Blastophaga*), Strepsiptera, or *Schistosoma*. In such cases sexual forms should be treated as if they were stages in the life cycle and thus male characters compared only with other male characters, and so on. A similar procedure should be followed in social insects when differentiation among castes is considerable.

We are on less sure ground in some of the most extreme examples of incongruence. It should, for example, be possible in principle to classify tissue cultures or spermatozoa, and we would hope to find their classifications congruent with those based on the whole adult. This has been done to some extent with pollen grains, whose classification was found to be reasonably congruent with orthodox taxonomy (see Erdtman, 1943). Similarly, it should be possible to make classifications of Fungi Imperfecti which are congruent with those based on the perfect forms. Nevertheless, in these cases the numbers of features may well be too few for numerical taxonomic methods. Very similar considerations apply to extremely modified parasites. There is evidence that comparative serology gives great assistance in cases such as these (Wilhelmi, 1940; Perlmann, 1953; Spiegel, 1960), and we believe that in principle numerical taxonomy can do the same.

The general agreement, frequently very close, between comparative serology (Section 3.2) and orthodox taxonomy is another piece of evidence in support of the hypothesis of nonspecificity, though detailed comparisons remain to be made. In studying serological aspects of metamorphosis, Telfer and Williams (1953) found in a silkworm that five out of six proteins were present in all stages examined, while one protein was absent in young larvae and in old adults. An additional protein was present in female but not male pupae. Perlmann (1953) found that eggs and pluteus larvae of a sea urchin shared ten out of thirteen antigens. The other three could not be detected in the eggs before the gastrula stage. Spermatozoa shared one antigen with the eggs. The relationships among galliform birds inferred from myology (Hudson et al., 1959) were compared to those indicated by serological data of DeFalco (1942) and Mainardi (1959c). There is no close correlation between musculature and serology, but unfortunately only a few forms were studied serologically and the data of DeFalco and Mainardi do not agree well. The evidence is therefore dubious.

Below we cite the few quantitative tests of the nonspecificity hypothesis available so far. Sneath (unpublished) has made a detailed analysis by association coefficients of the data on musculature of galliform birds cited above (Hudson et al., 1959), including also additional characters. Correlations between similarity coefficients based on leg characters and those based on foot characters were $r = 0.720$, while a similar correlation between similarity coefficients based on extensor and flexor muscles yielded an $r$ of 0.785. For comparison, correlations between similarity matrices based on odd- and even-numbered characters (an arbitrary division) yield $r = 0.826$. Since one could not expect on statistical grounds an agreement much better than the last, these correlations are quite good. It may be noted that this is a study of higher ranks—that is, several families of one order.

Haltenorth (1937) found good agreement between affinities based on 44 measures of bone length and 22 measures of the sagittal section of the skulls of eight species of large cats. Agreement between phenetic classifications based on the above sets of characters and 19 measures of head width was not satisfactory. The relatively small number of characters for the sagittal section and head width may make conclusions on nonspecificity tenuous for this study.

The opportunity to test the hypothesis of nonspecificity in a quantitative manner was also provided by a reanalysis of the bee data first published by Michener and Sokal (1957). The 122 characters originally studied were subdivided in two ways: 69 characters found in the female and common to the two sexes were placed in one set, 53 found only in the male bees were placed in a second set. In a second study these characters were divided differently: 60 head characters (both male and female) formed one set, and the 62 others were placed into the "non-head" set. When correlations between all pairs of species were computed (Michener and Sokal, 1963), they turned out to be similar to a considerable degree, regardless of the set of characters on which they had been based. The correlation coefficient between male and female classifications (based on product-moment $r$'s between pairs of species) was 0.71, and the analogous coefficient for head versus nonhead classification was 0.61. The magnitude of this correlation was partly a matter of scale. The analogous correlation between males and females on the distance scale was 0.35, while that between head and nonhead was 0.33. Similar discrepancies between various scales of measurement have been noted by Rohlf (1962). When the data were subjected to closer scrutiny, a number of differences among dendrograms prepared from them were noted.

Rohlf (1962), in a study of the hypothesis of nonspecificity, compared phenetic relations among 48 species of the mosquito genus *Aedes*, based upon independent analyses of characters of adults and larvae. Seventy-one characters were taken from the larvae and 77 from the adults. He found that on the whole the relationships were similar in the two stages but that there were many individual cases (somewhat more than would be expected due to chance alone) in which there were statistically significant differences between adult and larval interrelationships. The correlation between adult and larval correlations was found to be 0.29, and the correlation using distances was 0.59. Both correlations are, of course, highly significant, since there are 1,126 degrees of freedom.

In a quantitative study of two cyclomorphic adult forms (stem mothers and alates of the gall-producing aphid, *Pemphigus populi-transversus*), Sokal and Thomas (1963) were able to resolve the pattern of geographic variation into three factors for alates and two factors for the stem mothers. Only one of the factors determining variation corresponded in the two morphotypes. These data thus do not support the hypothesis of nonspecificity. However, the taxonomic rank investigated is near the lower limit—the local populations within a portion of the range of a species. It appears both from a priori principles as well as from the evidence so far collected that the hypothesis of nonspecificity will hold better, the higher the rank we consider. Thus, for example, there is little doubt that the orders of insects would be as faithfully mirrored in their larvae as by their adults, or that the classes of vertebrates would be recognizable from their skulls, their pelvic girdles, or their circulatory systems, and that these systems would yield roughly the same classifications. However, at lower taxonomic ranks this may no longer follow, and convergence resulting from adaptation to particular environmental circumstances may confuse the issue, yielding phenetic classifications which differ when based on different sets of characters.

In comparing classifications such as those based on females and those based on males it is not the absolute scale of resemblances that matters but the relative structure to be found in the two similarity matrices. Thus females may resemble each other more than males do; yet as long as the relative resemblances of the females among themselves are similar to those among the males, congruence would still obtain. Correlations among matrices of correlation coefficients, as carried out in tests of the hypothesis of nonspecificity by Michener and Sokal (1963) and Rohlf (1962), and the cophenetic correlation method of Sokal and Rohlf (1962) allow for unequal absolute scales of resemblance among dendrograms to be compared.

In summary of the above, we may conclude that the hypothesis of nonspecificity does not hold absolutely either for parts of the body or for stages of life history. It is more likely to be true for organs than for life history stages and at higher rather than at lower taxonomic levels. The extent of its validity will have to be examined by work in numerical taxonomy to be undertaken on a variety of groups. It should be added that only numerical taxonomy will be able to evaluate the degree to which the hypothesis holds because, as Hennig (1950) correctly and repeatedly points out, problems of this sort can only be solved when an exact method of estimating resemblances has been devised.

What if it can be shown that incongruences among different life history stages are the rule rather than the exception? The procedures of numerical taxonomy would not be invalid, but samples from all the available character sets would then have to be taken. This will have to remain an open question until more evidence has been collected. We would therefore recommend that until such a time undue reliance should not be placed on the hypothesis of nonspecificity and that characters should be distributed as widely as possible over the organisms to be studied.

### 5.4.4. The choice of characters: Some general considerations

It may be argued by the philosophically inclined that it is not possible to make absolute measures of resemblance because this would involve an arbitrary selection among the endless array of attributes which could in some sense be called characters of the organisms. Nevertheless, meaningful estimates of resemblance can be made once there is agreement on what characters are to be admitted as relevant in taxonomy. It is generally considered that only genetically determined characters should be used in orthodox taxonomy, and with this we concur. However, a study to investigate the influence of environment using numerical taxonomic methods could legitimately include environmentally determined characters.

It is, of course, quite impossible to give an adequate catalogue of all the taxonomic characters that can be used in various groups. Such a catalogue would comprise nothing less than a description of organized nature. Only specialists in the various groups will be in a position to define and describe unit taxonomic characters in the organisms they are studying. In their search for characters they ought to follow two guide lines, one of which at least is not included in customary taxonomic practice. The first is that all kinds of characters from all parts of the body and from all the stages of the life cycle should be used. When the hypothesis of nonspecificity is interpreted very strictly, a stratification of our sample from many body regions would not appear necessary. Any one part, such as the head, and any one kind of character, such as skeletal characters, should suffice. Many paleontological classifications are based, *faute de mieux*, on data of this nature. But this position can be reduced to the absurd or at least the questionable. If, on the basis of the hypothesis of nonspecificity, the skeleton suffices for a valid classification, so must the skull (as much of vertebrate and particularly primate paleontology has indeed inferentially claimed). But if the skull suffices, so must the jaw, or even a sliver or section of the jaw, reaching eventually the cellular level. A purist defending the hypothesis of nonspecificity may argue that jaws are indeed sufficient to establish *overall* phenetic relationships between taxa. The difficulty lies in finding and evaluating enough characters of the jaw. These may need special, refined techniques which are either not available to the paleontologist or (probably) have not even been invented. A conservative position would appear to be the employment of all available characters rather than restriction to a given region or kind.

The second guide line is to use all characters varying within the group studied, not merely conventional diagnostic characters. The latter are likely to be constant within the members of a given category. The exclusive use of such characters would prejudge the very issue—the establishment of taxonomic categories free from subjective bias—which numerical taxonomy wishes to solve. If the studies are based to a very large degree on characters previously described in the literature, there is some danger that diagnostic characters will be favored inordinately, since there is a historical weight in favor of diagnostic characters in the published literature. A number of critics have used such a possibility in order to question the validity of results obtained by Michener and Sokal (1957). The critics claim that since the characters employed in the study were those previously used to separate the groups concerned, it was not surprising to find that a classificatory technique utilizing these characters would yield a classification quite similar to the one described previously by conventional taxonomic methods. However, previous comparisons generally did not consider all characters simultaneously, so that the various diagnostic characters were each used only for portions of the systematic group studied. Thus the diagnostic value, or lack thereof, of any given character was rarely tested in any but a small section of the classificatory scheme.

Taxonomic characters can be roughly grouped into

(a) morphological characters (external, internal, microscopic, including cytological and developmental characters),
(b) physiological characters,
(c) behavioral characters,
(d) ecological and distributional characters (habitats, food, hosts, parasites, population dynamics, geographical distribution).

This list is far from being exhaustive. Readers interested in greater detail may wish to consult Mayr, Linsley, and Usinger (1953, p. 108 ff.), who have prepared a more complete classification and discuss each category in detail. Moll (1934) and Lawrence (1955) may be consulted on characters in botany. We have omitted serological characters; as these are analogous to similarity coefficients it would be underweighting them to use them as single characters. But we have as yet no criterion for applying weights to them in combining them with coefficients of similarity obtained by numerical methods.

Ecological and distributional factors, which have become much emphasized in recent years, require some comment in connection with their use for numerical taxonomy. While they are regularly reported, when known, they are not too frequently employed for classificatory purposes. Some difficulty may be encountered in coding them for numerical taxonomy. When an ecological character expresses some sort of gradient such as life zones in mountainous areas, depth in soil, temperature maxima, and the like, multistate coding is straightforward. However, how are we to code phytogeographic or zoogeographic distributional characters, host-plant preferences, or parasitic fauna? With distributional data, a two-dimensional breakdown into two characters is sometimes possible. In the other cases the information may have to be partitioned into a number of two-state characters. Thus, where several species or genera of hosts occur for a group of parasites under study, each of the former may have to be a single two-state character marked "present" when parasitized and "absent" when not. We may, however, wish to express systematic relations among host plants by appropriate coding. If a group of parasites live on four hosts, species $a$ and $b$ of genus $X$ and species $c$ and $d$ of genus $Y$, we could have one character for genus $X$ or $Y$ and one for species ($a$ or $b$ and $c$ or $d$) for each of the two genera.

Geographic distributions are characters which need special caution. In most cases it is not possible to be sure that they represent any character in the genotype. We may, for instance, have no evidence that there are genes conferring adaptation to life in North America as against life in Europe, and the distribution may reflect accidents of migration rather than any genetic attributes. In such instances the characters should not contribute toward estimation of phenetic relations, however useful they may be as pointers to the phylogeny. Similar care is needed with many ecological, behavioral, and parasitological observations. Ecological characters may sometimes be due to the recent invasion of a new habitat, and at first there may be no genetic differences between the population and its ancestral population. Behavioral characters may be acquired in youth by some accident, as for example song peculiarities of some birds, which may be learned by the young from adult birds of their own or different species (Lanyon, 1960). Parasitological characters may sometimes depend on chance infestation and not on the genotype of the host or of the parasite. Attempts to use the Mallophaga in classifying birds, for example, are made difficult by doubts as to whether some mallophagans are stragglers from other birds or have quite recently become established on their hosts through cross-infestation (for example, see Clay, 1949).

Characters such as host specificity also pose another difficulty, that of deciding what weight they should be given. Suppose several species of a genus of aphids live upon trees of several species, genera, and families. We wish to score the aphids so that the scores reflect those genetic attributes of the insects that restrict them to certain of the trees. It seems likely that wide host ranges involve greater genetic differences in the insects than narrow host ranges, and we may therefore require an estimate of the taxonomic resemblance of the trees, so that we may set up characters for wider and narrower host specificity. It would not be justifiable to carry this to extreme lengths, since the taxonomy of the trees themselves may be uncertain. In virus classification this problem is acute. Some viruses are restricted to one species of mammal, while others attack both birds and mammals. One might score class specificity, ordinal specificity, familial specificity, generic specificity, and so on (possibly introducing subclasses and tribes as well), and one might consider that higher categories should contribute more weight than lower ones. Since we have little detailed information on this problem, and hence no satisfactory method of allocating weights, we would suggest that only a few such characters be used and that each should be given equal weight. Although this may reduce the information it will avoid introducing bias.

Little need be said about avoidance of bias in choosing the characters. It is clear that when we use only a set of characters known to show affinity between certain groups, the similarity coefficients which will result from this study will reflect that choice. In an extreme case, by choosing only those characters which were the same in two organisms, one would obtain perfect but spurious resemblance between them. A systematic survey of all known characters or inclusion of all characters the investigator has been able to observe should avoid bias of this sort.

## 5.5. PHENETIC VERSUS PHYLETIC CLASSIFICATIONS

### 5.5.1. General considerations

Our major criticisms of the phylogenetic approach to taxonomy have been discussed in Section 2.3, and our reasons for preferring phenetic classification have been briefly stated in Section 4.6. However, there are some instances where the procedures of numerical taxonomy would yield erroneous results by the currently accepted criteria of phylogenetic taxonomy. These problems would all arise from the possibility of more or less serious discrepancy between relationships based on similarity and those based on descent. Issues such as monophyly, convergence, and parallelism come to mind immediately.

It is almost a truism that an intimate relation must exist between phenetic evidence and the degree of relation by ancestry. It should also be obvious that, while the two kinds of taxonomy are equally valid for their own purposes, they stand in a peculiar relationship to each other: if knowledge about phyletic relations is required, it must be obtained by conjecture from phenetic evidence; phenetic relations, however, should be deduced not from phyletic hypotheses but from the specimens themselves. A ready simile offers itself here: we may estimate the similarity between geometric objects on the basis of the nature and size of their dimensions, without any implication as to their past history or how they were developed or constructed by geometers. Yet under some conditions we may *deduce* from their geometrical form certain probabilities about their past history. We may, for example, suggest that a regular octahedron was developed by geometers subsequent to the development of the square. Inger (1958) has misinterpreted this point in referring to a hypothetical classification of nuts, bolts, and screws, which, he says, implies no historical relationship among the objects classified. On the contrary, as we must emphasize (see also Sokal, 1959), it does *imply* historical relationships without necessarily being based on these relationships. Any collection of such objects will show unmistakable evidence of their history: there will be nuts, bolts, and screws of simple design and crude workmanship, representing the early attempts at manufacture of these objects; there will be evidence that the simple slot across the head of the screw was an earlier invention than the four-armed crossed slots; there will be evidence of selection, since the most useful patterns will tend to be selected and manufactured by succeeding generations, a close parallel with natural selection and survival of the fittest. To comment that such evolutionary deductions are hazardous is to state the obvious: they are just as hazardous, or more so, in biology, and for the same reasons. We cannot be sure without dated "fossil" examples which form was the earlier and which was the later. It is also clear that, unless we had historical records of their development, we could only deduce the evolutionary relations from the objects themselves; without such records we could not make a genealogical classification directly but only by inference. The classification could not then be based on the evolution, or at most it would only be based on guesses about the evolution; the interpretation of the evolution would be based, rather, on the classification. In any event, it is plain that a classification of nuts, bolts, and screws (and equally, classifications of organisms) would not be fruitless nor lie outside the province of engineering (or biology), even if it took no account of evolution.

Let us take a closer look at the reasons for wishing to develop taxonomies which are in accord with phylogeny. This ideal is expressed mainly by the dictum that taxa should be monophyletic groups. There will therefore be difficulty only when the taxa given by numerical taxonomy are not monophyletic but polyphyletic. We believe that numerical taxonomy will in general give monophyletic taxa because we believe that phenetic groups are usually monophyletic. Before we can criticize numerical taxonomy on this score, therefore, we must have evidence that phenetic groups, created by adequate and acceptable numerical techniques, are not monophyletic. A clear example would be where convergence has occurred to an extent that causes confusion. But we must first show that this degree of convergence has indeed occurred. Figure 5-3 (p. 98) shows that there are several interpretations of what is at first sight a simple problem. There may indeed have been convergence, so that organisms **A** and **B** are more similar phenetically than their ancestors **A'** and **B'**, and **B** is convergent on **A**, though by ancestry related most closely to organism **C**; see Figure 5-3(a). But this conclusion may be uncertain. The evolution may have occurred as in Figure 5-3(b), where there is no convergence but divergence at different rates, with the phyletic line **B** evolving slowly (bradytely). Or, **B** may in fact have descended from **A'** so that **A**, **A'**, and **B** are monophyletic; see Figure 5-3(c). Finally, we may have been mistaken in thinking that **B** was convergent on **A**, for a careful estimate of phenetic affinity may show, taking all their attributes into consideration, that **B** is more similar to **C** than to **A**; here we had been misled by some striking but superficial or restricted set of features, as in Figure 5-3(d). It is clear that from a consideration of the organisms **A**, **B**, and **C** alone (without the evidence of the fossil forms **A'**, **B'**, **C'**, and **X**), we cannot distinguish between these alternatives except to recognize the last of them. Indeed, we have as yet no acceptable evidence that convergence of this kind—that is, overall convergence or convergence in phenetic resemblance—does take place to any marked extent. If it did, it would be exceedingly difficult to prove, for we would have to have an excellent series of fossils to be certain that we had not made any mistake in reconstructing the phylogenetic tree. The known examples of convergence are all open to the objection that relatively very few characters are affected.

Discrepancies between phenetic and phyletic taxonomies can also occur without convergence—for example by divergence at different rates, as in Figure 5-3(b), where **A** and **B** are more similar phenetically than either is to **C**, although cladistically they are equally related.

Even if we grant that overall convergence can occur (as, for example,

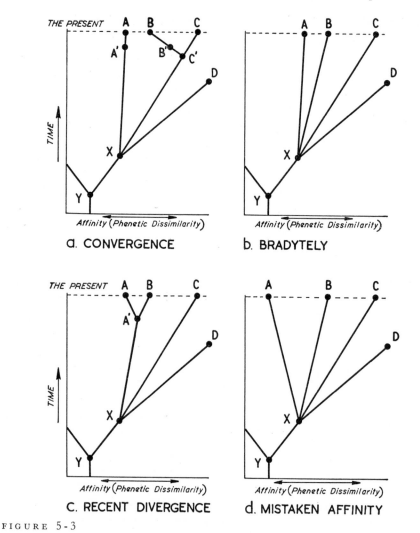

FIGURE 5-3

*Alternative interpretations of a case of apparent convergence (for explanation, see text).*

has been suggested for some groups of birds), we must ask ourselves why
we should wish to make taxonomies based on monophyletic groups.
Suppose the convergence had become so absurdly extreme that the two
forms are almost indistinguishable and can readily and successfully
hybridize: what is the purpose of separating them on grounds of ancestry
when in all other attributes they are virtually the same? The purpose
cannot be to emphasize minor dissimilarities, nor to serve as a guide to

their behavior with respect to genetic or any other class of properties. The purpose is presumably, therefore, to show that this convergence had occurred, a fact which could be expressed in simple terms without any need for setting up the whole apparatus of formal systematics, and, as is discussed above, the classification would thus be a special one for this special purpose and not a general classification. Where independent phyletic lines fuse into one, the whole problem becomes thoroughly confused, whether we know this has happened or not, since there are so many alternative ways of dividing the network of phyletic lines. This is a common occurrence in plants through the mechanism of allopolyploidy.

Simpson (1961, p. 120) has pointed out quite correctly that most definitions of monophyly are nonoperational because "they are so vague that they provide insufficient criteria for separating one from the other [monophyly from polyphyly] by analysis of evidence." We can ignore the naive statements of earlier authors defining monophyly as descent from a single pair of progenitors, statements made in ignorance of contributions of modern evolutionary theory. Hennig (1950, p. 307) defines as monophyletic groups of species which in the final analysis can be referred back to a common ancestral species (*Stammart*). He points out the sometimes neglected fact that the monophyletic group has to include *all* species derived from this ancestral species, not only those which the taxonomist wishes to classify. As Simpson correctly states, the problem with a definition of this sort is that it is difficult to know how far back one has to trace separate stems in order to arrive at the common stem form. For example, by Hennig's definition the mammals could be made monophyletic only by tracing them back to an unknown early reptile stem.

Remane (1956) solves the monophyly-polyphyly problem more drastically by not accepting as natural any groups with characters which do not conform to his criteria of homology. Thus, by not recognizing polythetic taxa, he decreases the probability of a taxonomist's having to recognize polyphyletic groups. Remane nevertheless does have to consider cases of reputed polyphyly—for example, the well-known case of the origin of the mammals, in which he attempts to show that polyphyly (or polygony, as he prefers to call this phenomenon) is not present. However, the evidence considered by him is rather outdated, and the interested reader is referred to newer papers (see Olson, 1959; Reed, 1960; Van Valen, 1960; Simpson, 1960). Indeed, in numerical taxonomy this problem is of no real consequence, except so far as it may lead to interesting conclusions about the parallel evolution of separate lines of mammal-like reptiles. To admit the existence of polyphyly would be quite fatal to Remane's system, since he relies upon a closed circle of reasoning from monophyly to a natural system, to homologous structures, and back to monophyly.

Bigelow (1956) has pointed out that in all supposedly monophyletic classifications overall similarities and differences are usually not disregarded. Even in those cases where the ideal of a monophyletic classification could be attained, it often is disregarded in favor of a phenetic classification by supposedly phylogenetic taxonomists. Bigelow feels that "if classification is to correspond with evolution, it must be based on the extent of overall difference, not on time."

The redefinition of monophyly (Simpson, 1960, 1961) is not free from ambiguity in its practical application: "Monophyly is the derivation of a taxon through one or more lineages (temporal successions of ancestral-descendant populations) from one immediately ancestral taxon of the same or lower rank" (Simpson, 1961, p. 124). We therefore need to know what is meant by the term taxon in each instance, and we need to decide the relative rank of the taxa. The difficulties can be illustrated by Figure 5-4. Presumably the descendant taxon, **X**, can be a phenetic group (of a rank indicated by its diversity $A$), and need not be itself a strictly monophyletic group, or the amended definition is superfluous. If the ancestral population, **Y**, is also a phenetic taxon and not a strictly monophyletic group, it can itself be a phenetic group (of rank indicated by its diversity, $B$). This would allow it to be composed of convergent lineages. If such a condition were not permitted (and possibly this is what is implied by "one immediately ancestral taxon"), the term taxon would be used in two different senses in the definition. It is improbable that the lineages ancestral to taxon **Y** would not have had some side branches, and if these had a phenetic rank $C$ less than $A$ (taxon **Z** in the figure), then taxon **X** would be monophyletic with respect to rank $A$ under the amended definition. Yet it would be considered polyphyletic by most workers. There seems little point in redefining monophyly simply to retain for polyphyletic or phenetic taxa the word "monophyletic." One must also specify the rank with respect to which a taxon should be monophyletic. Simpson does not give clear criteria for deciding this rank.

We would not ourselves be concerned directly with the problem of monophyly but would divide the lineages so as to yield phenetic groups as given by the vertical projection of the lines $D$ and $E$ (Figure 5-4), and taxon **Y** would remain with taxon **X**. This is not because it would put

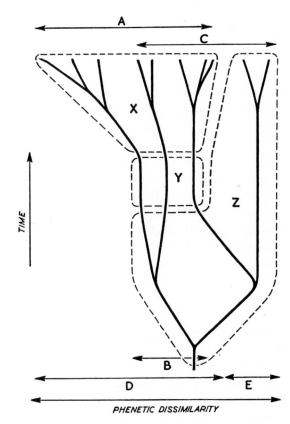

FIGURE 5-4

*Diagram of a phylogenetic tree to illustrate the problem of defining monophyly (for explanation, see text).*

into different higher ranks some species or genera that were very similar to one another, for this problem occurs wherever one divides the lineages, but because **X** and **Y** are phenetically similar.

Because of the difficulty of obtaining clear decisions on monophyly, Simpson (1961) describes four separate approaches for establishing classifications. The first of these is the empirical approach, advocated in this book but rejected out of hand by Simpson, although much of his discussion of this particular problem (particularly on p. 123) fairly cries out for an empirical solution. The other three approaches follow various types of phylogenetic reasoning, the details of which need not concern us here, in view of the general fallacy of the method. We need only quote from Simpson himself (1961, p. 122): "Choice among them is not a matter of right and wrong but of artistic judgment in each individual case. . . ." It seems to us that such an approach would exclude taxonomy from critical scientific inquiry.

The problem of phenetic *versus* phyletic classification arises also when considering the problem of vertical *versus* horizontal classifications. By a horizontal classification is meant relationships "among contemporaneous taxa of more or less distant common origin," while a vertical classification is based on relations "among successive taxa in an ancestral-descendant lineage" (Simpson, 1961, p. 129). It is not clear from his account whether vertical relations are entirely phyletic, nor to what degree phenetic considerations enter into horizontal classification. This problem is of most concern to the paleontologist. When based on neontological data entirely, the uncertainties of the relationships involved make a vertical classification indeed risky. Figure 5-5, modified after Simpson (1961), shows the dilemma faced by taxonomists in deciding between vertical and horizontal classifications and the relative simplicity with which a phenetic and empirical taxonomy such as numerical taxonomy would deal with this problem. The problems of grades and clades (Simpson, 1961) can be similarly treated by numerical taxonomy.

We may therefore here give a concise answer to the question: should taxa in orthodox taxonomy be in general monophyletic groups (clades) or phenetic groups? We believe that they should be phenetic groups, for the following reasons.

(1) Phenetic and phyletic relations are taxonomic dimensions formally independent of one another and must be so treated. In the great majority of cases we must deduce the cladal nature of the phenetic taxa by assuming that the phenetic resemblance does reflect the phyletic relations. Since we do not usually have any independent phyletic evidence, there can be no question of disagreement between the phyletic and phenetic data. The occurrence of scattered and incomplete fossil data does not materially alter the situation in such cases, since we have usually to decide whether or not these fossil forms are ancestral by employing largely phenetic criteria. Therefore, in such cases (the great majority) the classifications are de facto phenetic ones, and they are phyletic by lip service and wishful thinking only.

(2) We expect that in the great majority of instances the phenetic groups will indeed be clades, though we may not be able to prove this. This follows from our assumption that close phenetic similarity is usually due to close relationship by ancestry. It is only in cases where this appears to be untrue that any difficulty will arise. In such cases we must first verify that the phenetic and phyletic relations are indeed discrepant. This involves comparing affinities from a numerical taxonomic study with a phylogenetic tree obtained from independent fossil evidence (such

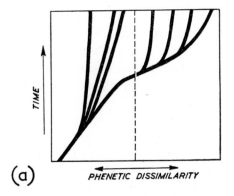

(a)

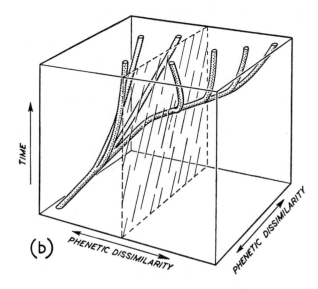

(b)

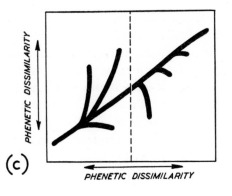

(c)

FIGURE 5-5

*Horizontal and vertical classification. (a) Diagram of a phylogenetic tree as commonly drawn, with a time dimension and one phenetic dimension. Vertical distances indicate temporal relationships and horizontal distances indicate phenetic relationships. (b) A more realistic representation with an added dimension of phenetic dissimilarity. In (a) is shown a horizontal projection of this three-dimensional tree, but a different horizontal projection might show very different horizontal relationships to that in (a). (c) The projection of (b) onto the base. The relations are now wholly phenetic. The relations between the tips of the branches are relationships among contemporaneous taxa, and hence are horizontal relationships in Simpson's usage.*

*It should be noted that even two phenetic dimensions are generally inadequate to represent phenetic relationships.*

as close sequences of fossil forms in which there can be no reasonable doubt as to the nature and branching of the phyletic lineages). No such studies have yet been made by acceptable numerical taxonomic methods, so the question is to this extent premature. A recent discussion on the evolution and taxonomy of mammals, summarized by Simpson (1960), illustrates this point well.

(3) If (and only if) we have acceptable evidence of disagreement between the phenetic and phyletic classifications, we may discuss which is the better classification to employ. The answer depends on our purpose. If our purpose is to study evolution, there may be advantages in employing clades, though as discussed below we may restrict the scope of our inquiries if we restrict our taxa to cladal taxa. If our classification is for "general purposes," then it is inescapable that we must prefer phenetic taxa to cladal taxa. To decide otherwise would be to imply that an evolutionary classification is a general classification, which by definition it is not. The most important point is that we must be prepared to recognize the disagreement if it exists and to recognize that biological data may admit many interpretations other than evolutionary ones.

To what extent should taxa be phylogenetic entities if the phylogeny is fairly certain? An example of current interest is the classification of the mammals. It is at present generally believed that the mammals are a polyphyletic group. Bigelow (1961), in discussing the implications of this, concludes that a horizontal (phenetic) classification is more satisfactory than a vertical (phyletic) classification. In the former the Mammalia would be a grade, while in the latter they would be a clade. Reed (1960) has advocated a cladal classification as being the more logical but admits that it is less convenient, even for paleontologists. Simpson (1960) prefers to retain the present horizontal classification, but his position is not very clear in view of his advocacy of cladal classification as a preferred general principle of taxonomy (Simpson, 1961, pp. 120–125, 189–191).

The evidence in the case of the Mammalia is itself not clear or easy to interpret. It is generally agreed among paleontologists that a minimum of two groups of reptiles (and possibly four or five) independently crossed the arbitrary line separating reptiles from mammals. The evidence for this (based on jaw and ear structure) is summarized by Simpson (1959) and by Olson (1959). Yet, as Reed (1960) points out, this implies an independent origin of an impressively large number of mammalian characters. This argument is of especial cogency in the case of the monotremes, which are thought by some to be one of the groups which crossed the line independently, although there is no pertinent fossil evidence of their origin (Simpson, 1945, 1960). The application of monophyly as a criterion would at the least require the inclusion in the mammals of the therapsid mammal-like reptiles, as Van Valen (1960) suggests. A consideration of the phyletic trees given by Olson (1959) and Reed (1960) shows a number of uncertainties about the origin of all the mammalian groups, and the authors cited by them and by Simpson (1959) are evidently not in agreement on the details. It may therefore be premature to discuss their taxonomic position, though it may be noted that the Multituberculata are the group which are hardest to explain on a monophyletic basis of the origin of mammals. The others might plausibly have arisen from a single therapsid stock, and, by excluding the Multituberculata from the mammals, the problem would be avoided (Simpson, 1960). Despite the uncertainty in this instance, there are some well-documented lineages in the evolution of mammals which pose the same problem (for example, see Simpson, 1951, pp. 204, 211, 280), though a critical examination by numerical taxonomic methods remains to be made.

However, it should be emphasized that even if the entire phylogeny of a group of organisms were known so that they could be arrayed in a dendrogram accurately representing descent (that is, who came from whom), we would still have a very limited representation of the organisms. In order to make a reasonable classification, even the most ardent phylogenist would wish to know something about the similarity between the organisms in order to make a meaningful classification. Unless we knew how much evolution had occurred and how this affects the phenotype of the organisms, it would be futile to construct a classification. Thus there is a place for numerical taxonomy even in the rare instances of completely known phylogenies. For this reason the application of numerical taxonomy to paleontological as well as neontological work is indicated (see Sneath, 1961).

### 5.5.2. Convergence

Convergence and parallelism are terms over which there is considerable confusion (see Haas and Simpson, 1946, for a full discussion). Convergence or parallelism may mean convergence or parallelism in one organ (or in one character complex) or of the entire phenotype. Many authors do not specify which they mean. In this book we use the terms with respect to overall, phenetic similarity, whether the changes are contemporary (isochronous) or not (heterochronous). The occurrence of convergence restricted to a small part of the phenotype would not, of course, produce convergence in overall similarity; for example, the bats are convergent on the birds with respect to flight, but in the remainder of their phenotype they are divergent from birds, when compared with the common reptilian ancestor.

A comment that is voiced more often than any other criticism of numerical taxonomy is that the frequent occurrence of convergence would confuse and invalidate its results. This question has been considered from the first (Michener and Sokal, 1957), and it is the position of numerical taxonomists that most cases of convergence would affect coefficients of similarity only slightly, since they would not involve more than a small proportion of the characters.

Considered strictly by the criteria of this book, convergence is no problem at all. So long as we are concerned with phenetic affinities the similarity value obtained by numerical methods will be truly representative. It is only when we wish to draw *phylogenetic* conclusions that convergence may confuse the issue. We hope to show in the following sections that even phylogenetic deductions will not be seriously affected by the inclusion of convergent characters in the computation of similarity coefficients.

It is necessary to specify in what respects lines are convergent. It is quite possible for two lines to converge in respect to one organ and to diverge in respect to others. The only kind of convergence which is pertinent to our present argument is that where the lines converge in so many respects (that is, characters) that it causes an increase in the overall similarity of the two lines. This, which can be called "overall convergence" to distinguish it from convergence in a few respects, might cause serious discrepancies between the taxonomy yielded by phenetic methods and that implied by reliable phyletic studies. Convergence in a few respects ("organ convergence") will not do this, since these few respects will have little effect on the affinity values of the many non-convergent attributes included in the analysis. There is of course no sharp line between overall convergence and organ convergence.

The pertinent question, then, is: Does marked overall convergence ever occur? And it is one which urgently needs study. There are many examples in which numerical taxonomy could be readily employed to test this question: *Canis* and the thylacine marsupial wolf, the marsupial and eutherian moles, the seals and sirenians, and some xerophytic or parasitic plants could be compared. We believe that the overall similarity of pairs of this kind is not high. Indeed, if this were not so, it is uncertain how they were recognized as "convergent pairs" and not just close relatives. The very obvious and striking similarities in appearance will, we believe, account for very few of the total features analyzed. Any reasonably random and unbiased selection would, we think, include far more features which did not show convergence. And even in habitus one finds many differences due to different modes of achieving the same function with diverse anatomical parts. Striking cases of overall convergence where the phylogeny is thoroughly known are not common, and none has yet been examined by acceptable numerical taxonomic methods.

Sneath (1961) has pointed out the ridiculous implications of total overall convergence in higher animals, though it may not be so ridiculous in viruses (see Section 8.1.2). It is perhaps worth noting that when considering many characters there is every expectation that evolutionary processes will *overall* be divergent. This is a consequence of variation, which has a strong element of randomness. In order to obtain convergence, the possible kinds of variation must be restricted; that is, there must be more change in differential features than in common features. We have no reason to believe that, in general, natural selection will have this effect (except possibly in situations like that described below), since it will act largely upon random mutations and in many different directions.

What we have said above applies to the higher levels of taxonomic rank. At lower levels, at the genus and below, there is a possibility of some degree of overall convergence. For example, the introduction of a new food plant into an archipelago possessing several island races of a fruit-eating bird (which had diverged slightly from one another over the course of time) might produce such a strong selection pressure—in the same direction and in all the islands simultaneously—that these races would rapidly evolve toward adaptation to feeding on the new plant, and this might outweigh the slow accumulation of genetic differences which had been continuously occurring in each race. The overall similarity between these races might then increase somewhat, and there would then have been some degree of overall convergence. In the absence of knowledge of the past, it is difficult to see how any systematic procedure would elucidate the case, and numerical taxonomy is in no worse position than others. It is possible that convergence on this level and of this degree may be frequent but undetectable, at least by any of the procedures known today.

Finally, we may emphasize an obvious but often forgotten point. If we do indeed wish to study convergence, we can only do this by comparing a phylogenetic arrangement with a phenetic arrangement. In no other way can we detect the process of convergence, and any attempt to restrict taxonomy to phylogenetic arrangements will then defeat its own ends.

### 5.5.3. Parallel evolution

Parallel evolution occurs when two genetically isolated stocks evolve so as to maintain constant the difference in those attributes which are under consideration. Parallel evolution seems to us to be similar to convergence and subject to analogous reservations of definition, but to a lesser degree. The same problems and dilemmas arise, and again there is very little clear evidence in favor of extensive parallel evolution if *all* the features are included in the taxonomic analysis. Possibly the best examples of what may be *overall* parallel evolution (the inclusion of the word "overall" implies a constancy in the overall similarity, as with convergence discussed above) are certain ferns (Holttum, 1949) and certain ammonites. The apparently parallel trends in the degree of convolution and ornamentation of the shells of ammonites represent very few characters out of the many present during life. In addition to this, these characters are likely to be selected by the environment in the same way; for example, it is possible that certain forms of the shell may have protected many different species of ammonite from a particular predator. Another example of this may be the repeated evolution of increased curvature of the shell in lineages of oysters, leading to the *Gryphea* phenotype, which has been interpreted as a recurrent adaptation to a muddy sea bottom (discussed by Joysey, 1959). This may well have involved only a few characters, since we do not know what changes occurred in the soft parts of these molluscs.

The reviews of Trueman (1930), Swinnerton (1932), George (1933), and Joysey (1959) may be consulted for some of the better-known instances of this phenomenon; these authors all emphasize the difficulty in deciding whether the apparently parallel lineages are indeed independent phyletic lines, or whether the forms found in any given stratum should be grouped together in a monophyletic taxon. If the latter procedure is correct, then parallel evolution is simulated by similar adaptive radiations in successive taxa (stages) of an evolutionary line.

As with convergence, we feel that most apparent examples of parallel evolution are due to parallel trends in a few characters. Again we urgently need quantitative studies of this problem. Even if overall parallel evolution does occur, it will be no easy matter to prove convincingly the validity of the phyletic lineages concerned, and the phenomenon will probably be of small degree.

Readers of the above two sections may feel at variance with our ideas because our definitions of convergence and parallelism, while not alien to the usage of systematists, are probably not the most common ones; hence our comments may be thought not relevant to the central ideas of convergence and parallelism as customarily conceived. While the terms convergence and parallelism permeate evolutionary literature, it is difficult to find definitions for them. Remane (1956), for example, uses but does not define convergence and parallelism. Rensch (1947) considers convergence to be simply nonparallel evolution. Simpson (1961, p. 78) has attempted to coin precise definitions for these terms. He defines parallelism as "the development of similar characters separately in two or more lineages of common ancestry and on the basis of, or channelled by, characteristics of that ancestry." Convergence he defines as "the development of similar characters separately in two or more lineages without a common ancestry pertinent to the similarity, but involving adaptations to similar ecological status." The inferences that are customarily made from such a definition, and that are also discussed by Simpson (1961, pp. 103 ff.), are that convergence occurs between forms that are relatively far apart, while parallelism occurs only among lines that are relatively closely related. Simpson mentions the occasional literal interpretation of convergence as the narrowing of differences between lines and the parallel change of these lines as constituting parallelism, but he does not consider that to be a particularly useful taxonomic concept.

It seems to us, on the contrary, that in any taxonomy based on a phenetic system (in fact any taxonomy that wishes to base itself on measurable quantities), the definition of parallelism and convergence should be entirely based on the parallel or convergent nature of the differences between the lines. We hold these beliefs for several reasons.

(1) It seems to us that no fundamental and useful distinction can be established between convergence and parallelism. To say that convergence takes place only between distantly related forms would prejudge the issue of relationship completely. We would no longer be able to use cases of convergence or parallelism in our classificatory schemes because relationships would have been predetermined before any deci-

sion could be taken on whether a convergence or parallelism is at hand.

(2) The definitions of Simpson (1961) and his subsequent discussions lead one to believe that by convergence is meant the construction of similar structures based on different genetic systems, while by parallelism is meant the construction of similar structures based on similar genetic systems. By inference one may conclude that different genetic systems occur in more distantly related organisms and similar genetic systems in more closely related organisms. This concept is, however, partly erroneous and of little utility. It is erroneous, because it has been shown in genetics, theoretically as well as by experimental evidence, that presumably identical populations when faced with an environmental challenge will not necessarily meet it by identical responses. For example, the challenge of insecticides to insect populations has been met by the same species in a number of different ways (Crow, 1957). Therefore it is not necessarily true that similar genetic systems will produce similar responses to a given environmental challenge. The converse point is granted, namely, that it is not likely that distantly related lines will develop similar genetic systems in response to similar environmental challenges.

(3) In the absence of knowledge about genetic homologies, we are faced in the main with phenetic changes which may be divergent, parallel, or convergent. It would therefore appear that the only useful distinction is whether changes are parallel or convergent, or better still whether there is relatively more or less divergence, since often less divergence between some members of two taxa than between the majority of the members of the taxa may be considered as convergence or at least parallelism. Of course, *sensu strictu*, this can only be done if fossil series of organisms are available. Where only living end points of evolutionary change are known, parallelism or convergence cannot really be demonstrated but must be inferred from recent evidence.

## 5.6.  THE REQUISITE NUMBER OF CHARACTERS

A problem of immediate and urgent importance in any numerical taxonomic study is the number of characters required to obtain reliable results. No general answers can as yet be given; however, there are some general considerations which must form the basis of this problem and which may be useful in guiding attempts at a solution. It is obvious that the problem of the number of characters relates to the hypothesis of nonspecificity. If the hypothesis holds rigorously, sampling a relatively small number of characters should still give an adequate idea of the classification. But if the hypothesis does not hold well in a given group, and separate characters exist in separate regions of the body representing different factors, then a relatively larger sample of characters must be employed. Two conceptual approaches were employed in obtaining an estimate of the number of characters required. The first, the hypothesis of the factor asymptote, did not prove fruitful; however, it is discussed here to give some insight into the reasoning we used. The reasoning eventually employed—the hypothesis of the matches asymptote—is given in the subsequent section. Any discussion of characters and the number necessary for the estimation of resemblance is inextricably linked to the question of what the taxonomic units are whose affinities are being investigated. We shall defer a consideration of this problem until Section 5.8. In the discussion that follows below we shall use the term operational taxonomic unit (OTU) for the unit that is to be classified without defining it further here.

### 5.6.1. The hypothesis of the factor asymptote

The following three statements are based on the nexus and non-specificity hypotheses. We label them collectively the hypothesis of the factor asymptote. This hypothesis concerns itself with information obtained about a single organism or operational taxonomic unit by studying its characters. First of all, it appears obvious that the more characters we study, the more information we will accumulate. We deliberately use "information" in a general, ill-defined sense here. For a recent discussion of the information content of biological classifications from the point of view of information theory, see Rescigno and Maccacaro (1960).

Second, a random sample of the characters should represent a random sample of the genome of the operational taxonomic unit. Our use of the term "random" is not in the strict probabilistic sense but rather in the sense of being haphazard or unbiased.

Third, as we include more and more characters, the gain in information with each additional character, while large at first, should decrease fairly rapidly and, after a certain number ($n_a$) characters have been recorded, should approach close enough to an asymptotic value to make further inclusion of characters in the study unprofitable. This last aspect of the hypothesis is most important for numerical taxonomy, since it would permit placing a limit to a theoretically boundless task. It is important to note whether the rate of gain of information slows down considerably before an appreciable proportion of the genetic factors of the operational taxonomic units have been described.

A simple model may help us to understand the process, although an even mildly realistic interpretation of the situation would have to be much more elaborate. Imagine an organism with 10,000 gene loci. Let us assume that each character yields information on 12 loci and that random choice of characters is therefore equivalent to random samples (with replacement) of 12 loci each time from the total of 10,000. The first character would present us with information on 12 loci. The

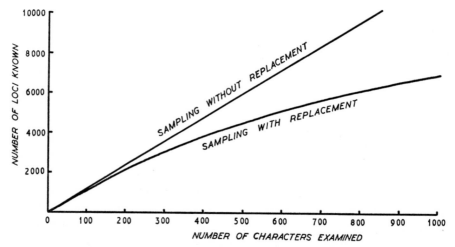

FIGURE 5-6

*The expected number of gene loci on which information will be given if each character provides information about 12 loci (for explanation, see text).*

probability that the next character will contain 12 *new* loci is extremely close to 1 (approximately 0.98567). Using an approximate method sufficiently accurate for our purposes, we can calculate the expected proportion of genes which will have been sampled by the formula $1 - (0.9938)^n$. In Figure 5-6 we see the results of such a computation graphed for studies involving 1 through 1000 characters, each assumed to be a sample of 12 independently occurring gene loci. If each character yielded information about different gene loci, the expected number of genes known would be a simple linear function of the number of characters studied. In view of the possibility that different characters will represent previously sampled genes, the expected number of genes known on the basis of a given number of characters is always less than the maximum possible number. While it is clear that the rate of actual recovery of new information (or new gene loci) is slowing down, loci are still being recovered at a fairly rapid rate after 200 characters have been studied. Thus not only do we not reach an asymptote of information recovery by the time an appreciable number of characters has been measured, but using what appears to us to be a reasonably realistic model we find that, after measuring 200 characters, information on only a little over one-fifth of the gene loci has been obtained.

To obtain information on 50% of the genes (5000 loci) we would have to study 579 characters, a procedure which would only be approximately 72% efficient, since that number of characters could yield a maximum of 6948 loci, if each sampled different loci.

A more realistic approach would be to permit the number of genes which a character represents to vary according to a plausible distribution, perhaps in Poisson fashion. While this would widen the confidence band of the graph, it would still not alter the general relations. Further realism could be added by considering the correlations among some of the characters sampled. This would reduce the rate at which the genome of the organism would be sampled.

The interesting conclusion from this model is that we are unlikely to learn about an appreciable proportion of the genotype (say $>15\%$) unless the average number of major gene effects on each character is considerably higher than 50 or unless an exceedingly large number of characters is studied. Thus a character survey of a taxon would fall short of the aim of obtaining a genetic characterization of it unless an impractically large number of characters is used.

A fundamental question may be raised at this point. If one cannot obtain adequate coverage of all genetic factors of a taxon from a reasonable number of characters (this was apparently not realized by any of the early writers on the subject), does this invalidate the practice of numerical taxonomy? The answer would appear to be "no," for two reasons. First, from the point of view of recognition and discrimination of taxa, the number of character states available when even a moderate number (say 100) characters are measured is far greater than is necessary. Thus, while our character sample may not be adequate to reveal the complete properties of a taxon they are likely to be quite adequate for its description and discrimination.

The second reason is that the coefficients of similarity on which numerical taxonomy is based do not rest directly on the absolute magnitudes and qualitative nature of the characters sampled but on the relative degrees of difference between the characters of the operational taxonomic units being compared, as will be shown below. This point of view leads us directly into the next hypothesis.

### 5.6.2. The hypothesis of the matches asymptote

When we compare two operational taxonomic units on the basis of a sample of their characters, we can express their resemblance as a proportion of characters agreeing (matching) out of the total number being compared and assume that the similarity between the two operational taxonomic units is some parametric proportion of character matches which we are estimating with a sample of characters. In other words, we are taking a random sample from a very large number of characters which we could in theory sample and which would yield us a single, definite proportion of matches if we were able to sample all the characters. This might, for example, be the matches in the nucleotide sequence of the DNA of the genotype. The hypothesis, then, simply assumes that, as the number of characters sampled increases, the value of the similarity coefficient becomes more stable; eventually a further increase in the number of characters is not warranted by the corresponding mild decrease in the width of the confidence band of the coefficient.

The justification of this hypothesis rests on ordinary sampling theory in statistics and needs no special defense, if we can conceptualize a parametric value of matches among all possible characters and if character sampling as actually practiced can be considered close enough to being random in a statistical sense. The fact that in correlational and distance techniques the magnitude of mismatches between characters is being taken into account should not affect the hypothesis, since the only consequence will be the automatic and quite appropriate weighting of mismatches by their magnitude. Suppose we think of the comparison of each character in two taxa as a sample of, say, 12 loci being matched, where comparison between the entire genomes of two taxa would yield a proportion $p$ of mismatches and $1 - p$ matches. Then a random sample of characters should provide an estimate of the value of $p$ based on simple binomial theory of sampling with replacement.

The hypothesis of a matches asymptote can be tested as follows. For a group classified on an adequate number of characters we may, by a systematic search, uncover another group of characters. If the hypothesis holds, the changes brought about in the matrix of similarity coefficients by the inclusion of the new characters should be no more than expected by sampling theory. We have some misgivings on this score. Sneath (1957b) has pointed out that a change of emphasis or technique on the part of the investigator may lead him, perhaps unconsciously, to look for matching characters in preference to nonmatching ones (or vice versa) and thus introduce bias.

### 5.6.3. How many characters?

We have as yet no unequivocal answer to this direct question. In the published literature on numerical taxonomy only Michener and Sokal (1957) have ventured to make a suggestion—not less than sixty characters. Their idea was based on the statistical consideration that the confidence limits of the correlation coefficients became too wide below that sample size. As we shall see, there are indeed two separate considerations involved.

First of all, there is the purely statistical problem of the reliability of the estimates, if we regard similarity as a parametric value which we are sampling. Figure 5-7 shows the changes in the 95% confidence band for two correlation coefficients as sample size (number of characters) increases. If association coefficients are considered simply as a proportion of matched character states out of a total of all possible matches, we can apply the standard error of the binomial to them ($s = \sqrt{pq/n}$; if we

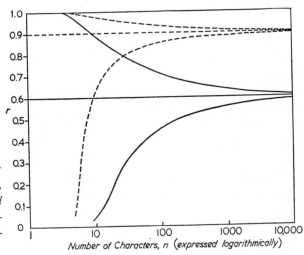

FIGURE 5-7

*The 95% confidence limits for two correlation coefficients, r = 0.9 and r = 0.6, plotted against the number of characters, n, on which the coefficients are based.*

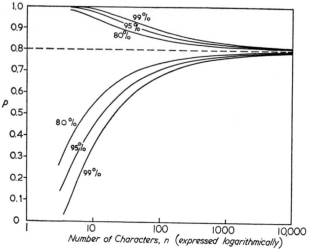

FIGURE 5-8

*The 80%, 95%, and 99% confidence limits of a proportion, such as the coefficient of association, $S_{SM}$, at a value of 0.8 plotted against the number of characters used to obtain the coefficient.*

assume the maximum error at $p = q = .5$, then $s = \sqrt{.25/n}$). Where $p$ is close to zero or unity and $n$ is relatively small, the binomial probability distribution $(p + q)^n$ should be expanded to obtain expected confidence limits for a given probability $p$. Figure A-4 in the Appendix provides a handy graph for so doing. Figure 5-8 shows the 80%, 95%, and 99% confidence bands for an association coefficient of 0.8. Figure 5-9 gives the expected value and 95% confidence band of a distance coefficient calculated as explained in Section 6.2.3.2.

We can see that as sample size increases the rate of decrease of the confidence bands becomes greatly reduced in all three instances. Thus the narrowing of the bands due to the increase of sample size from 50 to 100 is considerably greater than the subsequent reduction of the band between sample sizes 100 and 200. Therefore, after approximately $n = 100$, gains become unappreciable in general.

The above values should give some guide lines to the required sample size. The allowable width of the confidence band depends partly on the refinement with which one wishes to analyze the similarity matrix. If a rough classification is adequate, wide limits are permitted. But if fine structure is investigated and a detailed, nested classification is desired, the limits have to be sufficiently narrow that sampling error is not likely to be mistaken for real differences in affinity.

The second consideration is to think of each character as a sample of the genome and to inquire when a required percentage of the genome has been sampled at a required confidence level. We have seen in our discussion of the hypothesis of the factor asymptote that this approach is not very fruitful. Under plausible assumptions any reasonable number of characters would not represent more than a relatively small percentage of the genome. Thus we cannot use this consideration as a criterion for the necessary number.

Strictly speaking, the two ways of considering the effects of sample size would in any case be incompatible, since the required heterogeneity of the samples on which the second estimate is based invalidates the assumptions on whose basis the confidence bands have been computed. At best we can only claim the estimates of this section as indicators of the trends to be expected. As experience with numerical taxonomy of various groups begins to accumulate, we may learn empirically how an increase in the number of characters changes coefficients of similarity.

As a general rule we may stress that it is better to employ more, rather than fewer, characters. Certainly this should be the case whenever data on the characters are already available or can be easily obtained. By present methods of computation, limitations are generally set on the

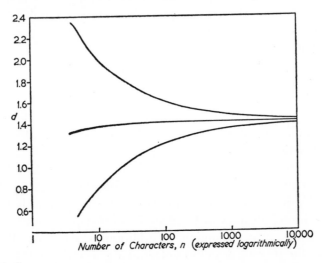

FIGURE 5-9

*Expected value of d and 95% confidence limits of the distance coefficient on the assumption that the observations on which the operational taxonomic units are based (that is, the n standardized characters used) are independent and normally distributed with a mean of zero and unit variance.*

number of operational taxonomic units rather than the number of characters, since computer operating time increases in general as the square of the number of taxa, but only in direct proportion to the number of characters.

## 5.7. THE PROBLEM OF WEIGHTING

Numerical taxonomy gives each feature equal weight when creating taxonomic groups (Sections 4.3, 4.4). This is unorthodox, but we will discuss its justification. We should emphasize that we are not here discussing the use of characters in identification. After a manner of speaking, "weighting" is used in such a procedure, and properly so. However, the construction of taxonomic keys and the identification of specimens belong to a late stage of taxonomic procedure and must not enter into the formation of the taxa concerned.

That every feature should be given equal weight is implicit in the work of Adanson and the writings of Gilmour (1937, 1940, 1951) and Cain and Harrison (1958), and it was stated explicitly by Sneath (1957a) and Michener and Sokal (1957). Verheyen (1960) holds the same opinion. Sneath reached this conclusion on considerations stemming from Gilmour's work on epistemology. It was argued that since natural taxa ideally contain the greatest possible content of implied information, this can only be measured in the number of statements which can be made about its members, which is independent of how important we may think any statement is. This argument has been developed at some length in connection with the "general" nature of natural classifications (see Sneath, 1958).

Michener and Sokal (1957) concluded that, even if desirable, there is no rational way of allocating weight to features, and therefore one must in practice give them all equal weight. Even if the entire genetic constitution of a form were known, it would be impossible to find a basis for weighting the genetic units, for these have no fixed adaptive, ontogenetic, or evolutionary significance. To mention only one possible criterion, the significance of the genetic units depends on their environment, which is always changing. In addition, when many characters are employed, the statistical analysis of similarity is only slightly affected by weighting some characters (unless this weighting is extreme). It is perhaps worth re-emphasizing this point, for if in practice the measures of overall similarity when based on many characters do yield substantially the same results, whatever the weighting (within reason) of individual characters, it would seem unnecessary to argue the point further.

The arguments in favor of equal weighting fall under seven headings.

(1) If we cannot decide how to weight the features, we must give them equal weight—unless we propose to allocate weight on irrational grounds.

(2) If we are to create taxonomic groups we must first decide how to weight the features which are to be employed for classification. We can therefore use no criterion which presupposes the existence of these taxa. For example, we cannot choose the constant features—to know if they *are* constant we must first set up taxonomic groups, and these we do not yet have. This was implied by Adanson's arguments, when he correctly asserted that one cannot make a priori judgments of the importance of characters.

(3) The concept of taxonomic importance has no exact meaning. If "importance" means "importance to me because I am interested in it," this is only special pleading. If "importance" means basic or fundamental, this can only mean that it sums up a number of other characters: if they are unknown, they are hypothetical; if known, the character is not single but multiple. If "importance" means essential to survival, the taxonomy can estimate viability, but not resemblance. If "importance" means "correlation with other features," then the added weight is due to these other features; where we observe the correlation to break down we do not regard the feature as important.

(4) If we admit differential weighting, we must give exact rules for estimating it. We must know whether the weight to be given to the possession of feathers is twice or twenty or two hundred times that given to possession of claws, and why. We do not know of any method for estimating this, and even if such a method were to be developed we doubt if any systematist would have the patience to use it because of the hundreds of characters he would need.

(5) The nature of a taxonomy depends upon its purpose: we could arrange living creatures in many ways, but we choose one way because we think it is the best for some purpose. We hold the view that a "natural" or "orthodox" taxonomy is a general arrangement intended for general use by all kinds of scientists (Gilmour, 1937; Sneath, 1958). It cannot therefore give greater weight to features of one sort, or it ceases to be a general arrangement. It can only be made if scientists are

willing to forego the claim that their own interests should be specially favored. It is not always clear to them that it is in their own interests to do this, but they need this general arrangement against which to compare their own special findings. Being general, it is best for general purposes but is perfect for none.

(6) The property of "naturalness" is, we believe, due to the high content of implied information which is possessed by a natural group. A group such as the Mammalia at once tells us much about its members with a high degree of certainty. A group such as "black animals" tells us nothing more than that they are all black. The content of information is measured by the number of statements which can be made about its members: each statement has unit value, and whether we think them important or not is irrelevant.

(7) As noted above and in Chapter 6, the use of many characters greatly evens out the effective weight which each character contributes to the affinity coefficient. In practice, therefore, the methods are equal-weight methods.

Equal weighting can therefore be defended on several independent grounds: it is the only practical solution, it and only it can give the sort of natural taxonomy which we want, and it will appear automatically during the mathematical manipulations. Singly, these arguments are cogent; taken together, we feel that they are overwhelming.

## 5.8. THE OPERATIONAL TAXONOMIC UNITS

What taxonomic units can be classified by numerical taxonomy? The logical fundamental unit in a large majority of instances is the individual organism. While this is usually an unambiguous entity, it is generally not feasible to use numerous conspecific individuals of each of several apparent taxonomic groups to compute a classificatory hierarchy. Matrices of excessive size would have to be processed—a formidable enterprise even by the standards of the most modern computers. Furthermore, such studies would throw light largely on resemblances among intraspecific variants and would not be likely to offer much scope for comparisons at the subgeneric, generic, and higher levels. Thus, except for special studies aiming at intraspecific classification, the most customary unit in zoology and botany will be the species (strictly speaking, the taxonomic unit with a binominal name, the *binom* of Camp, 1951, which is believed to correspond to one or other of the biological units which are given the name of species). Since the hierarchic level of the tax-onomic unit employed in numerical studies will differ, we cannot speak of fundamental taxonomic units but shall refer to them as *operational taxonomic units (OTU's)*.

Should numerical taxonomy rely on the validity of species erected by conventional methods? We believe (probably in agreement with most present-day biologists) that of the categories established in the present system of nature the different entities which have been called species have more reliability than any others, with the possible exception of the very highest taxa. So far as numerical taxonomy is concerned, it does not matter that there are many species concepts and species definitions, so long as these are clearly understood and used fairly consistently within a study. Some kinds of species, furthermore, can be defined by biological (analytical and experimental) criteria (see Mayr, Linsley, and Usinger, 1953, for some definitions) and differ in this respect from the higher and lower taxa, which are defined on more ambiguous bases. However, it should be pointed out that the criteria of specific difference actually applied by most systematists to most taxa are phenetic and do not satisfy the genetic definition of specific status (see also, Blackwelder, 1962, and Sokal, 1962b, 1964). Although taxonomists make objective tests of the criteria for specific distinction in only a small minority of cases, their judgment in this matter generally inspires confidence (certain difficult taxa and indifferent taxonomists excepted).

Zoologists in recent years have turned to a genetic definition of species (*sensu* Mayr, 1942). However, there are many groups—including, for example, the bacteria—where such a species definition seems at present inapplicable. Since a single bacterium can seldom be studied sufficiently, taxonomy is based on pure cultures of strains. In plants there are many genera in which the individuals are apomictic—vegetatively propagated, parthenogenetic, or self-fertilized—and here it is generally the clone which is taken as the unit of classification. Yet clones may throw off mutant forms, which may or may not be considered as distinct units. The important point is to avoid prejudice in choosing the OTU's and if need be to explore by preliminary analyses the phenetic relations of the specimens which are to form them. In both plants and animals there may be a choice between stages in the life cycle, or between different castes in social insects. The special problems raised by these possibilities have been discussed in Section 5.4.3.

Problems may arise if a taxon used as an OTU proves to be variable for one or more characters. This brings up the question of whether we can use as OTU's higher taxa (such as genera, families, and orders) in which the majority of characters within a taxon will of course vary. Such taxa can be used, in principle, for the reasons discussed in Section 6.4.

A second equally serious problem is the low degree of relevance of most lists of characters (see Section 6.5.5). Since these considerations have not yet been discussed, we shall postpone an evaluation of the analysis of higher taxa until Chapter 6.

CHAPTER **6**

# The Estimation
# of Taxonomic
# Resemblance

This chapter presents a detailed exposition and evaluation of the various numerical methods which have been advocated for expressing the similarity between taxa. We would like to remind the reader before proceeding that the terms "resemblance," "similarity," and "affinity" are used interchangeably throughout this book, and that unless specifically qualified they imply a solely phenetic relationship.

## 6.1. METHODS OF ESTIMATION IN VARIOUS SCIENCES

The problem of finding measures of the resemblance between pairs of entities based on a number of characteristics is not a new one; it has been encountered in a number of sciences whenever classificatory tasks have been undertaken. Besides taxonomy, the fields most frequently involved are psychology and ecology (see Section 10.6).

We adopt the convention used in psychology of arranging data for such an undertaking in the form of an $n \times t$ matrix whose $t$ columns represent the $t$ fundamental entities to be grouped on the basis of resemblances and whose $n$ rows are $n$ unit characters. Each entry $X_{ij}$ in such a matrix is the score of operational taxonomic unit $j$ for character $i$. The scale in which this score is expressed may simply allow for two states, such as present or absent. This is often conveniently symbolized by +

and — ; however, the use of 1 and 0 facilitates the numerical treatment of such data. Other scales may be ordinal, continuous, or percentages of the maximum expression of a given character. The consequences of the use of the various scales are discussed later.

Cattell (1952) has pointed out that most matrices of this sort can be examined from two points of view. The association of pairs of characters (rows) can be examined over all OTU's (columns). This is called the R-technique. The converse practice, the association of pairs of OTU's (columns) over all characters (rows), has been called the Q-technique.

In psychology the R-technique is used to quantify relations among various kinds of psychological tests computed from a number of subjects (individuals). It will yield groups of related tests. The Q-technique, on the other hand, will evaluate relationships among persons based on their performance on mental or personality tests. It should result in identifying and categorizing types of persons.

In ecology the application of similar techniques has been particularly fruitful in community studies. Rows in such studies would represent species (the floral or faunal composition), while columns would be stands or other sampled plots. In this field of research the R-technique aims at the quantification of the relation between the species sampled from a number of presumably homogeneous plots, which may be quadrats or entire stands, as the case may be. These methods have been helpful in: (1) discovering ecological relationships among different species, such as common environmental requirements or dependence of one species upon the other, and (2) the use of combinations of species in classifying and identifying ecological associations and communities. Difficulties have been encountered, since plant ecologists have been unable to extend this type of treatment to several species simultaneously. Recently Dagnelie (1960) has shown the way to a multivariate analysis of such data.

The application of the Q-technique in ecology is the computation of coefficients of relationship between stands or other sampling units based on lists of species common to such units. A great variety of coefficients have been developed and applied to this task, which has as its aim the grouping of similar stands into associations and communities. The analogies with taxonomic procedures are quite striking.

In taxonomy both techniques have been employed. In this field the R-technique refers to correlations among characters based on operational taxonomic units. These could be from the lowest possible rank (individual organisms) up through local populations, varieties, subspecies, species, and supraspecific taxa. At the infraspecific level, much R-type work has been performed (for example, Clark, 1941; Jolicoeur, 1959; Olson and Miller, 1958; Sokal, 1952, 1959, 1962a; Sokal and Hunter, 1955; Sokal and Rinkel, 1963). Such work contributes mainly to an understanding of ontogenetic processes and of minor genetic differentiation. At the higher taxonomic levels, analysis of R-type matrices should lead to information on phylogenetic factors at work within the group studied. So far as we are aware, the only taxonomic study of this nature has been that of Stroud (1953) on 43 species of the termite genus *Kalotermes*. We feel that much information of systematic value can come from such studies and shall discuss them in Section 7.6.

However, our main emphasis in numerical taxonomy is on Q-type studies. They refer to the quantifications of relations between pairs of taxa, frequently species, based on a preferably large number of characters. The history of this approach has been covered in Section 3.1. The resulting estimates of resemblance form the bases for the various procedures of numerical taxonomy. Criticisms of the Q-technique applied to problems in psychology (Cattell, 1952) have been shown not to apply to work in taxonomy (Sokal and Michener, 1958).

## 6.2. ESTIMATES OF RESEMBLANCE PROPOSED IN TAXONOMY

In a discussion of the various methods used for assessing taxonomic similarities, consideration must be given to the important problems of scaling and coding of characters and also to those of sampling (the reliability of the data used in a computation). However, these cannot be suitably discussed until the methods themselves have been presented. We shall therefore defer all consideration of these problems until the methods have been introduced and evaluated.

The various techniques for computing resemblances between taxa can be conveniently grouped into three types of coefficients—those of association, of correlation, and of distance. We would like to refer to them collectively as coefficients of resemblance or similarity.

### 6.2.1. Coefficients of association

These coefficients—also known as coefficients of similarity or relationship, or matching coefficients—have been widely used, particularly in ecology. Reviews of the different types of coefficients which have been proposed and used can be found in Cole (1949, 1957) and Dagnelie

(1960). We should point out at this time that all the terms employed here for these coefficients (such as association, similarity, relationship) have been used in a variety of meanings in English and in other languages. The designations adopted here are therefore arbitrary.

The basic arrangement of data for computation of coefficients of association is the familiar 2 × 2 table. An example of such an arrangement is shown here:

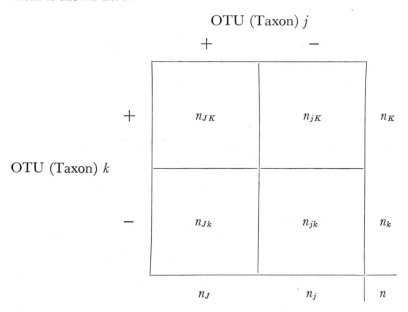

The data consist of $n$ characters scored for two OTU's labeled $j$ and $k$. They are subdivided into positive and negative classes for each of the two operational taxonomic units. We shall use capital letter subscripts to indicate positive or "1" states and lower-case letter subscripts to show negative or "0" states. The number of characters in which both OTU's are positive is labeled $n_{JK}$, the number in which both are negative $n_{jk}$. The number of characters positive for one OTU and negative for the other are $n_{Jk}$ and $n_{jK}$, respectively. Marginal totals are $n_J$ and $n_K$ for positive characters of OTU $j$ and $k$, respectively; similarly, $n_j$ and $n_k$ are the marginal totals for the negative characters. For convenience in writing formulas and in thinking about the coefficients, we establish the following symbolism: the number of characters in "matched" cells (of the 2 × 2 table), or $m$, will be $m = n_{JK} + n_{jk}$, and the number of characters in "unmatched" cells, or $u$, will be $u = n_{Jk} + n_{jK}$. The total number of characters, or $n$, is

$$n = m + u = n_{JK} + n_{jk} + n_{Jk} + n_{jK}$$
$$= n_J + n_j = n_K + n_k.$$

The $2 \times 2$ setup of the data in numerical taxonomy is primarily a convenient arrangement and must not be confused with the conventional $2 \times 2$ tables used for tests of independence in statistics. To elaborate this very important point, let us compare a typical example of data suitable for a test of independence in a $2 \times 2$ table with a Q-type arrangement between two OTU's. Suppose we wish to investigate the relation between smoking and heart disease in English males of a given age group. We would attempt to obtain a random sample of, say, 500 men of the specified age from different parts of England and various walks of life. We would then investigate each man to learn whether he smoked more than a specified amount and on this basis classify him as a smoker or nonsmoker (positive or negative). A thorough medical examination would establish whether each man suffered from heart disease according to a specified set of criteria; again the sample would be divided into positive and negative classes on the basis of the cardiac findings. The data would be arrayed in a $2 \times 2$ table. We would assume that the proportion of smokers and the incidence of heart disease in the sample are representative of their population statistics for the age group. The null hypothesis would suppose independence between the two properties, smoking and heart disease, and the test of this hypothesis could be carried out in the customary way.

In contrast, while we can legitimately assume that the characters based on a Q-type study in numerical taxonomy are a random sample from the infinity of characters that could be discovered, we cannot consider the proportions of positive scores in either taxonomic unit as representative of any parametric value. The meaning of "positive" and "negative" in connection with a $2 \times 2$ table for a coefficient of association can vary from the presence or absence of a structure or a chemical reaction to two alternative states of a dimorphic character, without the implication of absence or retrogression possibly carried by the term "negative." Thus in the latter instances the choice of which of the two states is to be called "positive" is quite arbitrary. When a strain of microorganisms becomes drug-resistant, should we call the resistant or the susceptible strain positive? We must not imply that there is a parametric value of positiveness which is estimated by the proportion in our sample. This proportion may change in quite an unpredictable manner when we add new characters and information. This difficulty is common to Q-type studies of association and correlation; we refer to it as heterogeneity of column vectors (of the original data matrix) and shall have more to say about it in connection with correlational studies. For the reasons stated, it would not be proper from the point of view of statistical theory to test these 2 × 2 tables with the customary chi-square test for independence (nor would we wish to do so, since our aim is to estimate resemblance).

An appropriate mode of thinking about Q-type data in a 2 × 2 table is to consider them a sample proportion of matches from an infinitely large population of character matches which could be attempted (see Section 5.6.2). If there is a parametric resemblance value between the two OTU's, this can be expressed as a percentage of matching characters. It is this percentage that we are estimating by our sample. In this manner the resemblance can be expressed as a single proportion, and the sampling error can be computed by conventional formulas based on the binomial distribution.

### 6.2.1.1. Possible kinds of coefficients

Much confusion exists in the literature regarding the terminology of coefficients of association. Since they have been used both for R- and Q-type studies, identical coefficients have often been proposed under different names for the two types of matrices. We have adopted the convention of calling the coefficient by the name of its originator (or the first we know to propose it), regardless of the type of study for which the coefficient was proposed.

The fundamental formula consists of the number of matches divided by a term implying the possible number of comparisons but varying in its detailed composition. Table 6-1 presents a scheme for classifying most coefficients of association, based on the nature of the numerator and the denominator. Of the fourteen possible combinations, only three have so far been proposed for use in numerical taxonomy. The others have either been suggested for ecological work or have not yet been used. The coefficients have been separated (vertically) into two groups in Table 6-1 by whether the numerator includes the "negative matches" or not. These are matches for the negative states of characters between the two OTU's.

Whether negative matches should be incorporated into a coefficient of association may occasion some doubts. It may be argued that basing similarity between two species on the mutual absence of a certain character is improper. The absence of wings, when observed among a group of distantly related organisms (such as camel, louse, and nema-

**Table 6-1.** *Coefficients of Association*

The coefficients of association are divided in two ways. The two vertical columns represent omission (left) and inclusion (right) of negative matches. The horizontal divisions of the table are based on the nature of the denominator indicated in the left margin of the table. Each coefficient is arranged in its box as follows. First line: author of coefficient and reference; second line: formula for coefficient; third and fourth lines: limits of coefficient and conditions necessary for coefficients to assume these limits; fifth line: expected value of the coefficient on the assumption of independence of positive and negative states in the two taxa being compared—that is, $\mathcal{E}(n_{JK}) = n_J n_K/n$ and similarly for the other three cells of the $2 \times 2$ table.

| Denomi-nator | Negative Matches in Numerator | |
| --- | --- | --- |
| | Excluded | Included |
| Matched and unmatched pairs are equally weighted | Jaccard, 1908 (Sneath, 1957b) <br><br> $S_J = n_{JK}/(n_{JK} + u)$ <br> $S_J \longrightarrow 0$ as $n_{JK}/u \longrightarrow 0$ <br> $S_J \longrightarrow 1$ as $u/n_{JK} \longrightarrow 0$ <br> $\mathcal{E}(S_J) = n_J n_K/[n(n_J + n_K) - n_J n_K]$ | Simple Matching (Sokal and Michener, 1958) <br><br> $S_{SM} = m/(m + u) = m/n$ <br> $S_{SM} \longrightarrow 0$ as $m/u \longrightarrow 0$ <br> $S_{SM} \longrightarrow 1$ as $u/m \longrightarrow 0$ <br> $\mathcal{E}(S_{SM}) = (n_J n_K + n_j n_k)/n^2$ |
| | Russell and Rao, 1940 <br> $S_{RR} = n_{JK}/n$ <br> $S_{RR} \longrightarrow 0$ as $n_{JK}/u \longrightarrow 0$ <br> $S_{RR} \longrightarrow 1$ as $(n_{jk} + u)/n_{JK} \longrightarrow 0$ <br> $\mathcal{E}(S_{RR}) = n_J n_K/n^2$ | (as above) |
| Matched pairs carry twice the weight of unmatched pairs | Dice, 1945 (Sørensen, 1948) <br> $S_D = 2n_{JK}/(2n_{JK} + u)$ <br> $S_D \longrightarrow 0$ as $n_{JK}/u \longrightarrow 0$ <br> $S_D \longrightarrow 1$ as $u/n_{JK} \longrightarrow 0$ <br> $\mathcal{E}(S_D) = 2/[(n/n_K) + (n/n_J)]$ | Unnamed coefficient <br> $S = 2m/(2m + u) = 2m/(n + m)$ <br> $S \longrightarrow 0$ as $m/u \longrightarrow 0$ <br> $S \longrightarrow 1$ as $u/m \longrightarrow 0$ <br> $\mathcal{E}(S) = \dfrac{[2(n_J n_K + n_j n_k)]}{[n(n_J + n_K) + 2n_j n_k]}$ |
| Unmatched pairs carry twice the weight of matched pairs | Unnamed coefficient <br> $S = n_{JK}/(n_{JK} + 2u)$ <br> $S \longrightarrow 0$ as $n_{JK}/u \longrightarrow 0$ <br> $S \longrightarrow 1$ as $u/n_{JK} \longrightarrow 0$ <br> $\mathcal{E}(S) = 1/[(2n/n_K) + (2n/n_J) - 3]$ | Rogers and Tanimoto, 1960 <br> $S_{RT} = m/(m + 2u) = m/(n + u)$ <br> $S_{RT} \longrightarrow 0$ as $m/u \longrightarrow 0$ <br> $S_{RT} \longrightarrow 1$ as $u/m \longrightarrow 0$ <br> $\mathcal{E}(S_{RT}) = \dfrac{(n_J n_K + n_j n_k)}{(n_{Jk} + n_{jK} + n^2)}$ |
| Unmatched pairs only | Kulczynski, 1927 <br> $S_{K1} = n_{JK}/(n_J + n_K - 2n_{JK})$ <br> $\qquad = n_{JK}/u$ <br> $0 \leqq S_{K1} \leqq \infty$ <br> $\mathcal{E}(S_{K1}) = 1/[(n/n_K) + (n/n_J) - 2]$ | Unnamed coefficient <br> $S = m/u$ <br><br> $0 \leqq S \leqq \infty$ <br> $\mathcal{E}(S) = \dfrac{[n_J n_K + (n - n_J)(n - n_K)]}{[n(n_J + n_K) - 2n_J n_K]}$ |

*continued on following page*

**Table 6-1.** (*continued*)

| Denomi-nator | Negative Matches in Numerator | |
|---|---|---|
| | Excluded | Included |
| Marginal totals | Kulczynski, 1927<br>$S_{K2} = \frac{1}{2}[(n_{JK}/n_J) + (n_{JK}/n_K)]$<br><br>$S_{K2} \longrightarrow 0$ as $n_{JK}/n_{Jk}$ and $n_{JK}/n_{jK}$ <br>   both $\longrightarrow 0$<br>$S_{K2} \longrightarrow 1$ as $n_{Jk}/n_{JK}$ and $n_{jK}/n_{JK}$ <br>   both $\longrightarrow 0$<br>$\mathcal{E}(S_{K2}) = (n_K + n_J)/2n$ | Unnamed coefficient<br>$S = \frac{1}{4}[(n_{JK}/n_J) + (n_{JK}/n_K)$<br>   $\qquad\qquad + (n_{jk}/n_i) + (n_{jk}/n_k)]$<br>$S \longrightarrow 0$ as $n_{JK}/n_{Jk}$, $n_{JK}/n_{jK}$,<br>   $n_{jk}/n_{Jk}$, $n_{jk}/n_{jK}$ all $\longrightarrow 0$<br>$S \longrightarrow 1$ as above ratios all $\longrightarrow \infty$<br><br>$\mathcal{E}(S) = \frac{1}{2}$ |
| Marginal totals | Ochiai, 1957<br>$S_O = n_{JK}/\sqrt{n_J n_K}$<br>$S_O \longrightarrow 0$ as $n_{JK}/n_{Jk}n_{jK} \longrightarrow 0$<br>$S_O \longrightarrow 1$ as $n_{Jk}n_{jK}/n_{JK} \longrightarrow 0$<br>$\mathcal{E}(S_O) = \sqrt{n_J n_K}/n$ | Unnamed coefficient<br>$S = n_{JK}n_{jk}/\sqrt{n_J n_K n_j n_k}$<br>$S \longrightarrow 0$ as $n_{JK}n_{jk}/n_{Jk}n_{jK} \longrightarrow 0$<br>$S \longrightarrow 1$ as $n_{Jk}n_{jK}/n_{JK}n_{jk} \longrightarrow 0$<br>$\mathcal{E}(S) = \sqrt{n_J n_K n_j n_k}/n^2$ |

tode), would surely be an absurd indication of affinity. Yet a positive character, such as the presence of wings (or flying organs defined without qualification as to kind of wing) could mislead equally when considered for a similarly heterogenous assemblage (for example, bat, heron, and dragonfly). Neither can we argue that absence of a character may be due to a multitude of causes and that matched absence in a pair of OTU's is therefore not "true resemblance," for, after all, we know little more about the origins of matched positive characters.

Sneath (1957b) excluded negative matches from consideration in his similarity coefficient. He felt that it was difficult to decide which negative features to include in a study and which to exclude. He stated that it is not pertinent to count "absence of feathers" when comparing two bacteria, but that this feature is applicable in comparing bacteria and birds. It is true that through reductio ad absurdum we can arrive at a universe of negative character matches purporting to establish the similarity between two entities. A similarly absurd procedure would be the introduction of positive matches for characters that are invariant over the group under study. The rules described in the section on inadmissible characters (Section 5.3.3) should forestall such improper procedures. In many two-state characters the two states in which they are expressed do not signify presence and absence of the character. Matches for "negative" states are thus of equal value and interest to those for "positive" states. A reasonable and logically defensible position appears to be the inclusion of positive as well as negative matches for those characters that vary within the group under study. In this respect our conclusion differs from that of Sneath (1957b) and Sørensen (1948) but agrees with Rogers and Tanimoto (1960) and by implication with Sokal and Michener (1958). Most of the applications of association coefficients since 1957 (largely in the field of bacteriology) have included negative matches in their coefficients.

In bacteriological work the problem may be slightly different because of the practice of applying a standard series of tests to a group of bacteria. In such cases appreciable blocks of invariant negative characters may result, which would artificially increase resemblance values between OTU's. Exclusion of negative matches from the computation of a coefficient of association may be the safe procedure here, especially since a large group of negatives may on occasion be due to an unrecognized metabolic block preventing the expression of many other characters. This case is similar to that of the missing organs discussed below (Section 6.5.3). The difficulty particularly with microorganisms is to know what characters are missing. In morphological characters this is determined by position—an insect, for example, cannot have wing veins in an absent wing. Thus we must code the veins NC (see Section 5.3.5). But our knowledge of metabolic characters is more limited. It may be impossible to decide if enzymes **A, B, C, D**, $\cdots$ are present but not expressed because of lack of **Z**, which is necessary for activity. This is analogous in a morphological context to being unable to decide how to score subsidiary characters because we do not know whether the organ is present. The coefficient of Jaccard (as employed by Sneath, 1957b) is appropriate when negative matches are to be excluded.

The horizontal subdivision of the coefficients in Table 6-1 is on the basis of the denominator of the fraction. The first row consists of coefficients whose denominator is the total possible number of matches. Matched and unmatched pairs are here given equal weight. Thus the ratio expresses the proportion of actual out of all potential matches. It appears to us to be the simplest of the various ratios proposed. The second row shows Russell and Rao's coefficient, which is "hybrid" in nature, excluding negative matches from the numerator but not from the denominator. This appears to be of questionable utility.

The third row shows coefficients with denominators in which the matched pairs carry twice the weight of the unmatched pairs. While the limits of these coefficients are identical to those of the values in the first row (similarity coefficient $0 \leqq S \leqq 1$), the intermediate values are bound to be larger. Thus, comparing the coefficients of Jaccard and of Dice, we find the latter greater at all times except when $u = 0$, at which time $S_J = S_D$.

The fourth row of coefficients uses a denominator in which the unmatched pairs carry twice the weight of the matched pairs. Again the limits remain as before, but now the coefficients are less than those in the first row except when $u = 0$—that is, when there are no unmatched pairs of OTU's. The coefficients in the fifth row differ from those in the first three rows in that they have infinity rather than unity as their upper limit. They represent the ratio of the number of matches to that of the nonmatches.

The sixth row represents the proportion of matches as the average of the proportion of matches in $j$ and $k$, while the seventh row represents the ratio of matches to the geometric mean of the marginal totals.

Next we consider three coefficients of association which balance the

**Table 6-2.** *Three Coefficients of Association which Balance Matched Pairs against Unmatched Pairs in the Numerator\**

---

Hamann, 1961

$S_H = (m - u)/n$

$S_H \longrightarrow 0$ as $m \longrightarrow u$

$S_H \longrightarrow +1$ as $u/m \longrightarrow 0$

$S_H \longrightarrow -1$ as $m/u \longrightarrow 0$

$\mathcal{E}(S_H) = \dfrac{1}{n^2} [(n_J - n_j)(n_K - n_k)]$

---

Yule, 1911 (refer to Yule and Kendall, 1950)

$S_Y = (n_{JK}n_{jk} - n_{Jk}n_{jK})/(n_{JK}n_{jk} + n_{Jk}n_{jK})$

$S_Y \longrightarrow 0$ as $n_{JK}n_{jk} \longrightarrow n_{Jk}n_{jK}$

$S_Y \longrightarrow +1$ as $n_{Jk}n_{jK}/n_{JK}n_{jk} \longrightarrow 0$

$S_Y \longrightarrow -1$ as $n_{JK}n_{jk}/n_{Jk}n_{jK} \longrightarrow 0$

$\mathcal{E}(S_Y) = 0$

---

phi coefficient (Pearson; refer to Guilford, 1942)

$S_\phi = (n_{JK}n_{jk} - n_{jK}n_{Jk})/(n_J n_K n_j n_k)^{1/2}$

$S_\phi \longrightarrow 0$ as $n_{JK}n_{jk} \longrightarrow n_{Jk}n_{jK}$

$S_\phi \longrightarrow +1$ as $n_{Jk}n_{jK}/n_{JK}n_{jk} \longrightarrow 0$

$S_\phi \longrightarrow -1$ as $n_{JK}n_{jK}/n_{Jk}n_{jK} \longrightarrow 0$

$\mathcal{E}(S_\phi) = 0$

---

\* The arrangement in the boxes for these three coefficients is the same as in Table 6-1.

number of matched and unmatched pairs in the numerator. These range from $-1$ to $+1$ and are shown in Table 6-2. All the coefficients of association which have so far been employed in numerical taxonomy are discussed below. The computation of the various coefficients of association is shown in Appendix A.2.

### 6.2.1.2. *The coefficient of Jaccard (Sneath):*

$$S_J = n_{JK}/(n_{JK} + u)$$

Sneath (1957a) used a coefficient he called the *similarity*, which has had a considerable history of application in R-type and Q-type studies in ecology. The earliest record of its employment we have found is by Jaccard (1908), and we shall therefore refer to it as the coefficient of Jaccard, $S_J$. It is clear that $S_J \rightarrow 0$ as $n_{JK}/u \rightarrow 0$, and that as $u \rightarrow 0$, $S_J \rightarrow 1$. In the latter case $n_J = n_K = n_{JK}$. The coefficient of Jaccard omits consideration of negative matches. In its class it is the simplest of the coefficients.

### 6.2.1.3. *The simple matching coefficient:*

$$S_{SM} = m/n = m/(m + u)$$

Sokal and Michener (1958), in a paper dealing with their numerical method for evaluating taxonomic relationships, introduced but did not employ a so-called "matching coefficient." This coefficient is the equivalent of the coefficient of Jaccard just discussed but includes negative matches. Because of its simple nature it must have been thought of and applied repeatedly; see, for example, du Mas (1955). In psychology Zubin (1938) proposed such a coefficient. Without tracing its history, we have called it the simple matching coefficient. This is $S_S$ in Sneath (1962). It is the affinity index of Brisbane and Rovira (1961). From the formula it follows that $S_{SM} \rightarrow 0$ as $m/u \rightarrow 0$, and that $S_{SM} \rightarrow 1$ as $u/m \rightarrow 0$, in which case $n_J = n_K = n_{JK}$ and $n_j = n_k = n_{jk}$. When first suggested by Sokal and Michener (1958), the coefficient was not restricted to characters with only two states. However, since we are here considering coefficients of association for dichotomous characters only, we are so restricting it now.

### 6.2.1.4. *The coefficient of Rogers and Tanimoto:*

$$S_{RT} = m/(m + 2u) = m/(n + u)$$

Rogers and Tanimoto (1960) developed a *similarity ratio* with flexibility to include characters with more than two states and also to take missing information into account. For purposes of this section we shall limit their coefficient, $S_{RT}$, to the case of two states per character and with complete information. Its mathematical formulation is then as given above. It follows that $S_{RT} \to 0$ when $m/u \to 0$ and that $S_{RT} \to 1$ when $u/m \to 0$, in which case $n_J = n_K = n_{JK}$ and $n_j = n_k = n_{jk}$. The coefficient of Rogers and Tanimoto includes negative matches, if we wish to call the second of the two states negative. It is more elaborate than the simple matching coefficient but is functionally related to it.

### 6.2.1.5. The coefficient of Hamann:

$$S_H = (m - u)/n$$

This coefficient has been employed by Hamann (1961) in a study of some families of monocotyledonous plants. It employs the difference between the matched and unmatched pairs as a criterion of association. Thus when the number of matched and unmatched pairs is equal, $m = u$ and $S_H = 0$. This coefficient can range from $-1$ to $+1$ when $u \to 0$ and $m \to 0$, respectively. It shares this property with the two coefficients listed next. These latter coefficients carry the determinant of the $2 \times 2$ table as their numerator. When two OTU's are independent on the basis of their characters, the determinant will be zero, yet the term $(m - u)$ is not necessarily so. As can be seen in Table 6-2, the expected value of $S_H$ will be zero only when $n_J = n_j$ or $n_K = n_k$ or both of these relations hold. This might appear an undesirable property of $S_H$, yet independence probably does not have a clear meaning in $2 \times 2$ tables in numerical taxonomy, as discussed above.

### 6.2.1.6. The coefficient of Yule:

$$S_Y = (n_{JK}n_{jk} - n_{jK}n_{Jk})/(n_{JK}n_{jk} + n_{jK}n_{Jk})$$

This coefficient, described as $Q$ in Yule and Kendall (1950), is symbolized by us as $S_Y$ in order to conform to the pattern adopted for designating coefficients of association. Its limits are $+1$ when $n_{jK}$ or $n_{Jk} \to 0$ and $-1$ when $n_{JK}$ or $n_{jk} \to 0$. Yule and Kendall describe it as the simplest possible (of its kind), although not necessarily the most advantageous that may be devised. It has been employed also by Brisbane and Rovira (1961).

### 6.2.1.7. The phi coefficient:

$$S_\phi = (n_{JK}n_{jk} - n_{jK}n_{Jk})/(n_J n_j n_K n_k)^{1/2}$$

This well-known coefficient can be found in many statistics books, as for example in Yule and Kendall (1950). It is also known as the fourfold point correlation coefficient. Its customary symbol is $\phi$, used by us in subscript form. The limits of $S_\phi$ are the same as those of $S_Y$, whose numerator it shares. The phi coefficient is frequently used in statistics and is important because of its relation to $\chi^2$; that is, $\chi^2 = \phi^2 n$. This permits a test of significance; however, because of the problem of heterogeneity of column vectors (Section 6.2.1), it is doubtful whether any meaning can be applied to such a test.

### 6.2.1.8. *Smirnov's coefficient of similarity and the generalized coefficient of Rogers and Tanimoto*

Two coefficients of association remain which we have not been able to bring into our general classification. These deal with characters whose number of states are not restricted to two. Such characters may or may not be linearly ordered. Rogers and Tanimoto (1960) treat these by a general formula, from which the formula given in Table 6-1 for two-state characters has been abstracted. The treatment by Smirnov (1960) approaches the problem in quite a different manner. Although these coefficients are quite different, the basic arrangement of data for both is identical.

Table 6-3 illustrates two OTU's scored for four characters $A$, $B$, $C$,

**Table 6-3.** *Four Multistate Characters to Illustrate the Computation of the Coefficients of Rogers and Tanimoto (1960) and Smirnov (1960).*

| | Character | | | | | | | | | | | | | | |
|---|---|---|---|---|---|---|---|---|---|---|---|---|---|---|---|
| | A | | | | B | | C | | | D | | | | | |
| State | 1 | 2 | 3 | 4 | 1 | 2 | 1 | 2 | 3 | 1 | 2 | 3 | 4 | 5 | |
| OTU 1 | − | + | − | − | − | + | − | − | + | − | + | − | − | − | |
| OTU 2 | − | + | − | − | + | − | − | − | + | − | − | − | − | + | |
| | States expressed by Smirnov's system | | | | | | | | | | | | | | |
| OTU 1 | $a_1$ | $A_2$ | $a_3$ | $a_4$ | $b_1$ | $B_2$ | $c_1$ | $c_2$ | $C_3$ | $d_1$ | $D_2$ | $d_3$ | $d_4$ | $d_5$ | |
| OTU 2 | $a_1$ | $A_2$ | $a_3$ | $a_4$ | $B_1$ | $b_2$ | $c_1$ | $c_2$ | $C_3$ | $d_1$ | $d_2$ | $d_3$ | $d_4$ | $D_5$ | |

and $D$. These characters have states ranging from 2 for character $B$ to 5 for character $D$. The two OTU's are scored positively if they possess a given state for a character and negatively if they do not. Thus we see that OTU's 1 and 2 agree in both exhibiting state 2 for character $A$ and state 3 for character $C$. They disagree in character states for characters $B$ and $D$. If a simple matching coefficient ($S_{SM}$) were applied to these data, this would imply that the mismatch in character $D$ is equivalent to the mismatch in character $B$. If the character states are scored entirely qualitatively, then this may well be a legitimate assumption; in such a case the simple matching coefficient might be indicated. The small fictitious example here would give a matching coefficient of two matches divided by four possible matches ($= 0.5$). When we give more weight to the mismatch in character $D$ than to the mismatch in character $B$ we presumably imply dimensionality in the character states. In such instances the coefficients of distance and correlation mentioned below would be more appropriate.

Rogers and Tanimoto's coefficient of similarity calculates the number of agreements in character states divided by the number of character states represented by at least one OTU. Thus the numerator of their coefficient would be 2 (one for the agreement on character state $A_2$, the other one for the agreement on character state $C_3$), and the denominator would be 6 (character states $A_2$, $B_1$, $B_2$, $C_3$, $D_2$, and $D_5$ all have at least one positive representative in the comparison). Thus Rogers and Tanimoto's similarity coefficient, $S_{RT}$, would equal $\frac{2}{6} = 0.33$.

In order to understand Smirnov's coefficient we first have to become familiar with his terminology. In Smirnov's coefficient the number of species (OTU's) involved in any given taxonomic study is of importance; this number is called $s$. Of importance also is the distribution of the states (modalities) for a given character among the $s$ species of the study. Thus Smirnov will write such a distribution as

$$(E_1) + (E_2) + (E_3) + \cdots + (E_{e-1}) + (E_e) = s,$$

where $(E_1)$ is the number of species exhibiting character state 1 for character $E$. The number of character states in character $E$ is symbolized by $e$. Thus character $A$ has $a$ states (four in the example in Table 6.3), while character $B$ has $b$ states (two in the same example). Since all the $s$ species in a study must exhibit one or the other character state, $\sum_{i=1}^{e} (E_i) = s$. Smirnov designates $(e_1)$ as the number of species not possessing character state 1 of character $E$. Obviously the following relation must hold:

$$(E_1) + (e_1) = s.$$

In an actual example we might have the following distribution of positive character states in one hundred species:

$$30E_1 + 20E_2 + 5E_3 + 45E_4 = 100.$$

Since 30 species possess character state 1, it is clear that 70 of the species will not possess that character state. We can therefore write the above relation as

$$30E_1 + 70e_1 = 100,$$
$$20E_2 + 80e_2 = 100,$$
$$5E_3 + 95e_3 = 100,$$
$$45E_4 + 55e_4 = 100.$$

The key to understanding Smirnov's method is that the similarity based on any one character is weighted as a function of the probability of the simultaneous occurrence of such a character state in two separate OTU's. If two forms share a rare character state, this is given much weight; if they share a commonly occurring character state, this is given little weight. Smirnov argues that when a character rare in the larger taxon under study (genus) occurs in two OTU's (species), then this is more important for determining similarity than if the concurrence is in a character state that is widely distributed. Thus, if in the fictitious example cited above an agreement occurred between two OTU's matching for character state $E_1$, the weight to be calculated would be as follows:

weight for character state match $E_1E_1$,

$$w_{E_1E_1} = \frac{(e_1)}{(E_1)} = \frac{70}{30} = 2.33.$$

However, an agreement in character state $E_3$ results in the following weight,

$$w_{E_3E_3} = \frac{(e_3)}{(E_3)} = \frac{95}{5} = 19.$$

Conversely, an agreement with respect to the absence of character state $E_3$ is weighted only very slightly:

$$w_{e_3e_3} = \frac{(E_3)}{(e_3)} = \frac{5}{95} = .053.$$

The minimum and maximum possible weights to be applied to an agreement are

$$(w_{EE})_{min} = \frac{1}{s-1},$$

$$(w_{EE})_{max} = \frac{s}{2} - 1.$$

Thus we see that weights are functions of $s$, the number of OTU's in the study. For any one character $E$, an average weight is calculated, representing the average of the weights for all the states of the character:

$$\bar{w}_E = \frac{1}{e} \sum w_E = \frac{1}{e}(w_{1,1} + w_{2,2} + \cdots + w_{e,e}),$$

where $w_{1,1}$ represents the weight for the positive match, negative match, or mismatch for character state 1 of character $E$, there being a total of $e$ states for this character. Mismatches are given a weight of $-1$. If we had two OTU's exhibiting different states of the fictitious character $E$ above, thus:

OTU 1 shows character state $E_1$

OTU 2 shows character state $E_3$,

then

$$\bar{w}_E = \frac{1}{e}\left[-1 + \frac{(E_2)}{(e_2)} - 1 + \frac{(E_4)}{(e_4)}\right]$$

$$= \frac{1}{4}\left[-1 + \frac{20}{80} - 1 + \frac{45}{55}\right] = -.233.$$

The similarity between any two OTU's—which Smirnov calls $t_{f,g}$ for OTU's $f$ and $g$, respectively—is calculated by summing the weights for the $e$ states of *all* characters and dividing by $n$, the sum of all the numbers of character states; that is

$$n = \sum_{i=1}^{m} e_i,$$

where $m$ is the number of characters employed and $e$ is the number of states per character. Finally,

$$t_{f,g} = \frac{1}{n} \sum_{i=1}^{m} (\Sigma w_{Ei}).$$

Thus, if we were to assume that OTU's 1 and 2 in Table 6-3 had been taken from 120 OTU's and that the frequencies of the states of characters $A$, $B$, $C$, and $D$ were equal in the sample (a highly artificial assumption), we would arrive at the following Smirnov similarity coefficient:

$$t_{1,2} = \frac{1}{14}\left[\left(\frac{30}{90} + \frac{90}{30} + \frac{30}{90} + \frac{30}{90}\right) + (-1 - 1)\right.$$

$$\left. + \left(\frac{40}{80} + \frac{40}{80} + \frac{80}{40}\right) + \left(\frac{24}{96} - 1 + \frac{24}{96} + \frac{24}{96} - 1\right)\right]$$

$$= 0.268.$$

The validity of Smirnov's coefficient must rest on the contention that a similarity coefficient should be placed on a probabilistic basis. Should similarity in rare structures be made more important than similarity in commonly occurring structures? We would hesitate to take such a step, since this would make the magnitude of the similarity coefficient much too dependent on the size and nature of the group investigated.

Superficially, the idea of weighting characters on the basis of the rareness of their occurrence has a certain attraction, particularly if the rarer structure or character is a complicated one. As it seems quite unlikely that independent evolution had produced this same structure, people tend to give more weight to such similarities, especially if they are deducing phyletic relationships. However, as we have stated elsewhere, we believe that in such cases the importance of the character would be shown by the presence of numerous correlated characters, which together automatically weight the character. We feel that such "built-in" weighting is preferable to Smirnov's system.

Smirnov's coefficient has one other disadvantage. It does not result in unity when comparing OTU's with themselves, but gives different coefficients for different OTU's. Smirnov interprets the magnitude of $t_{f,f}$ as a measure of the uniqueness of species $f$ with respect to the others with which it is being compared. A similar measure would be found in the *uniqueness* of factor analysis (see Section 7.3.3).

In view of the above drawbacks and the fact that multistate characters can usually be handled preferably by distance or correlation analysis, we cannot recommend Smirnov's coefficient for use in numerical taxonomy.

### 6.2.1.9. *Comparison of coefficients*

When we try to evaluate the relative merits of the six coefficients adapted to two-state characters, we must first consider whether inclusion of the negative matches is justified. If not, then the coefficient of Jaccard (or Sneath) appears appropriate as being the simplest of the coefficients in its class. There may be cases, particularly when there are many biochemical characters, in which sufficient grounds for rejecting negative matches can be found. But we have already stated that in most cases it would appear that all matches should be considered. Under those circumstances we would prefer the simple matching coefficient over that of Rogers and Tanimoto. The former is a simpler quantity and is easier to interpret, for $S_{SM}$ is functionally related to $S_{RT}$. The relation can be expressed as

$$\frac{S_{SM}}{S_{RT}} = \frac{m + 2u}{m + u}.$$

From this ratio it can be seen that in most cases $S_{SM} > S_{RT}$, that $S_{SM} \to S_{RT}$ when $u \to 0$ and that $S_{SM} \to 2S_{RT}$ when $m \to 0$. We can interpret $S_{SM}$ as the probability that two OTU's $j$ and $k$ will match for a given character selected at random. Such an interpretation leads directly to the concept that the probability of matching is an expression of the phenetic relationship between the two taxa (see Section 5.6.2).

Although ordinarily we would employ neither $S_J$ nor $S_{RT}$, it may be useful to describe the mutual relations between these two coefficients and $S_{SM}$. The relation between $S_J$ and $S_{SM}$ can be expressed as

$$\frac{S_J}{S_{SM}} = \frac{n_{JK}^2 + n_{JK}n_{jk} + n_{JK}u}{n_{JK}^2 + n_{JK}n_{jk} + (n_{JK} + n_{jk})u},$$

from which we learn that

$$S_J < S_{SM} \quad \text{when} \quad n_{jk} > 0,$$
$$S_J \to S_{SM} \quad \text{when} \quad n_{jk} \to 0 \quad \text{and} \quad u > 0,$$

when $u \to 0$ and $n_{JK}$, $n_{jk}$ are both $> 0$, then $S_J \doteq S_{SM} \to 1$. By comparison,

$$\frac{S_J}{S_{RT}} = \frac{n_{JK}^2 + n_{JK}n_{jk} + 2n_{JK}u}{n_{jk}^2 + n_{JK}n_{jk} + n_{JK}u + n_{jk}u}.$$

Hence

$$S_J > S_{RT} \quad \text{when} \quad n_{JK} > n_{jk},$$
$$S_J = S_{RT} \quad \text{when} \quad n_{JK} = n_{jk},$$
$$S_J < S_{RT} \quad \text{when} \quad n_{JK} < n_{jk},$$

when $u \to 0$ and $n_{JK}$, $n_{jk}$ are both $> 0$, then $S_J \doteq S_{RT} \to 1$.

Cole (1949) has discussed the relations among coefficients of association which range from $-1$ to $+1$. His preferred coefficient, $C_7$, would not be applicable to numerical taxonomy as it ignores negative matches. We have some reservations about using coefficients with this range. Should organisms be related quantitatively along a scale which permits them to be negatively correlated? Positive resemblance between organisms and absence of resemblance can be easily understood. What, however, is negative resemblance between organisms? In perfect negative correlation between OTU's **A** and **B**, every character on the basis of which the OTU's are being compared must have opposite character states in the two taxa. As a consequence, perfect negative association of this sort would result in an "anti-organism" whose organic feasibility and viability would be somewhat in doubt. On the whole, it seems to us that a similarity value scale ranging from 0 to 1 is to be preferred. On the other hand, we should point out that some coefficients such as $S_{SM}$ indicate a completely negative correlation between two OTU's as zero.

### 6.2.2. Coefficients of correlation

Coefficients of correlation have been repeatedly used in Q-type studies in both psychology and ecology. In the former science, Stephenson (1936) originated the Q-technique (under the name of inverted factor technique). The use of correlation coefficients in ecology is reviewed by Dagnelie (1960). These coefficients have been employed in numerical taxonomy by Michener and Sokal (1957), Sokal and Michener (1958), Sokal (1958), Morishima and Oka (1960), Ehrlich (1961c), Soria and Heiser (1961), and Rohlf (1962). Only the product-moment correlation coefficient has been used to date, and this on data where most if not all of the characters were present in more than two states. This coefficient, computed between taxa $j$ and $k$, is

$$r_{jk} = \frac{\sum\limits_{i=1}^{n} (X_{ij} - \overline{X}_j)(X_{ik} - \overline{X}_k)}{\sqrt{\sum\limits_{i=1}^{n} (X_{ij} - \overline{X}_j)^2 \sum\limits_{i=1}^{n} (X_{ik} - \overline{X}_k)^2}},$$

where $X_{ij}$ stands for the character state value of character $i$ in OTU $j$, $\overline{X}_j$ is the mean of all state values for OTU $j$, and $n$ is the number of characters sampled. Since this formula is based on moments around the mean, it takes into account the magnitudes of mismatches between taxa for characters with more than two states. In this respect correlation coefficients are superior to the coefficients of association described in Section 6.2.1. They resemble the three coefficients of association in Table 6-2 in that their limits range from $-1$ to $+1$. Thus negative correlation between taxa is at least theoretically possible.

Among the studies published to date, only that of Morishima and Oka (1960) shows high and significant negative correlations. We explain the generally positive nature of taxonomic Q-correlation matrices by saying that we are unlikely to find a pair of OTU's antithetical for an appreciable number of characters (the improbability of an "anti-organism"). Another explanation for the same phenomenon put forward by Michener and Sokal (1957) and Sokal and Michener (1958) appears on re-examination to be in error.

As a measure of phenetic resemblance, $r_{jk}$ has undisputed merit, but doubt must prevail about the significance of coefficients computed for a Q-type study. The heterogeneity of column vectors, noted in the previous section, is an equally irksome problem here. When the data are arbitrarily coded and the number of states varies for different characters, the correlations cannot meet the basic assumptions of the bivariate normal frequency distribution. This problem has already been faced by the psychologists, who have suggested standardizing rows of the basic data matrix. By this is meant calculating the mean and standard deviation of each character and transforming each character score into a standard deviate—that is, dividing its deviation from its mean by the standard deviation. This will create a mean of zero and a variance of one for every character. We can therefore postulate that the variates for each OTU (each of the column vectors) are sampled from n populations having a common mean (zero) and standard deviation (unity).

Studies of the effect of standardization of characters have been carried out by Rohlf and Sokal (1963) on the 97 species of bees of the *Hoplitis* complex first analyzed by Michener and Sokal (1957) and on the 48 species of the mosquito genus *Aedes* analyzed by Rohlf (1962). The above investigations have shown that standardization of characters reduces the average correlation within a matrix to approximately zero from the previous positive value. The standard deviations of the correlation coefficients based on standardized characters are larger than expected, and the coefficients are skewed to the right. Among correlations based on standardized characters, few negative correlations lower than −0.3 have been observed, while positive correlations can range almost up to unity. The phenetic relationships obtained from standardized correlation matrices are quite similar to those based on unstandardized correlation matrices. Standardization can also be achieved in a general way by various devices designed to equalize the variances of the different characters. Use of a percentage scale (Cain and Harrison, 1958) or a ratio of the variable against a standard (Haltenorth, 1937) are cases in point. In such instances negative correlations could occur.

Why did Morishima and Oka's (1960) study show appreciable negative correlations? These authors, who analyzed 16 strains and species of rice, may have initially coded their data in such a manner that means and variances of character state codes within a character were approximately identical. Such a view is supported by the fact that standardization of approximately half of their characters did not appreciably lower the mean of their correlation coefficients, which already was near zero.

### 6.2.3. Measures of distance

These statistics of resemblance between OTU's are based on a geometrical model. As we shall see later, we can relate them in special cases to the other types of estimates of resemblance. However, at face value they appear quite different. Since the techniques involved may be less familiar, we shall go into them in some detail.

Let us assume we have two OTU's for which $n$ characters have been studied. The states for each character have been assigned values along a scale ranging for convenience from zero to unity. We now draw a conventional pair of rectangular coordinates in which the abscissa

FIGURE 6-1

*Representation of four OTU's (T$_1$, T$_2$, T$_3$, T$_4$) as points on a plane determined by their character states for two characters, X and Y. Each character is represented by a dimension—in this case two. The quantity labeled d$_{2,4}^2$ in the figure is referred to as $\Delta_{2,4}^2$ in the text. To obtain the taxonomic distance, d$_{2,4}$, between OTU's T$_2$ and T$_4$ as defined in the text we must divide the quantity on the right side of the equation by n, the number of characters, and take the square root of the quotient (see Section 6.2.3.2).*

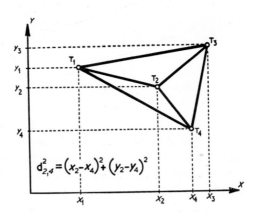

$$d_{2,4}^2 = (x_2 - x_4)^2 + (y_2 - y_4)^2$$

represents character $X$ and the ordinate character $Y$. Next we plot the position of the two OTU's with respect to these coordinate axes. A hypothetical case is shown in Figure 6-1. If the two OTU's are identical as regards the two characters under consideration, their positions will coincide and the distance between them will be zero. The greater the disparity between them, the greater will be the distance. Thus distance is seen to be the complement of similarity. From elementary analytical geometry we can show that the maximum distance possible between the OTU's would be $\sqrt{2}$ when they occupy respectively the tips of the two coordinate axes.

When we wish to estimate taxonomic distance on the basis of three characters, we must add a third coordinate ($Z$) to our diagram. On paper such a three-dimensional model can only be shown as a two-dimensional projection (Figure 6-2). The maximal distance is now $\sqrt{3}$.

We cannot visualize the geometry of adding a fourth and subsequent

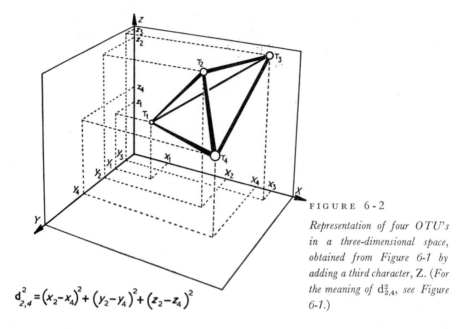

$$d_{2,4}^2 = (x_2 - x_4)^2 + (y_2 - y_4)^2 + (z_2 - z_4)^2$$

FIGURE 6-2

*Representation of four OTU's in a three-dimensional space, obtained from Figure 6-1 by adding a third character, Z. (For the meaning of $d_{2,4}^2$, see Figure 6-1.)*

characters. The requirements of each new coordinate axis are that it be at right angles with all previous ones. Although we cannot depict such an axis graphically, we can postulate its existence and demonstrate algebraically that most of the geometric theorems of conventional three-dimensional space can be extended to $n$ dimensions in so-called Euclidean hyperspace. Thus we are at liberty to postulate $n$ dimensions for $n$ characters. We can compute the distance between the two OTU's in hyperspace. The maximum distance will be $\sqrt{n}$ in an $n$-space, a hyperspace of $n$ dimensions. (It should be re-emphasized here that these maximal distances are based on characters with maximal values of unity.)

Before we describe the various techniques which have been suggested to establish measures of distance, we have to discuss the coding of the character states for distance analysis. Coding them between the limits of 0 to 1 (as is suggested by Cain and Harrison, 1958) seems a logical standardization, permitting maximum distances to be calculated. While this does not equalize the variances of the character states (rows) it does constrain them somewhat. A drawback of this scheme of coding would be its inability to admit OTU's with more extreme character states without recoding all characters.

Another technique is to standardize rows as described above for $r$—that is, to compute the mean and standard deviation of each row (the states of each character) and to express each state as a deviation from the mean in standard deviation units (Sokal, 1961). Since this would result in negative as well as positive values, adding 5 to each value would leave the variance unchanged yet would make computation easier when desk calculators are employed. When working with a computer, coding by the addition of 5 is generally unnecessary.

The standardization of the character states would make all character variances equal to unity. However, we are still faced with the problem of what to do when we wish to add a new species with one or more character states beyond the previous limits. Our coding system will now not have limits of 0 and 1 as before, and therefore it should not be difficult to express the new variate in standardized form. To give a concrete example, if the range of states for a character has been from 1 to 6, its mean 4.1 and its standard deviation 0.8, then the previous limits of the range must have been coded $(1 - 4.1)/0.8 = -3.875$ and $(6 - 4.1)/0.8 = 2.375$, respectively. A new state of 7 is now to be coded. It simply becomes $(7 - 4.1)/0.8 = 3.625$. This value is not really correct, however, since both mean and standard deviation of the character states have changed with the addition of the new state. We believe that when only few new OTU's and few cases of new extremes are involved this is not a serious problem, as the variance would be inappreciably altered. When a larger number of new states is involved (a case which we consider quite unlikely if fairly exhaustive comparative study has preceded the analysis), a fresh standardization of the affected characters will be necessary.

If desired, a normalization rather than a standardization can be carried out by means of rankits. (A rankit is the average deviate of the $r$th largest in a sample of $n$ observations drawn at random from a normal distribution with a mean of zero and a variance of unity; Bliss and Calhoun, 1954.) However, it seems to us that in the procedures outlined below this will not be necessary. For the purposes of the discussion which follows we shall consider our data to be either coded from 0 to 1 or to have been standardized.

We shall establish the following symbolism to deal with the examples in Sections 6.2.3.1, 6.2.3.2, and 6.2.3.3. Let $X_{ij}$ be the value of the state of character $i$ in OTU $j$, where $i$ varies from 1 to $n$ and $j$ varies from 1 to $t$. Thus, for example, the difference between OTU's 6 and 8 for character 3 would be written as $(X_{3,6} - X_{3,8})$. (The comma is introduced between the subscripts when dealing with numerals or triple letters in order to prevent confusion.)

### 6.2.3.1. Average differences

The expression

$$\frac{1}{n} \sum_{i=1}^{n} (X_{ij} - X_{ik})$$

is not particularly suitable for measuring the distance between OTU's $j$ and $k$, since the differences could be negative as well as positive. In a random, symmetrical model the expected value of this expression would be zero. The obvious correction would be to use

$$\frac{1}{n} \sum_{i=1}^{n} |X_{ij} - X_{ik}|,$$

the absolute (positive) values of the differences between the OTU's for each character. This is the *mean character difference* (*M.C.D.*), which has been proposed by Cain and Harrison (1958) as a measure of taxonomic resemblance. It had previously been used in anthropology by Czekanowski (1932), who called it *durchschnittliche Differenz*. Haltenorth (1937) employed this coefficient in an extensive study of 86 characters of eight species of the large cats. Each character was a mean based on a large number of specimens. In computing it Haltenorth counted as zero all differences which were not statistically significant. We consider this to be an undesirable feature of his system, as is explained in Section 6.2.4. However, a reanalysis of his original data by Sokal—employing $d$, the coefficient of taxonomic distance (Section 6.2.3.2)—resembled Haltenorth's results closely.

The simplicity of this statistic is in its favor; however, it does suffer several major disadvantages. It will always underestimate the true Euclidean distance between the taxa in space, and when some character differences are small while others are large, it will underestimate the actual distance considerably. It also lacks some of the desirable attributes of the alternative measure, the Euclidean distance or its square, described below. It cannot be partitioned into components. In general, it stands in the same relation to the distance as the average deviation to the standard deviation and suffers from similar disabilities as the former. In considering which of the methods to apply it might be argued that the mean character difference is simpler and hence to be preferred;

however, it is reasonable to expect that any worthwhile study in numerical taxonomy will depend on machine computation. As simple a study as 15 OTU's of 60 characters each will require 105 comparisons and consequently 6300 subtractions. Calculating the taxonomic distance on a good desk calculator would not be prohibitively more time-consuming than obtaining Cain and Harrison's mean character difference. Most numerical taxonomic studies will probably employ electronic computers, however. The limitations of these machines in relation to our work will be shortage of storage and slowness of input rather than computation time, which would not differ appreciably among correlational, distance, or mean character difference techniques.

### 6.2.3.2. *Taxonomic distance*

The distance between two OTU's in two- and three-dimensional spaces has been illustrated in Figures 6-1 and 6-2. We can generalize this concept of the Euclidean distance between two points in an $n$-dimensional space. The formula for such a distance, $\Delta_{jk}$, between OTU's $j$ and $k$, using the symbolism of the last section, is

$$\Delta_{jk} = \left[ \sum_{i=1}^{n} (X_{ij} - X_{ik})^2 \right]^{1/2}.$$

The symbol $\Delta_{jk}$ has been adopted in place of $\delta_{jk}$, suggested by Sokal (1961), in order to conform to conventional statistical usage, in which sample statistics are identified by Roman letters and parameters are symbolized by lower-case Greek letters. Since we are reserving the symbol $d$ for average distance (as specified below) and since $D$ is used for Mahalanobis' generalized distance, we assigned the symbol $\Delta$ for the above quantity. This convention has also been employed by Rohlf and Sokal (1963). It will sometimes be found useful to employ the square of the distance; the formula then becomes

$$\Delta_{jk}^2 = \sum_{i=1}^{n} (X_{ij} - X_{ik})^2.$$

Since $\Delta_{jk}^2$ increases with the number of characters used in the comparison, an average distance is commonly computed. This is

$$d_{jk} = \sqrt{\Delta_{jk}^2/n} \quad \text{or} \quad d_{jk}^2 = \Delta_{jk}^2/n$$

in square root and square form, respectively. The average squared distance, $d_{jk}^2$, was employed by Sokal (1961) and called $\overline{\delta_{jk}^2}$ by him.

The idea for such a coefficient has come to many people. So far as we can learn, this form of a measure of distance was first employed by Heincke as early as 1898. Schilder and Schilder (1951) demonstrated such a coefficient without standardizing characters. Clark (1952) has employed the same coefficient in comparing several populations of snakes, some only subspecifically distinct, others in different genera. His distances for each character are computed as a ratio varying between zero and unity. Thus his distance, called by him the *coefficient of divergence*, is computed as

$$CD_{jk} = \left[\frac{1}{n}\sum_{i=1}^{n}\left(\frac{X_{ij} - X_{ik}}{X_{ij} + X_{ik}}\right)^2\right]^{1/2}.$$

In Clark's original formula each of the $X$ terms actually represented a mean, $\bar{X}$, since he used a number of specimens to represent each OTU. For numerical taxonomy we have seen that single values will frequently suffice.

Bielicki (1962) describes a coefficient of distance for use in anthropology. Based upon an earlier statistic of Wanke (1953), it is similar to the coefficient of Clark (1952).

Sokal (1961) brought taxonomic distance to the attention of numerical taxonomists, employing the formulation of $d_{jk}^2$ and suggesting standardization of character state codes for each character.

Zarapkin (1934, 1939, 1943) employed a statistical approach related to distance although not identified as such. He employed a so-called standard population for which he would compute the mean and standard deviation of each character considered. Then for each character $i$ and for each OTU $j$ he computed $(X_{ij} - \bar{X}_{i,st})/s_{i,st}$, where $\bar{X}_{i,st}$ represents the mean of a standard population for character $i$, while $s_{i,st}$ is its standard deviation. This quantity is essentially a standardized deviation, except that the standardization is based on the $s$ of the individuals within the standard population rather than the $s$ of the character in question across all the OTU's of the study, which would seem to us to be a more reasonable scale of reference. When a standard population was unavailable and a single individual had to serve as an OTU, then the deviation was calculated as a proportion $(X_{ij} - X_{i,st})/X_{i,st}$. Zarapkin studied the frequency distributions of these deviations for many characters in a variety of populations, finding the shape and spread of these frequency distributions to be related to the taxonomic differences between the OTU's under consideration and the standard. To summarize his findings Zarapkin computed the standard deviations of all the deviations between each OTU and the standard population (that is, over all the characters). He called this quantity $\mathfrak{S}$. It is easily seen that, to the extent that the mean of the deviations between any OTU and the standard population approaches zero, the quantity is nothing but the distance between the OTU and the standard population expressed in the standardized units of the latter. The difference between $\mathfrak{S}^2_{jk}$ and $d^2_{jk}$ is the size coefficient of Penrose, $C^2_Q$ (see Section 6.2.3.3). In this manner Zarapkin was able to obtain distances of a variety of populations from a standard but not of the populations from each other.

We would not recommend this method. (1) It sets up an arbitrary standard population with respect to which the others are viewed, rather than considering them simultaneously (and thus from a multivariate point of view). (2) By standardizing on the basis of the standard population we may be introducing considerable bias into the interpretation of our findings. Worse yet, we may standardize interpopulation deviations on the basis of intrapopulation standard deviations. (3) Depending on the size of the standard population, $\mathfrak{S}$ may or may not represent taxonomic distance. An unequivocal statistic is preferable in this regard.

Related to taxonomic distance is the *coefficient of racial likeness*, developed by Karl Pearson (1926) for measuring resemblances between samples of skulls of various origins. The problem here differs in that continuous characters (lengths, ratios, and others) are measured, which vary from specimen to specimen and can only be expressed as means. This coefficient is computed as

$$\text{C.R.L.} = \left\{ \frac{1}{n} \sum_{i=1}^{n} \left[ \frac{(\overline{X}_{ij} - \overline{X}_{ik})^2}{\frac{s^2_{ij}}{n_j} + \frac{s^2_{ik}}{n_k}} \right] \right\}^{1/2} - \frac{2}{n},$$

where $\overline{X}_{ij}$ stands for the sample mean of the $i$th character for entity $j$, $s^2_{ij}$ for the variance of the same, and $n_j$ for the sample size of entity $j$.

In numerical taxonomy we can develop the following formula for the C.R.L., with Q-type data which have been standardized by rows. Since we have no means but only single values (with a variance of one) representing the OTU's, we obtain

$$\text{C.R.L.} = \left[ \frac{1}{2n} \sum_{i=1}^{n} (X_{ij} - X_{ik})^2 \right]^{1/2} - \frac{2}{n},$$

which approximates $\sqrt{\tfrac{1}{2}d^2_{jk}}$ for any of the cases in which we are interested ($n \geq 60$). The quantity $d^2_{jk}$ has therefore been called the reduced C.R.L. (Morant, 1936). The standard error of the C.R.L. approaches $1/\sqrt{2n}$ when $n$ is sizable. The C.R.L. is sometimes given in squared form (as in

Sokal, 1961). We prefer the plain form here, to be able to analogize it with $d$. The expected value of the C.R.L. for independent characters is $1 - (2/n)$. It should approach 1 for a large number of characters if the states are normally distributed.

On the assumptions that the observations (the $n$ standardized characters) were independent and normally distributed with a mean of zero and a variance of unity, Rohlf (1962) computed the expected value of $d$ for even values of $n$ as

$$\mathcal{E}(d) = \frac{(n-1)!}{\left[\left(\frac{n}{2}-1\right)!\right]^2 2^{n-2}} \left(\frac{\pi}{n}\right)^{1/2}.$$

Using Stirling's formula this reduces to

$$\mathcal{E}(d) \doteq \sqrt{2}\left(1-\frac{1}{n}\right)^{1/2}\left(1+\frac{1}{n-2}\right)^{n-1}\frac{1}{e}.$$

Thus for the large values of $n$ generally employed in numerical taxonomy the expected value of $d$ approaches $\sqrt{2}$ very closely. The expected variance of $d$ is

$$\mathcal{E}(\sigma_d^2) = 2 - [\mathcal{E}(d)]^2,$$

which approaches zero as $n$ tends to infinity. Figure 5-9 gives the 95% confidence limits to the expected value of $d$ at various sample sizes, $n$. We see that after $n$ approximately equals 75, the width of the band decreases very slowly.

*Generalized distance* is a statistic related to the coefficient of racial likeness. Developed by Mahalanobis (1936) and Rao (1948), it is a weighted coefficient similar to a squared distance in which both the variance of separate characters and the correlations among characters are taken into account. Generalized distance procedures are not appropriate for the usual type of work in numerical taxonomy, since in the latter field we recommend a single code value to represent the state of a given character in a given taxon. We do not, therefore, consider variation for a given character within a taxon. But the osteological material with which Pearson and the Indian statisticians were dealing had characters which were largely continuous, varying with the population; in their attempts to compute distance coefficients for such material they had to take into account the mean and variance of each of the characters considered. Since the material with which we are working consists of an appreciable proportion of discontinuous characters and since there is in many cases no variation of the particular state code within the taxon, the problem of intrataxon variation in state codes does not usually arise in our data, and we may assume their values to be fixed. Furthermore, as a matter of simple practicality we cannot consider using generalized distance in the study of numerical taxonomy, for these methods require inversions or similarly involved operations on matrices of the order of the number of characters considered. As we are often employing as many as a hundred or more characters, inversions of such matrices would be entirely impractical. No claim is made here that the characters which we are considering in numerical taxonomy are always invariable within taxa. On the contrary, in low-ranking taxonomic units (such as sub-species, races, or varieties) as well as high-ranking taxa, many character states are not constant for the entire taxon. The several methods suggested for treating such data are discussed in Section 6.4. But generalized distance allows for correlation among characters which the methods proposed so far in numerical taxonomy do not. Until R-type correlations are studied in numerical taxonomy the importance of this aspect of generalized distance for this work cannot be evaluated.

We might point out here that the simple matching coefficient $S_{SM}$ is related to distance in the following way. If we consider character axes ranging from zero to one so that the maximum difference between any two OTU's for any one character is unity, then the maximum distance between a pair of OTU's based on $n$ characters is $\sqrt{n}$. It can easily be shown that the average squared distance $d_{jk}^2 = u/n$; therefore $d_{jk}^2 = 1 - S_{SM}$.

Rogers and Tanimoto (1960) have also defined a distance coefficient, $d_{ij}$. This coefficient is defined as $d_{ij} = -\log_2 S_{ij}$, where $S_{ij}$ is an association coefficient between OTU's $i$ and $j$ and ranges from zero to unity. These distances define a semimetric space, rather than a metric one, such as is defined by the distances discussed above. It seems most appropriate to discuss the distance of Rogers and Tanimoto in connection with their method of clustering, presented in Section 7.3.2.5.

### 6.2.3.3. Size and shape

Penrose (1954) has suggested dividing the reduced C.R.L. ($d_{jk}^2$, or $C_H^2$ in his symbolism) into two parts: a coefficient of "size,"

$$C_Q^2 = \frac{1}{n^2} \left[ \sum_{i=1}^{n} (X_{ij} - X_{ik}) \right]^2,$$

and a coefficient of "shape,"

$$\frac{n-1}{n} C_Z^2 = \frac{1}{n} \sum_{i=1}^{n} (X_{ij} - X_{ik})^2 - \frac{1}{n^2} \left[ \sum_{i=1}^{n} (X_{ij} - X_{ik}) \right]^2$$

$$= C_H^2 - C_Q^2 = d_{jk}^2 - C_Q^2.$$

The "shape" coefficient, which is proportional to the square of Zarapkin's coefficient ($\mathfrak{S}^2$ of the previous section, identified as $C_Z^2$ by Penrose), represents the variance of differences between the character states of the OTU's being compared. The squared coefficient of Zarapkin is indeed nothing but the estimated variance (i.e., corrected for degrees of freedom). It is likely to be sizable when considerable discrepancy in the magnitude of the differences occurs, including a mixture of positive, negative, and negligible terms.

The $C_Q^2$ is identical to the correction term used in calculating the variance of differences between the character states. It represents the magnitude and direction of the differences. When $C_Q^2$ is large, the character states of the two OTU's being compared are quite different in magnitude, and the differences that exist are largely in one direction. A large $C_Q^2$ would appear, for example, if one OTU were very similar to another but much larger along most of the character scales. Thus where size is an important factor this should be revealed by the magnitude of $C_Q^2$.

In many studies of numerical taxonomy this partition may not be of too much significance, since $C_Q^2$ is not likely to be appreciable. This is so because coding is not along a uniform scale for all characters, and thus the sum of the differences is likely to be close to zero. However, when we are comparing organisms of different sizes, many of whose characters are size-conditioned, $C_Q^2$ is likely to yield valuable information. The magnitude of the shape coefficient will indicate whether the differences between characters are consistent or variable. Again, in much of our work we expect them to be variable. Although we still know too little about the relative importance of the size and shape factors to be dogmatic, we may note that the shape component may be the better estimate of affinity since we tend to reduce the size factor by our scoring procedures.

Rohlf and Sokal (1963) have pointed out that the shape coefficient is not a measure of similarity in proportions, as the name might imply. It is zero—indicating identity in "shape"—only if the difference between two OTU's is constant for all of the characters. These authors found that the product-moment correlation coefficient, $r$, is a better measure of similarity in shape between two OTU's.

If enough characters were available in a given study, one might segregate all those characters which manifest a size trend (such as skeletal dimensions in a vertebrate group) and recompute distances between OTU's on the basis of these characters only. One could then partition these distances into shape and size components, which should give some insight into the pattern of evolutionary change within the groups. It is not likely that the size component will be very large. The rules for treating empirical correlations (Section 5.3.3.6) would probably have reduced the importance of a general size factor even if many characters had shown its effects. To illustrate this problem, suppose we included in a study a number of different but approximately equally sized species of flies whose resemblances were computed from, say, 100 characters. If we add a species **A'**, which is apparently identical to a species **A** already in the study but several times as large, we shall have to add a number of new characters expressing size differences of various parts of the body. For all these new characters all the old species (including **A**) will exhibit the small state, while **A'** will show the large state. Since these new characters will therefore covary identically with each other, we must show cause, according to the procedure described in the section on empirical correlations, why more than one character should be employed. If, as we are likely to feel, a single size factor is responsible for the enlargement of the various parts of the body in species **A'**, we reduce the new characters to a single one and general size is *ab initio* an unimportant component of the distance coefficient.

## 6.2.4. Statistical significance of similarity coefficients

The reader may have wondered why the foregoing sections on statistics measuring similarity among OTU's have not made more than passing references to the significance of the coefficients being calculated. The computation of the separate significance of each individual similarity coefficient is not too important in numerical taxonomy. This is so for two reasons. First, we are concerned with the general significance of the similarity coefficient matrix among all the OTU's and not so much with the separate coefficients. Since we are concerned with the joint significance of the entire matrix, to omit values which are not significant, as was done for instance by Haltenorth (1937), is probably an improper procedure. Even values which individually are not significant are the best obtainable estimates of the relations between the two OTU's. This should of course not be interpreted to mean that statistical significance is to be ignored entirely. A matrix without a single significant coefficient (or with only a few such) is clearly not worth investigation. On the other hand, if a sufficient number of significant similarity coefficients are present, it is not necessary to demonstrate the individual significance of every coefficient.

The second consideration is that the significance levels of individual similarity coefficients based on $n$ characters are not likely to be those customarily given in textbooks of statistics. This problem has been previously referred to as the heterogeneity of column vectors. We mean by this that variables $j$ and $k$ representing OTU's $j$ and $k$ are not taken as random samples from a common population, as is required by statistical theory, but are really taken from a heterogeneous sample wherein each variate estimates a different character. This problem is somewhat alleviated by standardizing characters—that is, standardizing the rows of the data matrix. Such a procedure results in all characters having a mean of zero and a variance of one. However, there is obvious correlation among the rows or the characters. This means that when a correlation between two OTU's is based on $n$ characters it is not really based on $n$ independent dimensions of variation, and the number of degrees of freedom on the basis of which its significance is to be computed is likely to be less than $n$. Since we have as yet no way of approaching this problem, we have to put general faith in the validity of the matrices, just as persons working on multiple factor analysis, a closely related field, have had general confidence in the validity of factor loadings without being able to assign standard errors and confidence limits to their estimates. The conventional standard errors can therefore serve as guide lines toward the significance level of the similarity statistics. Type I errors, however, are likely to be greater than the standard statistical tests indicate.

## 6.3. SCALING AND CODING CHARACTERS

The logical basis for coding characters has already been discussed in Section 5.3. We are therefore concerned here only with the numerical and statistical consequences of the procedure adopted. The nature of the scale in which the character is coded will limit the choice of possible similarity coefficients to be adopted.

When we consider the scaling of each character, we have to distinguish between (1) phenetically discrete and (2) phenetically overlapping characters.

(1) By a *phenetically discrete character* we mean a character that does not vary appreciably within the OTU's; consequently the taxa under study can be easily grouped according to the various states for the character in question, with little or no possibility of misclassification for any given OTU. Meristic characters will often fall into this category. Where the number of antennal, palpal, or tarsal segments, the number of vertebrae of a given region, or the number of petals of a flower is constant for a certain taxon, but varies among taxa, the character may be taken to be phenetically discrete. In an entomological study, if a group of species were either apterous, micropterous, or macropterous but did not vary intraspecifically in this regard, we could again consider the character phenetically discrete. On the other hand, if, as in some Heteroptera, species occurred which were dimorphic or polymorphic with regard to their wingedness, the character could not be so considered. "Presence-absence" characters with perfect penetrance are included among phenetically discrete characters and are likely to constitute a considerable proportion of characters in botanical and zoological studies and the preponderant part in microbiological analyses.

It may be argued that phenetic discreteness does not necessarily imply genetic discontinuity. Indeed, there is good reason to believe that many stepped characters (such as polydactyly in mammals or tolerance to toxicants in insects) are caused by thresholds superimposed upon continuously varying effects (genes or gene products). However, these cases are usually recognizable by the variation in the expression of the character within a given class (taxon). If meristic characters are phenetically discrete characters, we must conclude that the variation ranges widely and is multimodal and that the thresholds are spaced in such a way as to effectively split up the distribution into nonoverlapping segments.

"Presence-absence" characters, whose states are expressed as 0 and 1, respectively, can be handled by any of the coefficients of association. If a coefficient of correlation is desired, some consideration as to the nature of the underlying variation is necessary. The tetrachoric correlation coefficient, $r_t$ (Treloar, 1942), is to be computed when a continuous distribution of the character is assumed, with the division into two classes established as a convenience for the taxonomist; when, on the other hand, basic dichotomy is believed to exist, the fourfold point correlation coefficient $\phi$ appears appropriate. The two coefficients are not identical. Hence the correlation between taxa will quite properly depend in part on the assumptions behind their characters. Since it is not very likely that all characters used in a study will be subject to the same assumptions, it may be difficult to agree on any one set of assumptions. The use of distance as a measure of relationship is possible with presence-absence data. In such a case the taxa are located at some corner of the hyperspatial cube represented by the positive manifold.

The use of phenetically discrete characters divided into more than two states will result in the substitution of the Pearson product-moment $r$ for the correlation coefficients mentioned previously.

Of the coefficients of association so far employed for taxonomic work, only those by Rogers and Tanimoto and by Smirnov make special allowance for characters with more than two states. The probability of matches occurring in such characters becomes greatly reduced. Let us consider for the sake of simplicity a random model with an equal frequency of occurrence of each state. While in the case of two states the probability of a match for a given character (negative matches included) is $1/2$, and $(1/2)^n$ for matches on all of $n$ characters, in the case of 3 states these probabilities are $1/3$ and $(1/3)^n$ respectively and in the general case of $c$ states $1/c$ and $(1/c)^n$. Thus values of the association coefficients would be much reduced. There would also be no opportunity to allow for the magnitude of a mismatch in computing the coefficient. For these reasons association coefficients are not very suitable for multistate characters. In these characters negative matches as such usually do not have any meaning, unless one of the states of the character refers to its absence. It thus becomes difficult to array the data in a 2 × 2 table; only 2 cells can really be filled in—the number of matches ($m$) and the number of non-matches ($u$). Hence the appropriate coefficients of association are the simple matching coefficient and that of Rogers and Tanimoto.

The distance formulas are equally applicable in the cases of phenetically separate characters of two or more than two states. It is somewhat difficult to predict the effect of dividing a character into several states as compared to a zero-or-one scale. Distances between taxa should in general decrease when a previous two-state case is recoded into more states. However, if the previous example had many matches at zero or one, which on finer classification would be shown to be short distances, the overall distance may well increase somewhat.

(2) *Phenetically overlapping characters* differ in their means from taxon to taxon but exhibit considerable variation within taxa and overlap between them. Characters such as those expressing size, color intensity, and ratios of body measurements would quite likely fall into this group. How-

ever, statistically discontinuous or meristic characters, such as segment or tooth number, may also be phenetically overlapping characters. Numerically they present no special problems in the computation of product-moment correlation coefficients and of distances. The coefficients of association discussed in this paper cannot be computed from such information directly, since matches along the scale of a continuous variable would be quite unlikely. However, with the device of grouping the means into a small number of classes, the approach suggested in the previous section can be utilized.

The employment of phenetically overlapping characters gives rise to problems of a statistical nature. Since the expression of a given character varies within an OTU, the mean used to describe the state of the character for a given taxon is merely an estimate subject to sampling error. No difficulty occurs in setting confidence limits to individual means, but the distribution and hence the validity of coefficients of resemblance based on such measures are difficult to evaluate. This problem arises constantly in physical anthropology. Estimates of distance (particularly Pearson's coefficient of racial likeness and Mahalanobis' generalized distance) therefore take the variance of the estimates into consideration. Coefficients of association do not. This whole problem is treated in greater detail in the next section.

A measure of similarity between the gene pools of freely interbreeding populations conforming to the Hardy-Weinberg equation has been proposed by Sneath (unpublished) for studying the overall similarity between the blood groups of human races. This compares not the phenotypes but the gene frequencies in the populations; the measure is

$$S.B._{.1.2} = \frac{1}{L}(K_{\alpha 1.2} + K_{\beta 1.2} + \cdots + K_{\lambda 1.2}),$$

where $S.B._{.1.2}$ is the overall similarity between populations 1 and 2, $L$ is the number of gene loci, and $K_\alpha$ to $K_\lambda$ are the proportion of matches at each of these $L$ loci; the value of $K$ for each locus is

$$K_{1.2} = (a_1 a_2 + b_1 b_2 + c_1 c_2 + \cdots + h_1 h_2),$$

where $a_1$ to $h_1$ are the gene frequencies of the different alleles, $a$ to $h$, at that locus in population 1, and $a_2$ to $h_2$ are the respective gene frequencies in population 2.

This formula in effect excludes negative matches, for reasons discussed in a forthcoming paper by Sneath.

## 6.4. CHARACTER VARIATION WITHIN TAXA

How should we record characters if they vary within the operational taxonomic units which we employ? In the earliest studies of numerical taxonomy this was deliberately ignored, and Michener and Sokal (1957) were fortunate in not having many characters that varied within the species they studied. Wherever intraspecific variation of a given character occurred, the commonest state was chosen to represent the species. However, in much of the work to be done in the future, and particularly in taxonomic studies involving categories above the species, character variation within taxa is going to figure prominently in the analysis of the data. Whenever intrataxon variation of characters occurs, one necessarily takes the risk that these groups are not valid natural taxa, with the consequent danger that the analysis will give misleading results. In order to understand fully the implications of variation of characters within taxa, we have to digress for a moment into related fields—psychology and ecology.

Workers in psychology and ecology engaged in the computation of coefficients of correlation and of association are much concerned with the question of the reliability of single variates used in their computations. The responses of an individual to a particular psychological test repeatedly administered are rarely the same. Even in controlled situations, where learning and conditioning can be ignored, responses vary, owing to a variety of pyschological and physiological conditions mostly unknown and subsumed under the heading "individual variability" or "error." From this comes the concept of the reliability of a test, its correlation with itself when repeatedly administered. This problem occurs with most biochemical estimations, which usually have rather low accuracy, and is especially troublesome in microbiology. It occurs even when a single strain is tested. If the observational variation is sufficient to make a character seriously unreliable it should of course be omitted.

Sampling problems in ecological work are similar. Let us study, for example, the ecological associations of arthropods found in decaying tree stumps in a mixed hardwood forest. We attempt to compute coefficients of association in a Q-type study between faunas collected from individual stumps. Sampling error may arise in one or both of two ways: (a) species **X** may not be found in tree stump **A** since the sample taken from it did not contain **X** (other areas of stump **A** would have **X**, however); (b) no members of species **X** may be in the tree stump at all, although it may be ecologically quite suitable for it. In the dispersal process of the species **X**, stump **A** has (at least so far) been missed. This does not mean that species **X** may not invade the stump at a later time.

Error (a) is a relatively straightforward problem of sampling, its magnitude depending among other factors on the density and distribution of species **X** in stump **A** and the size of the sample taken in relation to the size of the stump. Error (b) is complicated by the time dimension and requires an answer to the question of whether the absence of **X** from the fauna of stump **A** should be considered an error at all. Ecologists have debated whether an "archetypal" association including all possible species exists at all. We tend to support the more recent views (Whittaker, 1953) of associations as relatively undefined entities (stands) containing an assemblage of species with varying probabilities of occurrence. An association is therefore a cluster of stands whose species compositions do not fully overlap but which possesses centers of greater density representing the most typical form of the association. Thus absence of species **X** from stump **A** should not be thought of as an error; rather, it is an essential item of information about the latitude in species composition in the association and the cohesion of the cluster of stands. In summary, we would feel that allowance should be made for sampling errors within a stand but that we need not be concerned with "errors" in the faunal or floral composition of various stands.

We have digressed so fully into these problems of ecological research because the question of error in such analyses has analogues in numerical taxonomy. A sampling error of type (a) in numerical taxonomy might occur in the following situation; if we sample one or a few specimens from a polymorphic population, we might observe and record only one character state, while two or more were to be found in the population. An error of type (b) would consist of using a local population (or subspecies) to represent an entire species, ignoring the fact that some characters had different states in different local populations. Such errors can, of course, occur at higher levels, too. Some sampling error of type (a) is unavoidable so long as the OTU is to represent a hierarchic level higher than single individuals. Whether the error of type (b) should be called an error is dubious. As in ecology, the variation itself represents an important property of the system. In numerical taxonomy it would be a measure of the heterogeneity of the OTU under study, worth investigating in its own right. We shall now treat the subject of errors in character state coding in numerical taxonomy in a more systematic fashion. Errors in coding the phenetic value of a character in a given taxon may arise from the following four sources (apart from observational errors).

(1) If, as is not infrequently the case, a species is known and described from a single specimen, we run the danger of employing in our computation data that may not be typical or representative of it. Even in the case of phenetically discrete characters, occasional variants and mutants are bound to occur, and while it is not very likely that a single specimen taken at random from the population will show one of these, the possibility should not be neglected. With one variant per 1000 individuals and a consideration of 100 characters, a specimen picked at random has almost a 10% chance of carrying at least one variant. However, in most studies, particularly in those applications of numerical taxonomy which may be expected in the reasonable future, one would expect that a fairly representative sample of each OTU has been examined and that aberrations have been recognized as such.

(2) Cases of phenetically overlapping characters present more of a problem. Whether they are qualitative (melanic forms in a group of moths), meristic (number of antennal segments in a group of grasshoppers), or continuous (size of leaves in species of elms, rate of sugar fermentation in bacterial substrains), their means are not very representative if they have been derived from a single, reasonably homogeneous population from a limited geographical area. However, even if very complete knowledge of the variation within each taxon were available, it would still be difficult to decide how to compute a mean and its variance for every character of the taxon. One way might be weighting based on frequency in the population. If, for example, a mean for skin color in the human species is to be computed, one could multiply the various color values by the respective frequencies of these colors and thus obtain a mean for the species. It might be felt, however, that the actual frequencies of the various types at present living were not really representative of the common stock from which they presumably originated. Since we do not really know the color of the ancestral stock for *Homo sapiens* and are unlikely to know ancestral character states in most instances, such considerations are not particularly useful. An unweighted mean or midpoint of the range of variation may therefore be preferable to a weighted mean.

We are unable at this early stage in the development of numerical taxonomy to present recommendations for the various alternatives. Experience in comparing several of these will have to be gained. Two alternatives which have not yet been mentioned are (a) to omit the variable character from the analysis and (b) to employ a character state for a taxon postulated for its archetype or ancestral form. We may immediately dismiss the latter alternative by saying that it will nearly always introduce an unwarrantable element of speculation, prejudice, or vagueness. The first alternative also has disadvantages. In most instances it may not greatly matter, although many features may have to be eliminated on this account, leaving too few for good work. Yet if a feature is rare in one taxon and very common in the next and would be excluded, it could not then contribute to the dissimilarity between the taxa, as it clearly should.

(3) If a numerical taxonomic study of higher categories is to be undertaken, the problem of how to weight different types just discussed reappears in a new guise. Should a higher taxon which is to be used as an OTU be represented as the weighted mean of its constituent taxa and, if so, how should the weighting be done?

One solution to this dilemma is to introduce into the study one representative of each varying constituent of each polymorphic taxon and analyze them all together. If our notions about affinities are correct, the first clusters should represent the various polymorphic taxa; that is, the variants composing them should correlate much more closely with each other than any one of them or their common taxon does with any other taxa. However, introducing many variants adds much labor and expense to a study and may make it prohibitive.

Another solution is to use only a single representative of the polymorphic group. This would be done in the expectation that the variance of the polymorphic forms within their taxon is less than the variance among the taxa of the study. Thus the error introduced by choosing a single representative of a taxon should not be large enough to seriously affect the estimation of the similarity among the taxa of the study. If this were not so it would raise the question of the validity of the represented taxon. We have called this approach the *exemplar method*. The single representatives of the OTU's are exemplars of the taxa they represent.

Thus, to cite an example, if we were studying the relationship of *Homo sapiens* to various anthropoids, we could use a specimen from any of the races of man. The correlation of such an individual with any given anthropoid should be independent of his race, on the average, and would therefore approximate that of some hypothetical average man with the same anthropoid.

The above paragraph was written before the authors became acquainted with a paper by Zarapkin (1943) comparing hands and feet of man and three apes. In this study Zarapkin compared the deviations of single specimens of the animals and found clear distinctions at the racial, specific, and generic levels which transcended individual variation. In a test of the exemplar method carried out by Sokal (1962b) on Smirnov's (1925) data on genera of syrphid flies, two taxa (genus groups), **A** and **B**, joined at a (coded) similarity level of 850. The average value of the similarities between members of **A** and **B** turned out to be 851, with a standard deviation of 20. The range of individual similarity coefficients is from 900 (upper value) to 813 (lower value). Thus we are able to estimate the amount of possible error involved by taking at random a member of taxon **A** and one of taxon **B** as exemplars of their respective groups. In this particular example, also, the magnitude of error is quite tolerable. Other tests of the exemplar method are currently underway.

A solution of the problem of intrataxon variation of characters will partly depend on what the investigator wishes to study. If he wishes to compare a typical mammal with a typical bird, he must himself decide what he means by typical—whether "central" or commonest. He must also take the consequences of his decision, for it may be that the commonest form is very eccentric. If he is in doubt, he will do well to use several forms to represent the taxon, using, when necessary, single specimens for this. We suggest that in general a combination of the two approaches will prove of most value.

(4) A problem peculiar to microbiology is that many biochemical tests can select for mutations. A single strain may then give different results on two occasions, depending on whether a mutation had occurred. This is likely to affect few of the characters, and it may therefore not matter which state is scored, but if a mutation is regularly observed, this fact (and the mutation rate if measured) is a perfectly valid character of the strain. Such problems in clones of higher organisms, though rare, can be treated similarly.

## 6.5.  UNWARRANTED COMPARISONS

Up to this point we have ignored a major problem which must have occurred to most readers: there are likely to be numerous cases in which, for a certain OTU, no information is available for a particular character, making it impossible to compare this OTU with others. We may distinguish several ways in which this situation may occur.

### 6.5.1. Missing data

More frequently in some studies than in others, certain items of information may be unobtainable. The only available specimen may be damaged and have some structures missing; museum regulations may prevent dissection for the study of internal characters; distributional or ecological facts may be unknown; equipment for complex chemical or physical tests may not be available. Yet in many OTU's of the study we may have information on the character in question, and the one obvious and simplest solution—the elimination of the character from consideration—would seem deplorable. Where such missing data occur, the character state should be labeled with some agreed code for "inapplicable," which should be clearly distinguishable from a minus or a zero. Sneath (1957b) labeled such cases NC ("no comparison").

### 6.5.2. Missing characters

Many instances will arise where a given character present in one OTU is absent in another. In most cases the zero or minus state of the character will be the appropriate code for this condition. In some cases, however, a character may be masked by another so that we cannot score it; for example, black pigment would prevent our scoring for the character "presence of yellow pigment." The latter character would then in a sense be a missing character, and this would be another form of missing data discussed above. When this occurs the character state should be labeled inapplicable.

### 6.5.3. Missing organs

More frequent are instances where organs or relatively major parts of the body are absent or strongly modified in a given OTU, with the result that logically subordinate characters contained within the missing part cannot be scored. If, in a study of a group of insects, we have included "presence or absence of a wing" as one character and also five wing vein characters, we cannot score the venational characters in a wingless taxon. We cannot be sure whether the difference between the two taxa involves one character or all six, since the wingless form may have maintained its wing vein genes which cannot now be expressed as such. The only consistent procedure is to consider the wing vein characters inapplicable in the wingless taxon. Thus they cannot be compared with the corresponding states in the winged form. They also cannot be compared with the wing vein characters in another wingless taxon, since the fact that they are both not manifested does not provide a basis for comparison. Thus the wingless and the winged forms could be compared only on the basis of the single character "presence or absence of wings." We can compare the two wingless forms on the basis of the same character if we accept "negative matches" (Section 6.2.1.1). This may seem to be splitting hairs, and we must admit that it is not always easy to decide when a character is inapplicable and when it is negative or absent. However, once the decision has been made the subsequent procedure is logical and consistent. A block in a metabolic pathway poses a similar problem (Section 6.2.1.1).

### 6.5.4. The estimation of resemblance when some characters are inapplicable

No problem exists in the estimation of resemblance when coefficients of association are used. Any pair of character states including the code for "inapplicable" is simply excluded from the 2 × 2 table of matches and from the computation. This is an acceptable procedure unless too many of the characters are inapplicable, in which case the inclusion of the responsible OTU is inadvisable (see Section 6.5.5 on relevance).

When the resemblance between two OTU's is calculated by means of a correlation coefficient or a distance coefficient, characters which are inapplicable for either one are omitted in the calculation of the coefficient for the pair. It is obvious that the divisor in calculations of either coefficient has to be adjusted. In the distance coefficient the number of characters has to be reduced by the number of inapplicable comparisons, but in the correlation coefficient it is often necessary to compute separate sums of squares for the denominator of each individual $r$, since different characters are likely to be inapplicable in different OTU pairs. Such operations can, of course, be programmed but result in slowing down the speed of computations appreciably and also require greater storage (or repeated passes through the computer), since we have to recompute the sum of squares of each variable for each correlation coefficient rather than only once for each matrix. When possible, therefore, inapplicable characters are to be avoided. While a desk calculator operator would not be likely to be slowed down by a few inapplicable values, since he can easily scan the data and use standard procedures when records are complete, prior scanning is not feasible on most electronic computers unless their capacity is such that all the data can be stored before the outset of the computations. A computer program would therefore have to proceed with the time-consuming checking of all input for inapplicable data and the separate computation of sums of squares. When a given table of data contains inapplicable entries for only a few characters or a few OTU's or for a few of both, we recommend the removal of the responsible rows and columns rather than processing by the slower method.

One final consideration: if the coefficients in a resemblance matrix are based upon different samples of characters, the resulting coefficients are subject to two sources of error. First, they may be different because of the qualitative differences in the characters from which the coefficients are computed. We believe that adequate sample sizes will minimize this error, basing our belief on the hypotheses of nonspecificity and the matches asymptote. A second error is statistical. Confidence limits of the coefficients will vary, and a difference which is statistically significant between two coefficients in a matrix may be nonsignificant between another two coefficients in the same matrix, based upon a smaller sample of characters. We are particularly concerned with this fact when an elaborate statistical treatment of the resemblance matrix such as factor analysis is planned. We therefore hope that the number of character state codes labeled "inapplicable" can be kept at a minimum in a given study.

### 6.5.5. Relevance

Cain and Harrison (1958) have introduced the useful concept of the relevance of a comparison. They define this as the ratio of "twice the number of applicable characters considered (since these are shown by both forms) to the number of inapplicable ones (each of which will be shown by only one of the forms)." This ratio has the undesirable property of being indeterminate at its upper limit, and it is also not clear whether Cain and Harrison included those characters inapplicable to both forms being compared [such as character (6) for taxa **D** and **E** in their study]. We prefer a simpler coefficient of relevance,

$$R_{jk} = \frac{a_{jk}}{n},$$

where $a_{jk}$ is the number of characters applicable in taxon $j$ which are also applicable in taxon $k$ (or vice versa), and $n$ is the number of characters employed in the study. By this formulation $R_{jk}$ ranges from zero to unity.

We do not yet have enough experience with numerical taxonomy to know what relevance values are likely to be found in comparisons involving OTU's at various hierarchic levels. Nor do we know whether different groups of organisms would exhibit appreciable differences in this regard. However, it is obvious that low relevance values are undesirable; minimal values of 0.7 in most studies and of 0.5 in those based on many characters would seem indicated. In studies where widely varying relevance values seem unavoidable, the values may be used to indicate the reliability of the similarity coefficient to which they are pertinent.

## 6.6. COMPARISON AND EVALUATION OF METHODS

Evaluations of the three major approaches to estimates of affinity must at this time remain quite tentative. Although an appreciable number of studies employing numerical taxonomy have by now been published and all three types of coefficient employed, there are only five studies known to us in which different types of coefficients are compared. These are studies by Rohlf and Sokal (1963), Rohlf (1962), Sneath (1961), Gilardi et al. (1960), and Hill et al. (1961).

Rohlf and Sokal (1963) and Rohlf (1962) suggest that a correlation coefficient should be used, rather than a distance, whenever most of the characters used in a study are measurements of various parts of an organism and the OTU's differ much in overall size. When characters are independent of size, distance coefficients seem more meaningful. Until more experience is gained in numerical taxonomy, these authors suggest that both distance and correlation be applied and that taxonomies be erected that take both into consideration.

Rohlf (1962) in his study of the 48 species of *Aedes* mosquitoes found relationships indicated by correlations and by distance to be correlated to the extent of $r = -0.52$. Rohlf decided to employ distances based on standardized characters for establishing his classification because (a) these coefficients gave higher correlation between adults and larvae in his study, and (b) the relationships indicated by distances corresponded more closely to the previous classification of the genus.

Sneath (1961) compared the mean character difference (M.C.D.) and correlation ($r$) in *Knightia*, which though based on few characters showed quite good concordance. Gilardi et al. (1960) and Hill et al. (1961) compared the $S_J$ and $S_{SM}$ values for a series of bacteria, and again there was good concordance for most values, but one or two results suggested that with $S_{SM}$ inapplicable features were being counted as similarities in some cases.

Thus our discussion of the relative merits of the various methods must have a tentative aspect and be based mainly upon deductive inferences of the properties of the coefficients and the procedures used to compute them. Our comments will be restricted to the three coefficients (one from each method) which we at present feel have the most justification and the best promise for further work. In association coefficients this is the simple matching coefficient (or that of Jaccard, if negative matches are to be excluded); among correlation coefficients it is Pearson's product-moment $r$; and among distance measures it is the coefficient of taxonomic distance, $d$, based on standardized characters. Association and distance are easier to interpret conceptually than correlation. We can think of an association coefficient as the proportion of agreements to be found in unit taxonomic characters between two organisms. The concept of distance in a hyperspace bounded by coordinates representing the characters of the study is self-evident (see Figure 6-2). Of the various conventional interpretations of a correlation coefficient perhaps the most applicable for numerical analysis is through its square, the coefficient of determination, which identifies the proportion of the common variance of the two OTU's. This is not an altogether satisfactory idea. While not likely to be found in practice, we can hypothesize an OTU which has the same numerical code for its state in every character. Since the variance of this OTU would be zero, its correlation with another OTU would be indeterminate. Such a case would not, however, invalidate the coefficients of association or distance.

As regards simplicity of computation the correlation coefficient is the most complicated, followed by that of distance; the association coefficient is the simplest of all. However, such considerations are probably not very important. The computations even for a small numerical taxonomic study are so tedious that they will almost inevitably be processed by electronic computers. The differences in computation time will consequently be negligible. If necessary, correlation and distance computations can be satisfactorily carried out on a desk calculator. The association coefficient involves mostly matching of two-state characters, which can conveniently be performed by inspection or with a tally counter. This method lends itself most easily to mechanical improvisations, which should simplify the counting procedure. Punched strips of paper superimposed one on top of the other, mechanical sorting of punched cards, or specially marked X-ray plates (Sneath, 1957b) are among such devices.

From the point of view of utilizing the coefficients for the classificatory procedures outlined in Chapter 7, cluster analysis can be performed on

all three of them, although the distances would first have to be transformed into a complementary function (or the cluster analysis procedure
revised to pick out the lowest rather than the highest coefficients). If we
wish to use factor analysis for our classificatory procedure, the coefficients
must be correlations.

# The Construction of
# a Taxonomic System

In this chapter we discuss how a taxonomic system can be constructed from the resemblances among operational taxonomic units in a study. By this we mean the grouping together of those OTU's to form taxa, employing the affinities found by the methods described in Chapter 6. In order to do this we must discuss the requisites of a taxonomic system, the techniques for creating it, and problems of taxonomic rank.

It must be clearly understood that taxonomic systems are inevitably oversimplified representations of the matrix of affinities among the forms studied. One cannot therefore demand perfection of such systems. The principles of their construction have been little studied, and we feel that this part of the subject would generously repay the attention of taxonomists.

## 7.1. REQUISITES OF A TAXONOMIC SYSTEM

There are many ways in which we can construct taxonomic systems, according to the purpose in mind. We have assumed throughout this study that we wish to make taxonomic systems which are "natural," and we have discussed in Sections 2.2 and 4.5 the conceptual bases for natural systems. There are, however, a number of requirements essential to any practical taxonomy, whether natural or not.

Every taxonomy is built from units of some sort, and in biological taxonomy these are the organisms and the characters which they possess. We have been considering how one classifies the organisms, from their correlations and resemblances (Q-technique), but one can also consider

the correlations among the characters (R-technique); as an adjunct to
the usual systematics this may be valuable, particularly in the making of
keys and in the study of causal relations in biology (see Section 7.6). In
making taxonomic systems we are impelled by one consideration of overwhelming importance: we can neither list nor remember all the characteristics of various organisms and higher taxa, and we therefore need
a system of grouping them into a manageable number of groups whose
characters are preponderantly constant. Because of high constancy and
mutual intercorrelations of characters, such a grouping will carry a high
predictive value. Thus, if we read of a new aphid species we can immediately predict a number of characteristics which this species is expected to
possess. Being an aphid, it will with almost complete certainty be a plant
feeder, possess a particular type of wing venation, be parthenogenetic in
part of its life cycle, produce males by nondisjunction of the sex chromosomes, produce honeydew, secrete wax from cornicles or other glands,
and so on. Since an aphid is a homopteran, we can forecast with some
accuracy the general construction of its mouth parts, the texture of its
wings, and other homopteran characteristics. This type of argument can,
of course, be extended to the hexapod and arthropod levels of classification and even higher. It is obviously much easier for us to remember
this of the group Aphididae than of each individual aphid. Furthermore,
it is impossible to remember or appreciate the innumerable relations
between the various OTU's to be classified, but this is easier when they
are grouped into fewer inclusive taxa. Work is at present going on to see
whether there may be some groups of actinomycetes characterized by the
production (at least in a proportion of the strains) of certain kinds and
classes of antibiotics (see Silvestri et al., 1962; Arai, Kuroda, and Ito,
1962). If the groups are based on well-correlated characters we may
hope that type of antibiotic will also be correlated with the groups.

The prime purpose of a taxonomic system is therefore one of economy
of memory. This economy is achieved in one of two ways: (1) either we
employ the attributes one at a time in order to cluster our taxonomic
entities, which gives us a system such as that used in indexing books by
the names of their authors or by their size (monothetic systems), or (2)
we attempt to cluster them according to all their attributes considered
simultaneously, for which we use measures of affinity between the entities. Intermediates between these two may also be employed. The first,
or monothetic, method is "artificial" (though by chance or by selection
of the right attributes it may happen to be very nearly "natural"), while
the second method is "natural" but incomplete, since the matrix of

affinity values is itself too complex to serve the purpose required and must be analyzed so as to cluster the entities into "natural" taxonomic groups. In either case some form of nomenclature is needed for the resultant groups, but we may postpone discussion of this to a later chapter. In either case, too, the number of resultant groups must not be too large, and their properties must be consistent with the principles on which they were set up. When the groups are monothetic, this is simple; we must only obey our own criteria and put white objects into the pigeonhole labeled "white" and black ones into that labeled "black" (though even this elementary point is often overlooked, as Metcalf, 1954, pointed out in an amusing discussion on artificial keys). When the groups are polythetic ones, we must bear in mind that it is never certain, but only more or less probable, that a member possesses any given feature (see Section 2.2).

The most powerful method of achieving economy of memory is the method of the nested hierarchy. This device allows us to group a large number of taxonomic groups into fewer composite groups of higher rank, and it is only when these groupings are mutually exclusive that it gives the best results; for example, a given genus can belong to only one family, and this family to only one order, and so on. If it is found that some attributes are possessed by all members of one group, the task of remembering the attributes of the group is therefore less. The natural group of mammals has many attributes which are not possessed by the natural group of birds. This property of natural hierarchies is presumably due to the evolution of the natural groups, since it need not be always true—for example, in classifying the members of an interbreeding population, where it may not be possible to establish any satisfactory system of mutually exclusive hierarchies. The advantages of hierarchies are so great that we will generally employ them, even when this means we must distort the system of affinities to some extent.

It is not generally realized that hierarchies, other than purely arbitrary ones, can only be made with certain sorts of distributions of affinities between organisms. Figure 7-1(a) shows a random distribution of organisms envisaged as occupying points in a two-dimensional phenetic space, and Figure 7-1(b) shows a uniform distribution. In neither case can hierarchies be made except by arbitrary lines. In order to make hierarchies, one needs a clumped distribution, as shown in Figure 7-1(c), where the dotted lines indicate a nested hierarchy. The random distribution may give some hierarchical groups, since some parts are clustered by chance, but there are too many "intermediate" types for a satisfactory

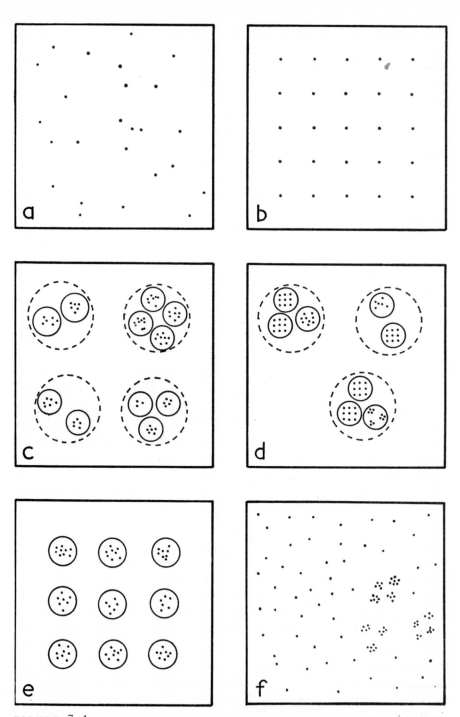

FIGURE 7-1

*Different types of clustering (for explanation, see text).*

hierarchy. We have no evidence that uniform distributions occur in taxonomy, and random distributions seem likely to occur only at low levels
of taxonomic rank, such as among geographical races or panmictic populations (see Section 8.2.3). Note that the clumped distributions must be
clumped at each level at which it is wished to make a hierarchical division; whether they are uniform, random, or clumped *within* this level is
immaterial for that hierarchical level. Figure 7-1(d) shows a hierarchical
arrangement which at the two higher levels is clumped; in Figure 7-1(e)
the hierarchy is only possible at the intermediate level, since the circles
are regularly spaced. For satisfactory complete hierarchies the taxa must
be clustered at every level. Only part of the distribution in Figure 7-1(f)
could be arranged hierarchically.

The nature of these distributions should be made clear, for they have
received much attention from ecologists; Greig-Smith (1957, pp. 50–84)
gives a full discussion of them as applied to two dimensions (see also
Thompson, 1956). A random distribution is one in which the probability
of occurrence of an entity is independent of the occurrence of other
entities in any sampling unit; that is, the presence of an entity at a given
point neither raises nor lowers the probability that another entity will
occur close to it. A uniform (overdispersed) distribution is one in which
there is a decreased probability of another entity occurring close to the
first, while in a clumped distribution the probability of this is raised.
Although developed for two-dimensional systems, these principles can
probably be safely extended to the multidimensional systems of taxonomic affinities.

It is evident that in making clusters of OTU's we place the dividing
lines between the groups at places where there are distinct gaps in the
combinations of characters we have observed. Above the rank of species
(or perhaps of genus) there is no great problem, and gaps are larger and
evident on cursory study. So far, there has been no work specifically
directed toward measuring such gaps by numerical methods, but there
is no reason why they should not be elaborated, if needed, from the
numerical techniques described in Chapter 6.

However, when we group a number of quite distinct taxa into a higher
taxon, such as grouping genera into families, the presence of the gaps is
itself of little help. If there are clear gaps between genera **A**, **B**, **C**, and **D**,
this will not tell us whether they should—on grouping them into two
families, 1 and 2—be grouped into Family 1 = (**A** + **B** + **C**) and Family 2 = (**D**) or into Family 1 = (**A** + **B**) and Family 2 = (**C** + **D**). The
problem is to define the sort of grouping which is to be considered a

natural taxon. This definition may not be easy to state precisely. Clearly the taxon (or taxa) must possess the property of "naturalness" to the highest possible degree. Sneath (1961) has defined natural taxa as "sets composed of all those elements which share $x$ or more features out of $y$ features, where $x$ and $y$ are large numbers, but in which an element may have any combination of features as long as the total number of features shared with every other element of the set is $x$ or more." Note that the qualifying word "all" is inserted in the phrase "sets composed of all those elements." This is necessary, since otherwise one can select a few of the contained entities, and such a selection may not itself be a natural taxon. For example, the selection mice plus whales plus bats is not itself a taxon, but is only an "unnatural" part of the taxon Mammalia, which is composed of all the known kinds of mammals. Also the definition given above yields overlapping taxa, which for convenience are converted into non-overlapping, hierarchical systems. The study of such systems has not yet been adequately developed, though Woodger (1937, 1951, 1952) and Gregg (1954) have made a start on this.

At a lower level of rank, the problem of division between intergrading groups remains to be discussed. This problem is generally not acute with the higher ranks, except perhaps in microbiology, where there may possibly be large "spectra" of gradually merging forms (see Cowan, 1955). In ecology intergrading groups may be the rule rather than the exception (Goodall, 1953). Discrete, nonoverlapping classes of vegetation or of fauna may be desirable from a practical viewpoint; however, they may have no theoretical validity (Whittaker, 1953). There is no reason why phenetic groups should not be recognized even when all intermediate forms are found between two kinds of creature—for example, where two species hybridize. If the hybrids are in the minority, the division between the two species lies through them, and again this is a problem of cluster analysis. It is analogous to two mountains joined by a saddle: the saddle is the division between them.

One further point requires emphasis: we can only make hierarchical natural groups on the basis of the organisms which are known to us. This is easily seen if one considers a study upon a few forms which appear to fall into two distinct clusters. The two clusters would be two taxa. Yet if it is later found that the forms are connected by a chain of intermediate forms which are more numerous than the extreme forms, we would now have a single cluster which we would have to consider as a single taxon.

To summarize, a taxonomic system should be "natural" in an empirical sense, and thus should be of high predictive value. The system is best arranged in the form of a nested hierarchy, and dividing lines are to be placed at gaps in the combinations of characters observed.

## 7.2. FREQUENCY DISTRIBUTIONS OF SIMILARITY COEFFICIENTS

Illuminating insights into the phenetic relationships among the OTU's in a numerical taxonomic study can be obtained by an inspection of the frequency distributions of the similarity coefficients. A frequency distribution of correlation coefficients between pairs of species was published by Michener and Sokal (1957) in their study of the bees of the *Hoplitis* complex. A primary mode among these correlation coefficients was shown at $r = 0.38$. This represented the most frequent class of correlation coefficients found between the species in this study (mostly intergeneric relationships). A secondary mode at $r = 0.78$ indicated relationships among closely related species. Bimodality or multimodality of this sort substantiates the nested arrangement of clusters of the OTU's in a given study. Rohlf and Sokal (1963) observed similar multimodal structure in distributions of correlation and distance coefficients based on standardized and not standardized characters. Standardization of characters generally accentuated the multimodality of the distributions. Even when multimodality was not clearly indicated, observed variances of similarity coefficients were greatly in excess of expectations. A pronounced bimodal distribution (each peak approximating to a normal curve) is apparent for the similarity values for strains of two species of bacteria (Sneath, 1957b); one peak indicates the interspecific similarity values, the other the intraspecific values. These findings and others lend some initial justification to the procedures for clustering the matrix, by demonstrating that the arrangement of the OTU's in the general study is not entirely at random.

The variation of similarity coefficients may be useful as an indication of the homogeneity of the OTU's. If to a homogeneous nucleus of OTU's we add other OTU's of the same homogeneous group, the variance will in general remain about the same. As we add OTU's of a markedly dissimilar group, the variance will rise steeply, and bimodal or multimodal curves of the affinity value distribution may appear.

## 7.3. TECHNIQUES FOR DESCRIBING TAXONOMIC STRUCTURE

Several techniques have been employed in numerical taxonomy to ascertain and describe structure in matrices of similarity coefficients.

Such techniques have been used in various fields such as ecology and psychology to group related items into ecological associations or personality types. Since the requirements for clustering methods in taxonomy differ sufficiently from those in other fields, we shall restrict our account to taxonomic techniques. These methods are still somewhat in a state of flux, and modifications are to be expected in the next few years, especially as they relate to the development of ever faster and more sophisticated computational equipment.

The clustering techniques described below are generally applicable to all three types of coefficients of similarity—coefficients of association, correlation, and distance. Distance coefficients are conventionally coded in such a way that the larger the coefficient the greater the distance between OTU's. Hence there is a negative relationship between coefficients of association and correlation, on the one hand, and of distance, on the other. Since most cluster methods are designed to recognize the greatest similarity first and lesser similarities later, distance coefficients are for purposes of computation conventionally changed in magnitude in such a way that the greatest distances appear small and the smallest distances great. A convenient scheme for such a conversion is to calculate the complement of the distance from a convenient number, usually ten. We therefore define the tens-complement of the distance as $10 - d_{jk}$. When the similarity coefficients in a clustering method are limited in range from zero to one, the tens-complement of the distance is divided by 10. This results in a similarity value of one for a distance value of zero.

Three techniques for describing taxonomic structure in similarity matrices are discussed below. The simplest of these is differential shading of a similarity matrix (Section 7.3.1); more complex, but more usefully descriptive, are the various types of cluster analysis, described in Section 7.3.2; the most complex of the methods is factor analysis, described in Section 7.3.3.

## 7.3.1. Differential shading of the similarity matrix

This is the most obvious technique for recognizing in one overall glance the groupings among the OTU's of a similarity coefficient matrix. The method consists of adopting a system of grouping the similarity coefficients into from five to ten evenly spaced classes arrayed by order of magnitude and representing each of these classes by a different degree of shading in the squares of a half matrix. Generally, the highest value is shown darkest and the lowest value lightest. The shading patterns need to be chosen with care, so that visually they present an even progression. It has been found empirically that for seven shades, ranging from white to black, the following densities of shading (expressed as the percentage of the area of the square that is black) give good results: 0, 12.5, 25, 50, 75, 87.5, 100. Barring and crosshatching are easier to use than stippling. One can then see the half matrix represented as a pattern of different shades, generally limited by a diagonal of squares of the darkest value, representing the similarity of the individual OTU's with themselves (see Figure 7-2). Alongside these can be found densely shaded triangular submatrices, representing groups of related OTU's. Such groups are frequently found on first inspection, unless the array of OTU's has been deliberately randomized, when the squares containing the darkest shade will be scattered throughout the matrix. A shaded similarity coefficient matrix exhibiting reasonably good initial clustering is shown in Figure 7-2. By skillful rearrangement of the sequence of the OTU's, these clusters can be more sharply defined and areas of light and dark can be separated with greater precision. An example of such a "cleaned up" diagram is shown in Figure 7-3. Although this has not been generally done, it might be of advantage to represent such figures as symmetrical

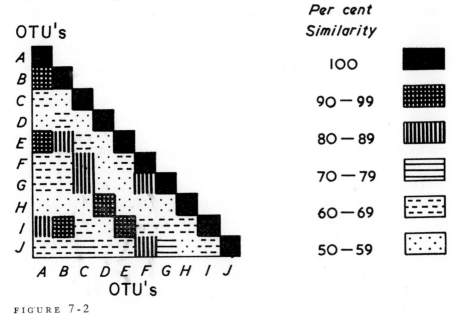

FIGURE 7-2

    *A shaded similarity matrix with the OTU's arranged in a haphazard order (for explanation, see text).*

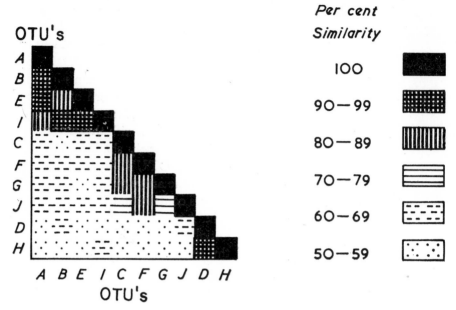

FIGURE 7-3

*The similarity matrix of Figure 7-2 after rearrangement by clustering, or the bringing together of OTU's that are very similar to one another.*

matrices. In such cases the clusters will be represented as dark squares, as shown in Figure 7-4, which is the symmetrical representation of Figure 7-3 above. One can then visualize the search for group structure as a rearranging of the rows or columns of this matrix in such a way as to obtain the optimum structure in the system. Such a procedure has been suggested by Robinson (1951). But this rearrangement of the rows of a matrix is not as simple as it sounds, because every time the position of a row changes the position of the corresponding column will change. Criteria for optimum structure in a shaded matrix, which must be a function of both the size of the groups as well as the depth of shade, have not yet been developed. When many taxa are used, such diagrams become quite unwieldy. All the individual squares have to be kept very small, making a clear definition of taxa difficult.

## 7.3.2. Cluster analysis

We mean by this general term a large class of numerical techniques for defining groups of related OTU's based on high similarity coefficients.

### 7.3.2.1. *Elementary cluster analysis*

This is the simplest of the various methods of clustering. It consists of arbitrarily selecting a level on the scale of similarity coefficients. All coefficients above this level are written down and the relationships expressed by these coefficients are indicated by lines or links connecting the OTU's, which are represented as points. Selection of a very high coefficient of similarity as criterion for clustering would yield only a few small clusters, just as only the higher peaks of a mountain range would appear as islands on a topographic map if all the area below some high contour line were obliterated. When the criterion for admission of similarity coefficients is lowered, more OTU's join the established clusters, new clusters form, and old ones coalesce. This is analogous to the joining of mountain peaks on a map by successively lowering contour lines. Sooner or later clusters will overlap by this method, some OTU being a member of two clusters simultaneously. Because of the possibility of overlapping clusters, elementary cluster analysis is generally an unsatisfactory procedure. When carried out in large matrices, it must be done by means of a systematic procedure. This is, of course, also necessary if the compu-

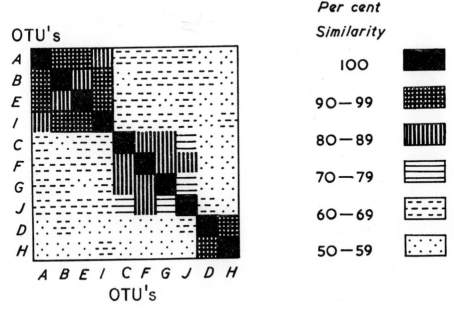

FIGURE 7-4

*The symmetric matrix derived from Figure 7-3, as if by reflection in a mirror set along the principal diagonal.*

tation is to be carried out by a computer program. Diagrammatic methods of this type, using heavy lines (or multiple lines) for high similarity links, have been used by several authors, for example, Boeke (1942).

### 7.3.2.2. Clustering by single linkage (Sneath's method)

The clustering methods which follow differ from elementary cluster analysis in that they do not group taxa related above a certain fixed criterion (level of similarity coefficient), but instead first cluster those OTU's most related, gradually admitting more members into the cluster by lowering the criteria of admission. The method practiced by Sneath (1957b) and followed by a number of authors is directly related to elementary linkage analysis. First it clusters together those strains mutually related with the highest possible similarity coefficient; then it successively lowers the level of admission by steps of equal magnitude. Thus if the first criterion is a similarity coefficient of 0.99, the next ones may be 0.98, 0.97, and so on. The computer program designed to process data according to Sneath's technique lists in successive stages the code numbers of the OTU's in the groups as they coalesce. One might, for instance, obtain a record as follows:

| $S$ | OTU's | |
|------|---------|-----|
| 0.99 | 1, 2 | |
| 0.98 | 1, 2, 3 | 4, 5 |
| 0.97 | 1, 2, 3 | 4, 5 |
| . | . | |
| . | . | |
| . | . | |
| 0.80 | 1, 2, 3, 4, 5 | |

This indicates that OTU's 1 and 2 join at a similarity value of 0.99; OTU 3 joins them at 0.98, while OTU's 4 and 5 join at the same level; not until $S = 0.80$ do 4 and 5 join 1, 2, and 3.

The admission of an OTU or a cluster into another cluster is by what we may call the criterion of single linkage. By this we mean that if a similarity level of 0.88 would admit an OTU into a cluster, a single linkage at that level with any member of that cluster would suffice to warrant admission. Similarly, any pair of OTU's (one in each of two clusters) related at the critical level will make their clusters join. Thus, while two clusters may be linked by this technique on the basis of a single bond, many of the members of the two clusters may be quite far removed from each other.

In order to overcome this difficulty, Sneath suggests recalculating the mean similarity values both within groups and between groups. This can, of course, be done at any of several hierarchic levels. The average similarity value is calculated by computing one of two quantities. The first quantity $\Gamma S$ is the so-called square mean—the mean of all $t \times t$ similarity coefficients including the self-comparison in the principal diagonal. The other quantity, $\Delta S$, the triangle mean, is based on the so-called "strictly triangular matrix," which includes only the triangular portion of the similarity coefficients, excluding self-comparisons. These quantities are related. The $\Delta S$ is lower than $\Gamma S$ or approaches it when $t$, the number of taxa in a cluster, becomes large:

$$\Delta S = \frac{\Gamma S t - 1}{(t - 1)},$$

$$\Gamma S = \frac{\Delta S(t - 1) + 1}{t}.$$

On the whole it would appear that the $\Delta S$ method of averaging would be preferable, since self-correlations are a function of the number of taxa included and would distort the estimates of the relationships among OTU's.

### 7.3.2.3. *Clustering by complete linkage (Sørensen's method)*

This method, described by Sørensen (1948) for ecological studies, has not been used in numerical taxonomy. It corresponds in most details to Sneath's method, except that admission of an OTU into a cluster is by what we might call the complete linkage criterion. A given OTU joining a cluster at a certain similarity coefficient $S_i$ must have relations at that level or above with every member of the cluster. Thus single bonds with just one member of the cluster would not be sufficient to effect the juncture. Where the possible groups overlap (where there is a choice of two attachments which a given OTU can make), Sørensen prefers fusion to yield the larger group, or the cluster with the greater number of OTU's. If these are equally large, he would choose the juncture so as to have as few as possible residual groups; and if this criterion turns out to be indecisive, he recommends choosing the combination with the highest average similarity coefficient.

After all junctions permitted at a given criterion have been made, he computes a new similarity matrix, using means of similarity coefficients.

It is obvious that with different initial levels of similarity coefficients the resulting clustering is likely to vary. Sørensen does not feel that these differences in appearance of the final dendrogram, based on differences in the limits by which he admits groups to a cluster, matter very much. However, we feel that the computational procedure leading to dendrograms should be an unequivocal one; therefore we prefer the recalculation of the similarity coefficient matrix at regular and short intervals, as practiced in the following clustering method.

### 7.3.2.4. Clustering by average linkage (the group methods of Sokal and Michener)

These group methods are a class of clustering techniques proposed by Sokal and Michener (1958). These authors suggested their techniques for the analysis of correlation coefficient matrices, but with some minor exceptions, to be mentioned below, the group methods can be applied to all types of similarity coefficient matrices. We shall discuss them here in this general context. They base admission of any individual into a cluster on the average of the similarities of that individual with the members of the cluster. This average similarity was called $\bar{L}_n$ in the original paper, but now is called $\bar{S}_n$. By members of the cluster we mean either the original OTU's or the smaller clusters composing a higher ranking cluster (see below on how these are formed). As the cluster grows and more remote relatives are considered as prospective members, the value of $\bar{S}_n$ of necessity becomes lowered. In their original study Sokal and Michener suggested that when any one prospective member would lower the $\bar{S}_n$ value of a cluster by 0.03, the prospective member should not be included, and that similarity coefficients should be recalculated among all clusters already formed at that level as well as between all clusters and those OTU's that have remained single. The value of 0.03 was empirically arrived at and referred to correlation coefficients employed by Sokal and Michener (1958) in their study. With different studies and different similarity coefficients this value may need to be adjusted.

By such a method the size of the clusters at any level is likely to vary, and the number of OTU's joining a new cluster is also liable to vary. Perhaps no OTU would join a given cluster in any one computational cycle; this would be because all prospective members had higher relationships to other clusters than to the one under consideration or because prospective members would cause too large a drop in $\bar{S}_n$ values. In other situations an appreciable number of OTU's might join the groups before the $\bar{S}_n$ level is depressed by 0.03. Since the number of OTU's joining a cluster varies, the above procedure has been called the variable group method, contrasting with the so-called pair-group method. This latter method permits only one OTU to join a cluster during any one computational cycle. This OTU is always the one having the highest average similarity value with the cluster. As soon as all prospective members have joined their clusters, a new similarity matrix of all clusters with each other and with single stems is recalculated. Thus by the pair-group method more recomputation of similarity coefficient matrices is necessary, because during any one clustering cycle only one OTU or cluster can join with another OTU or cluster.

In their original study Sokal and Michener (1958) tried both the pair-group and the variable group method and found little difference between them. They preferred the variable group method at the time, but more recently the pair-group method has been recommended because it is considerably easier to program, particularly for computers of medium capacity and speed. The relative merits of the two methods will be further discussed in Section 7.3.2.6.

The recomputation of the correlation coefficients analyzed by Sokal and Michener (1958), after each clustering cycle had been completed, was originally carried out by Spearman's sums of variables method (Spearman, 1913; Holzinger and Harman, 1941). The general formula for this computation is

$$r_{qQ} = \frac{\Box qQ}{\sqrt{q + 2\,\Delta q}\,\sqrt{Q + 2\,\Delta Q}},$$

where $\Box qQ$ is the sum of all correlations between members of one group with the other group, $\Delta q$ is the sum of all correlations between members of the first group, $\Delta Q$ is a similar sum between members of the second group, $q$ is the number of OTU's in group 1, and $Q$ is the number of OTU's in group 2. The details of this computation are shown in Appendix A.3. Spearman's sums of variables method correlates the sums of the variables making up any one cluster with sums of variables in any other cluster. In the special case where we would wish to calculate the correlation between a single OTU ($x$) and a new group ($q$), the formula is amended to

$$r_{xq} = \frac{\sum r_{xq}}{\sqrt{q + 2\,\Delta q}}.$$

A peculiarity of Spearman's method is that so-called reversals in correlation level are possible; that is, the sums of variables may be correlated at a slightly higher level than the variables composing them. For example, if **A** and **B** have formed the nucleus of a group at $r_{AB} = 0.9$ and **C** is about to join them, by the rules of the variable group method both $r_{AC}$ and $r_{BC}$ must be $<r_{AB}$. It can then be shown that $r_{(A+B)C}$ (the correlation between cluster **A** + **B** and OTU **C**) must be $<0.925$. Thus $r_{(A+B)C}$, while it will usually be $<r_{AB}$, could be slightly greater. Similar situations can be shown to exist with larger groups. The increases found by Sokal and Michener were well below the mathematically possible limits. In all such cases the relations were represented as multifid furcations of all the stems involved in the reversal and at the highest of the several $\bar{S}_n$ levels considered. When $\Delta q$ and/or $\Delta Q$ are very small or negative, large reversals are possible. When $\Box qQ$ is negative, reversals will also be negative. Therefore, when Rohlf (1962) employed correlation coefficients based on standardized characters, he found that the reversals for the coefficients near zero occurred in a negative direction, depressing the mean correlations appreciably. This would indicate that Spearman's method is not suitable for such correlations.

When the group methods are applied to distances or coefficients of association it would not be proper to recalculate correlation coefficients at the end of each clustering cycle. For this reason the new relationships among the clusters are calculated as arithmetic averages of all the coefficients involved in the correlations of any two clusters. This method has been used by Rohlf (1962) and Sneath (1962); an example is given in Appendix A.3. Using this simple method of averages, reversals of similarity coefficients during clustering are, of course, impossible, and clusters

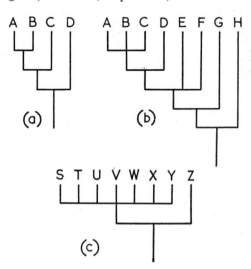

FIGURE 7-5

*The weighting of stems in building clusters, modified from Sokal and Michener (1958) (for explanation, see text).*

will then decrease steadily or at worst retain the same $\bar{S}_n$ value through several clustering cycles.

A consideration which we have not so far discussed is the problem of weighting stems. The simple diagram of Figure 7-5(a) will clarify this issue. The **A** and **B** represent two OTU's with the highest similarity coefficient. The $\bar{S}_n$ for **C** against **A** and **B** is significantly below $S_{AB}$, so that **A** and **B** represented as being closer to each other than they are to **C**. When studying the relation of a fourth OTU, **D**, with group **ABC**, we face the following problem: should we calculate the correlation of **ABC** against **D** with **A**, **B**, and **C** equally weighted or should we weight **A** = **B** and **AB** = **C**? Rephrased biologically, the problem is whether to relate **D** with the homogeneous group **ABC**, or with the stem **AB-C**, where **C** carries as much weight in determining the relation with **D** as do **A** and **B** together. In such a simple case the two alternatives may not produce very different results, but in a situation such as that depicted in Figure 7-5(b), OTU **H** might be weighted as $\frac{1}{8}$ of the group **A-H** or $\frac{1}{2}$, depending on the system adopted. Similarly, **B** would be weighted $\frac{1}{8}$ in the former case but only $\frac{1}{72}$ in the latter. When dealing with fairly large groups the second method would therefore reduce the weight of the members admitted early and increase the weight of those OTU's admitted later. The same problem is found in a situation such as that shown in Figure 7-5(c). By the first method **T** is weighted $\frac{1}{8}$; by the second method it is weighted only $\frac{1}{14}$. Neither of the two methods is entirely satisfactory. By the first method we are reducing the importance of OTU's **H** and **Z** in representing groups **A-H** and **S-Z**, respectively. The clustering methods discussed in Sections 7.3.2.1 to 7.3.2.3 have all been of the unweighted kind. Most of the applications of the technique of Sokal and Michener have employed weighted methods. The relative merits of the two approaches are discussed in Section 7.3.2.6.

### 7.3.2.5. *Central or nodal clustering (the method of Rogers and Tanimoto)*

The method proposed by Rogers and Tanimoto (1960) is a clustering method, but its actual procedures are markedly different from the preceding ones. Rogers and Tanimoto started with an association coefficient ranging from zero (absence of association) to one (complete association).

The coefficient which they used was their own similarity coefficient, $S_{RT}$, but their methods can be applied to any such coefficient, as was shown by Silvestri et al. (1962), who applied Rogers and Tanimoto's method to the simple matching coefficient $S_{SM}$.

Rogers and Tanimoto's clustering technique can be summarized as follows. After a matrix of similarity coefficients has been obtained, a value $R_i$ is obtained, which symbolizes the number of nonzero similarity coefficients that a given OTU $i$ has with other OTU's. It is obvious that in a matrix of $t$ taxa the maximum value of $R_i$ is $t - 1$. Rogers and Tanimoto originally developed the criterion for $R_i$ as the number of OTU's with which OTU $i$ has at least one attribute in common; hence $S_{RT} > 0$. It might seem questionable whether such small similarity values should be considered in computing $R_i$. Alternatively one might consider only those similarity coefficients greater than the expected value or greater than a given criterion which had been shown empirically to give useful clusters. This latter approach was adopted by Silvestri et al. (1962), who in setting up their $R_i$ values considered only similarity coefficients larger than 0.65. These $R_i$ values are indices of typicality. The larger the $R_i$, the more "typical" a given OTU is of the group under study.

Next to be computed is the quantity $H_i$, which is defined by

$$H_i = \prod_{j=1}^{j=t} S_{ij}, \qquad j \neq i, S_{ij} > 0.$$

This is the product of all the similarity coefficients of OTU $i$ with those of the other OTU's, except with itself, and with those coefficients equal to zero (or not considered for evaluating $R_i$). The higher the value of $H_i$, the more "typical" will be OTU $i$. All the OTU's are then grouped in a table in order of descending value of $R_i$; in those cases where $R_i$ is equal for two or more OTU's the order is by descending value of $H_i$.

The OTU having the highest $R_i$ and the highest $H_i$ value is considered the most typical one in the whole study, as will be shown below. It is in fact the centroid of the system, when the matching coefficients are expressed in logarithmic form. The most typical OTU is called the prime node of the study and around it is formed a cluster of OTU's having high similarity coefficients with it. The problem now is to find a criterion to determine the number of OTU's that are to go in the cluster. In order to do this a second node has to be found, which is generally the second highest member in the typicality array, although not always. The radius of the cluster of OTU's around the prime node must be such that it does not include the OTU forming the secondary node.

At this point we should introduce the concept of distance as used by Rogers and Tanimoto (1960). They convert the similarity coefficients ranging from zero to one into distances defined as $d_{ij} = -\log_2 S_{ij}$. These distances will range from zero (when $S_{ij} = 1$) to infinity (when $S_{ij} = 0$); therefore, similarity values of zero are not so converted and, as has been seen above, are omitted from consideration. These distances permit the visualization of taxonomic similarity as taxonomic distance similar to the distances previously discussed in Section 6.2.3. However, they define a so-called semimetric space in which Euclidean properties of distance are not necessarily obeyed—the sum of two sides of a triangle is not necessarily greater than the third. Thus similarity between OTU's **A** and **B** and also between **B** and **C** need not necessarily imply similarity between **A** and **C**. By using the logarithmic formulation we can now calculate

$$-\log_2 H_i = \sum_{j=1}^{j=t} d_{ij} = \sum_{j=1}^{j=t} (-\log_2 S_{ij}), \qquad i \neq i, S_{ij} > 0,$$

expressed as distances. The most typical OTU—the one presumably forming the primary node—will have the lowest $-\log_2 H_i$ value expressed as the sum of the distances.

The formulation of similarities as distances and the expression of them as the negative logarithm of the similarity coefficient permit the relation of these procedures in numerical taxonomy to information theory. These are interesting relationships, even though not particularly useful at this stage in the development of the concept.

If a second node has been determined, the distance to this node can be computed. If we call this distance $d_{1,2}$, then all OTU's related to the primary node OTU at distances less than $d_{1,2}$ are to be included. The resulting cluster now has to be tested for homogeneity. Rogers and Tanimoto (1960) do this by computing a quantity $u_n[(d_{ij})]$, which is a measure of the inhomogeneity of the cluster. The exact definition of $u_n[(d_{ij})]$ is given by the equations

$$u_n[(d_{ij})] = \frac{\mathcal{E}_n(g, h) - E_n[(d_{ij})]}{\mathcal{E}_n(g, h)} = 1 - \frac{E_n[(d_{ij})]}{\mathcal{E}_n(g, h)},$$

$$\mathcal{E}_n(g, h) = \log_2 \left[ \frac{n - g}{2} (n - g - 1) - h \right],$$

where $n$ is the number of OTU's in the cluster in addition to the primary node OTU. (Please note that $n$ is used here with a different connotation than throughout the rest of this book.) The matrix $(d_{ij})$ is the symmetric distance matrix of the OTU's in the cluster, $g$ is the number of zeros in $(d_{ij})$ which lie above the principal diagonal, and $h$ is the number of infinite elements above the principal diagonal which are not also in the same rows and columns as the $g$ zeros. The term $E_n[(d_{ij})]$ is defined as

$$E_n[(d_{ij})] = -\tfrac{1}{2} \sum_{ij}' \frac{d_{ij}}{T_n[(d_{ij})]} \log_2 \frac{d_{ij}}{T_n[(d_{ij})]},$$

where $d_{ij}$ represents the elements of the matrix $(d_{ij})$, $\sum'$ indicates summation of finite terms only after repeated rows and columns are deleted, and

$$T_n[(d_{ij})] = \tfrac{1}{2}(\sum_{ij}' d_{ij}).$$

This measure of inhomogeneity is successively computed as OTU after OTU is added to the primary node cluster in the order of their distances from it. When this measure suddenly takes a large jump in value, the "natural" limits of the cluster have been exceeded and, again, the last OTU to be added is removed. Sometimes it is necessary to remove also the OTU closest to the periphery of the cluster, exchanging it for another possible contender in order to see whether the cluster would be more homogeneous with a different composition. After the primary clump has been determined, it is removed from the study and a secondary clump is found among the remaining OTU's. This procedure is repeated with the residual number of OTU's until such a time as all the OTU's have joined clusters or until only a few residual ones remain. These are then attached to those clusters to which they seem to fit best.

The measure of inhomogeneity devised by Rogers and Tanimoto necessitates fairly complex computational facilities, and for this reason Silvestri et al. (1962) simplified it by studying the $R_i$ values of the OTU's in a cluster and rejecting those OTU's with an $R_i$ value much inferior to the possible maximum of $c - 1$ (if $c$ is the number of strains in the cluster, $R_i$ max $= c - 1$).

A new clustering method is proposed by Lockhart and Hartman (1963) in a recent publication. The groups, although polythetic, are made monothetic by discarding all characters which vary within them. This method avoids the main disadvantage of monothetic methods—the moving of an aberrant OTU to a place removed from its "natural" polythetic place. It employs the number, $d_c$, of characters in which it differs from a given index OTU (after discarding those characters that are not constant as the group is built up). For details of the method the reader is referred to the original source. The authors report that monothetic groupings obtained for 50 representative microorganisms were found to be essentially similar to the polythetic groups obtained by other methods.

### 7.3.2.6. Comparison and evaluation of clustering techniques

We have not as yet a systematic study comparing the effects of the different methods of clustering discussed above. For this reason the discussion which follows must be largely based upon theoretical considerations whose significance remains to be empirically validated.

A technique for evaluating different clustering methods by means of cophenetic correlation coefficients has been developed by Sokal and Rohlf (1962). These coefficients are described in greater detail below (Section 7.4). But for the purpose of such a comparison we would compute a correlation between the original similarity coefficients on which a dendrogram is based and the so-called cophenetic values, which are a matrix of coded similarity values extracted from the dendrogram. We may postulate that in an ideal case the dendrogram should reproduce exactly the amount of information on similarity available in the similarity coefficient matrix. Thus a perfect correlation between original similarity coefficients and the cophenetic values in a given dendrogram would show that there has been no distortion whatsoever on converting the data into a dendrogram. It is most unlikely that this would happen in any actual set of data. The extent to which the cophenetic correlation departs from 1.0 will be a measure of distortion which the clustering technique and the dendrogram impose on the taxonomic relationships. We may evaluate different methods of clustering by comparing the magnitude of cophenetic correlation coefficients between the original similarity coefficients and cophenetic values based on a variety of different dendrograms prepared for the same OTU's. When such a study was made, using 23 selected species from the 97 species of the *Hoplitis* complex analyzed by Michener and Sokal (1957), Sokal and Rohlf (1962) found that among the four clustering methods tested—weighted pair-group method, weighted variable-group method, unweighted variable-group method, and unweighted pair-group method, using averages rather than Spearman's sums of variables method—the last of the methods gave the highest correlation with the original correlation coefficients ($r = 0.86$). The differences were not very impressive since the greatest distortion, which occurred in the weighted pair-group method, still gave a cophenetic correlation of 0.80 with the original correlation coefficient. Comparing an average linkage method and a single linkage method with original similarity coefficients for the data by Hamann (1961) as processed by Sneath (unpublished), we found cophenetic correlations of 0.59 and 0.34, respectively, showing that the average linkage method represented the data considerably better, although not too well.

Each of the clustering methods described in the previous section is valid in its own right if consistently applied. It is to be expected that the single linkage method will provide for the very rapid coalescing of groups, and hence may not provide a sufficient amount of taxonomic detail. But the complete linkage method may require the lowering of the similarity criterion by a considerable amount in order to establish groups by that method. In both cases the admission of a new member depends upon a single $S$ value, the highest or lowest, which may be unrepresentative for many reasons. It seems to us, therefore, that methods based on averages, such as the various group methods of Sokal and Michener, have an advantage in bestriding a middle path between the extreme positions. Certain problems remain, particularly when a given OTU **A** has much similarity to another OTU **B** but not to **C**, while **B** has higher relations with **C** than it has with **A**. In such a case, average clustering is necessarily unrepresentative of the true relations. In clustering work in fields other than biological taxonomy this problem is not so serious because overlapping clusters are permitted.

A comparison by Sneath (unpublished) of Hamann's (1961) similarity coefficients among families of Monocotyledons shows that clustering by the average method draws out the differences in similarity coefficients considerably, so that the lowest stems unite near a coefficient of zero, while with single linkage methods the lowest stems unite at a coefficient of 60 (out of a maximum of 100). Furthermore, in addition to this condensation of detail produced by the single linkage method, some rearrangements of the families of plants are suggested. In particular, one family (the Cyanastraceae), which shows uniformly low similarity to all other OTU's except one (the Liliaceae), was grouped with the Liliaceae by the single linkage method but was widely separated from all OTU's by the average linkage method. The cophenetic correlation coefficient (see Section 7.4) between the two dendrograms was only 0.28.

If we adopt the method of average linkage, the problem of weighting OTU's within joining clusters assumes importance. The nature of the problem has already been discussed. Sokal and Michener (1958), in discussing the merits of the two methods, felt that the optimum system of weighting would be one between the two extremes—weighting late arrivals more than earlier members of the group, yet not weighting them equally to the entire early stem. Since this was not possible without the renewed introduction of a subjective element into the procedure, they adopted the method of weighting each new member as equal to the sum total of all old group members. They thought such a procedure to be the less objectionable method of the two, in view of the underlying assumed phylogenetic causes of the phenetic relationships under study. Thus it was felt that clusters of several OTU's or stems bearing a single OTU equally represent independent evolutionary lines. Weighting of stems in this manner does not provide the best classification, yet we lack a better criterion for the moment. A computer could be programmed to apply a series of different weights, where the weight could be some function of the size of the group. Thus, if a cluster representing ten OTU's has another OTU joining them, there are two extreme choices: to weight the single joiner equal to all ten, or to weight the newcomer only one-eleventh. The weight furnished by the computer could be in between these values as a function of the number of OTU's in each stem. But it may legitimately be argued that weighting of stems distorts the affinities among the OTU's. Computation of similarity coefficients among clusters on an unweighted basis is the most faithful method of condensation of the original coefficients. Rohlf (1962) has found this to be true in his data, when tested by cophenetic correlations. However, to follow a consistently unweighted policy may lead to absurdities in certain situations. For example, if we wish to know the affinity of a reptile with the mammals and represent the latter by 100 rodents but only 5 representatives of other orders, an unweighted reptile-mammal affinity would represent mainly a reptile-rodent affinity. A further advantage of the unweighted scheme is that a true average similarity is computed for which confidence limits can be estimated (Rohlf, 1962). Each system of weighting is defensible on several grounds, and we do not as yet have sufficient experience to decide the relative merits of the various systems. In light of our knowledge to date it may well be that the differences between the two extreme choices are so slight that a compromise solution such as suggested above would be generally acceptable.

In deciding between pair-group and variable-group procedures, we note that the former will show less distortion of the original similarity coefficient matrix and be devoid of an arbitrary criterion of group formation. But the variable-group method does not differentiate between fine differences in order of clustering, which may be nonsignificant. Again, we need more experience to decide on the preferred procedure; however, in this instance it is well known that the two alternatives produce very similar results. Also, limitations of computational equipment may determine the choice of method.

In devising our method in such a way as to avoid overlapping clusters, we are in fact biasing the data to yield discrete definable clusters. Such biases are deliberately introduced as a regular function of the system because of the nature of the classification we are attempting to construct. Biological classification should be constructed by nested nonoverlapping categories, if only for purposes of convenience. The underlying phylogeny makes such an arrangement the only reasonable one, at least among the higher categories. This may well be an aspect of the clustering process in which numerical taxonomy differs from classificatory procedure in related sciences such as psychology, ecology, or language classification. Overlapping language forms are permissible, as are overlapping psychological types and overlapping ecological associations. Overlapping taxa of the same rank are, however, not permissible. (For a contrary view see the paper by Michener, referred to in Section 10.7.)

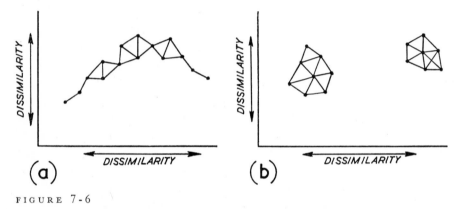

FIGURE 7-6

*The effects of different methods of linkage in forming clusters. (a) Single linkage; the clusters may be long and narrow. (b) Complete linkage; the clusters are compact.*

Computer programs for average linkage clustering which take into account the variance of the members of the clusters that are formed have so far not been developed. If single linkages are permitted, complicated serpentine clusters may be formed; see Figure 7-6(a). The actual affinity between the "end links" of the serpentine cluster may be very remote indeed. On the other hand, if complete linkage is practiced, the clusters are likely to be very compact and well defined; see Figure 7-6(b). Such clusters could also be conceived as clouds of OTU's in a hyperspace, and they could be defined as hyperspheroids in that space. No attempt at such a definition has yet been made, although the method of Rogers and Tanimoto does in fact delimit clusters by defining hyperspheres around central points. It would seem that straggly, serpentine types of clusters are not very desirable in biological taxonomy; for that reason also the use of average cluster methods is recommended.

The method of Rogers and Tanimoto has the advantage that when carried out in its original formulation—by computing a coefficient of inhomogeneity—one is able to obtain a measure of the homogeneity of clusters which, as discussed above, would be a desirable feature of a clustering procedure. At the end of the clustering procedure the groups themselves are re-examined, to test whether the most natural groupings have been obtained. Through the mathematical relations to information theory concepts we may be nearing an understanding of the information content of natural taxa in biology.

However, on the debit side we find that the method of Rogers and Tanimoto defines only a series of primary nodes without connecting these into a dendrogram. It centers these nodes around the most typical OTU in each case and, instead of studying the mutual relations among the OTU's simultaneously in a similarity matrix, disperses these as it were to several centers of attraction, the nodal points. Furthermore there is much indeterminacy in the clustering solutions obtained by this method. A number of decisions during clustering are left to the discretion of the operator. This feature was deliberately built into the routine by its authors and has been made a part of the computer classification program (The IBM 704 Taxonomy Application). Such flexibility goes counter to our aims to make the clustering procedure repeatable. Furthermore, viewing the prospects of numerical taxonomy for the immediate future, it is unlikely that an appreciable number of taxonomists will become familiar enough with computer techniques that the kind of close computer-man association necessary for running this program is going to be realized. It would be preferable to have a program which, once the data are fed into the machine, will yield an unequivocal similarity scheme. In our limited experience with this particular technique, we have found that the results obtained by the Rogers and Tanimoto clustering method are usually reflected in various other types of clustering methods yielding more conventional dendrograms. These other methods have also the additional features of joining clusters at precisely calculated levels. Hill et al. (1961) and Silvestri et al. (1962) compared the Rogers and Tanimoto method and the single linkage method on the same affinity coefficients. The dendrograms were on the whole very similar. We cannot at this stage wholeheartedly recommend the procedure of Rogers and Tanimoto, although it does have interesting features which may on further development lead to fruitful results.

In summary we might recommend, at this stage in the development of numerical taxonomy, the average linkage method of clustering employed as a variable-group method or as a pair-group method. The decision which to employ will often depend on available computer facilities. The weighted method is to be preferred until such time as functions for intermediate weighting are developed. There may, however, be legitimate reasons for preferring unweighted clustering methods in a given study. Recomputation of similarity matrices at the end of each clustering cycle is to be done by Spearman's method for correlation coefficients based on unstandardized characters and by ordinary averages for correlation coefficients based on standardized characters and for all other similarity coefficients.

### 7.3.3. Factor analysis

A method of representing taxonomic structure which is related to but considerably more involved than the clustering methods is factor analysis. Sokal (1958) appears to have been the first to employ factor analysis to indicate taxonomic relationships from a similarity matrix expressed in the form of correlation coefficients. Morishima and Oka (1960) followed Sokal's proposal, applying factor analysis to a taxonomic correlation coefficient matrix but without rotation to simple structure. Factor analysis of Q-type matrices, originated by Stevenson (1936), has been used repeatedly in psychology.

Factor analysis when applied to correlations among taxa may be interpreted as a statistical method for describing the complex interrelationships among taxa in terms of the smallest number of factors. An OTU is placed in the taxon corresponding to the factor to which it is most closely related. The degree of similarity between an OTU and the average aspect of the taxon which a factor represents is given by the factor loadings. The higher the factor loading, the more typical is the OTU of the taxon. In a sense each factor represents the "type" of a taxon. Hence there is a superficial similarity between factor analysis and the type concept, now generally in disrepute (see Simpson, 1961). The distinction between such essentially idealistic concepts and the empirically and statistically based typology of numerical taxonomy is made by Sokal (1962b).

Multiple factor analysis is a branch of multivariate statistics which, in examining a complex set of phenomena stated in terms of correlations among the variables under consideration (in our case the correlations among OTU's), attempts to express these phenomena as functions of a small number of new variables. These new variables (called factors) should contain the maximum amount of information for describing these relationships. Two different methods of factor analysis are customarily practiced: the principal components method is largely employed by British factor analysts, while multiple factor analysis with rotation to simple structure is widely accepted in the United States. Factor analysis is sufficiently complex that a detailed discussion and explanation of the subject would require a book in itself. Computational details for the method can therefore not be given here, but readers are referred to Cattell (1952), Fruchter (1954), Harman (1960), and Thurstone (1947) as suitable introductory texts.

In the most extensive application of factor analysis to classificatory work, Rohlf and Sokal (1962) employed centroid factor extraction with subsequent rotation to simple structure. This is the most commonly employed form of multiple factor analysis. Centroid factor extraction describes the interrelationships among OTU's in terms of an arbitrary orthogonal (uncorrelated) system; that is, the new variables (factors) are uncorrelated. The first centroid factor accounts for most of the covariation among the OTU's, the second centroid factor for somewhat less, the third still less, and so on. The relative amounts of information contained by each factor can be determined and are usually expressed as a percentage of the total amount of information. The problem of how many factors should be extracted is a complicated subject, and readers are referred to the books mentioned in the previous paragraph for a discussion of this issue.

After the factors have been extracted they are transformed by rotation of coordinate axes to another coordinate system, no longer restricted to orthogonality, which reveals the interrelationships among the OTU's in their simplest form. The criteria for this constellation, known as "simple structure," require that any one factor influence only some of the variables (OTU's) in each study and affect other variables little or not at all. In a simple structure solution, therefore, we do not find a general factor but instead find group factors. Furthermore, any one variable (OTU) should not be affected by all factors. Correlation between the factors is permitted and is frequently necessary if simple structure is to be obtained.

Rotation to simple structure was an immensely tedious and partly subjective method only a few years ago; however, the recent development of so-called analytical (computational) procedures has simplified the process considerably. The concept of simple structure is somewhat controversial, but factors which emerge in a simple structure solution have been shown to correspond to meaningful entities which reappear in different related studies (Cattell, 1952).

Rohlf and Sokal (1962) applied these methods to sets of 40 species from among the 97 of the *Hoplitis* complex of Michener and Sokal (1957) and obtained the results illustrated in Figure 7-7 for one of these sets. In general they found very good agreement between results of the weighted pair-group method and factor analysis. In Section 8.1.3 we will discuss in some detail the so-called pregroup-exgroup problem. The apparent isolation of exgroup OTU's by the weighted pair-group method, compared to their position by orthodox classification, is probably due to the computational procedures implied in these group methods. The group methods, as well as most other forms of cluster analysis, consider only the highest correlations in a matrix at each clustering cycle. Since relatively isolated OTU's do not have very high correlations with most of the OTU's in the matrix, they are in effect left out until $\bar{S}_n$ is decreased to the average level of correlation of these relatively isolated OTU's with the other OTU's, which exaggerates their degree of isolation. Factor analysis, on the other hand, simultaneously employs all the correlations of each OTU with every other OTU. Therefore the isolated OTU's are considered from the start with the group of OTU's with which they have the highest relationships. All of the species designated by Michener and Sokal (1957) as being exgroup species (see Section 8.1.3) were placed by factor analysis (Rohlf and Sokal, 1962) in the same general groups of species in which they had been placed by Michener and Sokal after the pregroup-exgroup corrections had been made. It would therefore seem that at least for the pregroup-exgroup problem in the *Hoplitis* complex the phenetic classification based on factor analysis is close to the one which Michener and Sokal presumed to be the evolutionary one.

Factor analysis should also predict (by low communalities; see Rohlf and Sokal, 1962) which OTU's might be incorrectly placed by the weighted variable-group method. One difference between factor analysis and the weighted variable-group method is that the latter gives more detail of taxonomic structure, especially at the lower levels, whereas factor analysis only indicates the cluster to which an OTU belongs and the degree to which each of the OTU's resembles an "average" representative of the cluster. This limitation of factor analysis might be an advantage in that it prevents one from attempting to interpret differences which are probably not reliable (see Michener and Sokal, 1957, p. 161). If more detail is desired within a cluster, one has to limit the scope of the study.

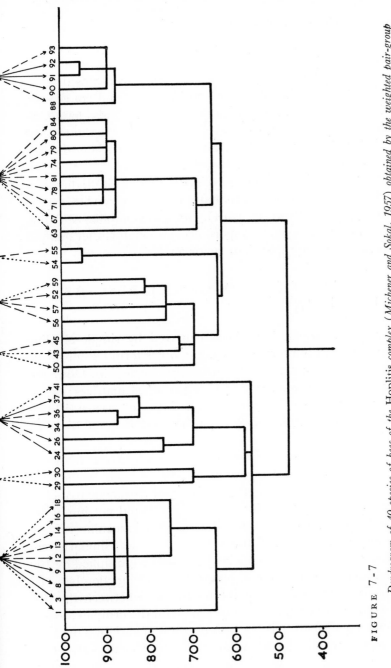

FIGURE 7-7

Dendrogram of 40 species of bees of the Hoplitis complex (Michener and Sokal, 1957) obtained by the weighted pair-group method. The results of centroid factor analysis with rotation to simple structure are shown across the top in the form of arrow diagrams from the factors to the species. The numbers at the top of the dendrogram are code numbers for the species. Ordinate of dendrogram: magnitude of correlation coefficient between joining stems multiplied by 1000. In the arrow diagrams solid lines correspond to standard partial regression coefficients (primary patterns) >0.9, dashed lines to coefficients between 0.70 and 0.89, and dotted lines indicate the relatively highest coefficient between a factor and a species without very high coefficients with any factor. [Redrawn from Rohlf and Sokal, 1962, Figure 1.]

On comparing the results of factor analysis with the dendrogram given by the weighted pair-group method, Rohlf and Sokal (1962) found that no straight line could be drawn across a dendrogram to yield exactly the groups given by the corresponding factor analysis. This means that the groups formed by the factor analysis are approximately, but not exactly, at the same hierarchic level. Morishima and Oka (1960) also found the weighted pair-group method yielding results quite similar to those of the factor analysis which they employed, although these authors did not rotate their factor matrix to simple structure.

The main limitation of the usefulness of factor analysis in finding taxonomic structure is the amount of computation necessary with even a small number of OTU's. However, with increased availability of digital computers this limitation is of less importance, although cluster analysis will always be much more rapid than factor analysis.

## 7.4.  THE REPRESENTATION OF THE RESULTS OF CLUSTERING

Similarity matrices which have been clustered by simple shading methods are not generally represented in any other form except as the dark triangles in the original shaded matrix (see Figure 7-3). However, if the clusters are grouped again, one or more secondary matrices may be shown in which each new OTU represents a cluster of former OTU's. One could conceive of such shaded diagrams as cross-sectional transects through a dendrogram.

The most common and convenient representation of the results of numerical taxonomy is by dendrograms. Except for their rectangular nature they appear very much like the customary phylogenetic trees, but they are strictly based on phenetic evidence and should not imply descent. The abscissa of such a dendrogram has no special meaning, serving only to separate the OTU's, while the ordinate is in some similarity coefficient scale usually from zero to one and frequently multiplied by 100 or by 1000 in order to avoid decimal places. Points of junction between stems along such a scale mean that the resemblance between the two stems is at the similarity coefficient value shown on the ordinate. When using correlation coefficients and Spearman's sums of variables method, the highest level of correlation is customarily chosen in the case of reversals, and the level of juncture indicates a correlation no higher than the given value. Michener and Sokal (1957) drew their dendrograms with the tips pointing upward and the final joined stem pointing down-

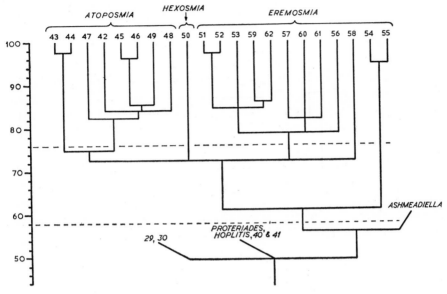

FIGURE 7-8

*Dendrogram for the bee genus* Anthocopa, *a portion of the* Hoplitis *complex (Michener and Sokal, 1957). This dendrogram was obtained by the weighted variable-group method.* Ordinate: *magnitude of correlation coefficient multiplied by one hundred. Correlations between any two joining stems can be found by reading the value on the ordinate corresponding to the horizontal line connecting the stems. This value becomes approximate and maximal in cases of multifid furcations. "Roofs" over the species numbers at the tips of the lines delineate subgenera. These subgenera are based on Michener's formal classification established by conventional methods before the numerical taxonomic study was carried out. "Stubs" at the base of the dendrogram indicate connections with related taxa. Broken horizontal lines were drawn across the dendrogram by Michener and Sokal in an attempt to delimit genera and subgenera (at r levels of 76 and 58, respectively). More recent practice would tend to label these lines phenon lines yielding 76-phenons and 58-phenons, respectively. Using this terminology, we arrive at six 76-phenons in Anthocopa, which are (43 . . . 44), (47 . . . 48), (50), (51 . . . 56), (58), and (54 . . . 55). [Redrawn from Figure 7 in Michener and Sokal (1957).]*

ward on the page, as shown in Figure 7-8. Most authors have followed their lead. Another version is to present the dendrogram lying on its side with the tips of the OTU's pointing to the right. Such an arrangement has been chosen by Sneath (1962), for example (see Figure 7-9). It has the advantage that if the nomenclature of the classification is to be listed in the same diagram this can be done more conveniently with the diagram lying on its side.

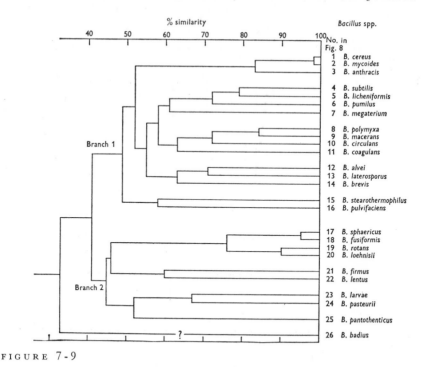

FIGURE 7-9

*Dendrogram of 26 species of bacteria of the genus* Bacillus. [*Sneath (1962), Figure 9. Reproduced by permission from the 12th Symposium of the Society for General Microbiology.*]

Taxonomic rank can be assigned to OTU's by drawing horizontal lines across (vertically oriented) dendrograms at given levels (see next section for details). While the scale alongside any one dendrogram is a reliable indicator of the level at which two stems come together, it is not to be construed as representing relationships among the tips of the dendrograms, which are impossible to represent adequately in a two-dimensional graph. As we have seen in Chapter 2, representation of phenetic relationships among the OTU's in a study is not possible by a dendritic scheme in two or even three dimensions.

Comparison between the methods of representation by different clustering techniques can be carried out by the technique of cophenetic correlations devised by Sokal and Rohlf (1962). These authors divided the similarity values along the ordinate into a suitable number of equal class intervals by drawing *phenon lines* as class limits across the dendrogram (see Figure 7-10, where the range of similarity values has been divided into eight classes). The number of classes into which the variation should be divided will depend upon the number of OTU's being classified. As a very rough guide, dendrograms of less than ten OTU's need not be divided into more than four classes, while dendrograms involving as many as 100 OTU's should be divided into at least ten classes. A further consideration should be that the class intervals should be fine enough to reveal a reasonable amount of structural detail in the dendrogram to be analyzed. Persons planning to do such computations on a desk calculator should employ the minimum number of classes necessary. But increasing the number of classes never does any harm from a statistical point of view. A computer program developed by Rohlf divides the range of similarity values into 50 classes. Schemes could also be developed which would handle the actual similarity value at which two stems join. The statistical consequences of using actual juncture levels rather than co-

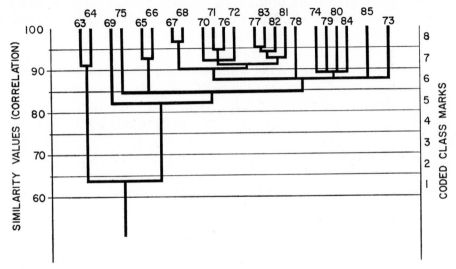

FIGURE 7-10

*Dendrogram or diagram of relationships among 23 species of the bee subgenera* Chilosmia *and* Ashmeadiella s. str., *taken from Rohlf and Sokal (1962) and based on data by Sokal and Michener (1958). The relationships were obtained by the weighted pair-group method (WPGM). The ordinate is graduated in a Pearson product-moment correlation coefficient scale (coded by multiplying by 100). Numbers across the top of the figure are species code numbers which are identified in Rohlf and Sokal (1962) or Michener and Sokal (1957). Horizontal lines across the dendrogram are phenon lines defining taxa at the minimum level of similarity at which the phenon line cuts the ordinate. Class intervals delimited by phenon lines along the similarity scale have had their class marks coded (on the right side of the dendrogram). [From Figure 1, Sokal and Rohlf (1962). Permission of the editors of* Taxon.]

phenetic values are probably slight, based on the well-known effects of grouping of frequency distributions.

Once the class intervals along the ordinate have been established, each class mark should be coded on a scale starting with unity at the low end (the end having the lowest similarity value) and increasing by unit steps. Thus with ten classes the highest class should be coded 10. These values will then be proportional to the similarity values, except in the case of distances, where they will be complementary and where inverse coding —starting with unity at the highest level—might be advised. The coding is a computational convenience for desk calculator operation; actual class marks can be used in digital computer programs.

The cophenetic value of two OTU's was defined by Sokal and Rohlf (1962) as the class mark of the class (between phenon lines) in which their stems are connected. For example, in Figure 7-10 we can see that species 65 and 66 are connected in class interval 7. Hence their cophenetic value is 7. Similarly, the cophenetic value of species 69 with species 74 is 5, since that is the level at which these OTU's are connected. The closer the relationship between the two OTU's, the higher their cophenetic values. It is convenient to record cophenetic values in matrix form, resembling a matrix of similarity values (see Appendix Table A-17).

A comparison of dendrograms is made simply by calculating an ordinary product-moment correlation coefficient between the corresponding elements of the two matrices of cophenetic values to be compared. These coefficients have been called cophenetic correlation coefficients. For this procedure, each half matrix can be imagined as strung out in single file, column by column. For $t$ OTU's there will be $t(t-1)/2$ elements in a half-matrix of similarity coefficients. The magnitude of the cophenetic correlation coefficient will describe the amount of agreement between the two dendrograms being compared. In their original study Sokal and Rohlf (1962) found that the weighted variable-group method was closest to the weighted pair-group method; the dendrograms prepared by the weighted variable-group method resembled those prepared by the weighted pair-group method at a cophenetic correlation coefficient of 0.95. Comparison between average cluster methods and single linkage cluster methods on Hamann's (1961) similarity matrix of monocotyledonous plants gave a value of only 0.28.

In view of the difficulty of representing the phenetic relations among all the OTU's by means of a dendrogram, other graphic methods of representation have been attempted. Models or projections of models which represent the taxa as points or little spheres in a character space have frequently been used. It is of course generally impossible to represent all the relations among $t$ taxa in a three-dimensional space except in unusual cases, as where the rank of the matrix does not exceed 3. However, in a surprising number of instances one can represent a relatively small number of taxa in a three-dimensional space without doing too much violence to their distances. It is, of course, distance matrices particularly which can be so represented (see Figure 7-11). These representations are not particularly useful for purposes of publication (however, see Lysenko and Sneath, 1959) but are often of great interest for private study by the investigator who can get a different "feeling" for the quantified relations among the taxa by seeing them in this particular

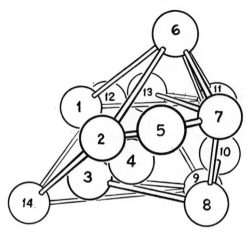

FIGURE 7-11

*Taxonomic model of the Enterobacteriaceae. The taxa are represented by spheres connected by rods indicating taxonomic distance. [After Lysenko and Sneath (1959).]*

form. Looking at these models and photographing them from different angles and points of view also helps in this connection.

Correlations among taxa can also be represented as angles (angle = arc cos $r$) between vectors, the tips of which represent the OTU's (Rohlf and Sokal, 1962). Various taxa can then be represented as clusters of vectors, more or less like knitting needles sticking out of an orange. However, we again run into the problem of showing relations which need more than three dimensions for a true representation.

## 7.5.  CRITERIA OF RANK

We believe that rank should be based on phenetic criteria, as indeed we believe is the usual practice of taxonomists. These criteria have usually been based on two points: (1) that the internal phenetic diversity of taxa of equal rank should be as nearly equal as possible; (2) that gaps between taxa of equal rank should be as nearly equal as possible. The second point is to cover the cases of monotypic genera, families, and so on, as with *Gingko biloba*, which is the only species of its order. These two rules may sometimes be inconsistent, and we must then decide which to choose. This depends on the kind of cluster analysis employed. Simpson (1961, pp. 133–134) would, for instance, retain as a genus the very diverse taxon *Rattus*, although the divergence among its species is greater than the average distance between *Rattus* and the closely related genus *Thallomys*.

A case in point is the birds, a class which has much suffered from "splitters" and from the naming of trivial variants as subspecies. There is evidence that phenetically and genetically they are, for vertebrates, a group of small variability. The most aberrant are the penguins and some ratites, but these are not as different from "typical" birds as whales and bats are from "typical" mammals. Birds are remarkably similar to one another serologically (DeFalco, 1942), and interspecific and intergeneric hybrids are relatively highly fertile (Huxley, 1943, p. 146; Sandnes, 1957). The difficulty of making satisfactory classifications (either phyletic or phenetic classifications based on comparative morphology as discussed by Stresemann, 1959) and the large number of monotypic genera also suggest that the category of genus in birds is of lower rank than the genus in other vertebrates. Possibly a more uniform scheme would treat the birds as a class containing only one subclass, with the latter containing only a few orders, and would reduce most avian orders to families and most families to genera.

Those who have devised techniques for numerical taxonomy have suggested that they can be used to decide the rank of the taxa which they yield, and some suggestions have been made that agreement might be reached by biologists on the similarity levels which should define the categories of rank. To say that this is premature is to state the obvious, but the likely developments deserve some discussion. Sneath (1961) has pointed out that there is a lower limit to the groupings which can be fitted into a nonarbitrary hierarchy. For example, different mutants of one species cannot be so arranged; it is impossible to decide whether white cats are of higher rank than long-haired cats. Such groups are not phenetic taxa; they are "rankless taxa" and cannot be satisfactorily handled by hierarchic subspecific nomenclature. Many so-called subspecies are of this nature.

The criteria which have been proposed are all very similar in essence: the same criterion for a given rank must be applied to all parts of an analysis. That is, where a hierarchical tree has been made, the line defining a given rank must be a straight line drawn across it at some one affinity level. The line must not bend up and down according to personal and preconceived whims about the rank of the taxa. We believe that in the foreseeable future each major group will have to be standardized separately. No useful standard can yet be applied to both bees and jellyfish, but within the megachilid bees, or perhaps within all the bees, some worthwhile standardization might obtain. To make this practicable there would have to be agreement on the rank of the whole group under study; we also would have to decide on the rank of the OTU's employed, which will frequently be a category considered to be a species. The other ranks could then be intercalated evenly.

The particular body of data to which this agreed primary scale was to be fitted would also need to be agreed upon. Any subsequent studies should always include these characters (if at all possible), even if they were augmented by new characters. There is something to be said for choosing certain type specimens and defining these as points of reference, for in the event of disagreement on whether the original data were representative it would be possible to make further analyses using additional features of these types or of acceptable replacement types. Nevertheless, it is our conviction that if adequate and representative samples of the known taxa and of the characters are chosen, subsequent analyses will seldom show marked discrepancies in rank. Such a reference system should obviously make the least alteration of well-established systems of taxonomy. Another useful convention would be to use a parallel system based on affinities, such as 80-phenons, which would on each occasion be equated with that rank which the worker accorded to it (see Section 9.1.1). This would be preferable to any attempt to give fixed taxonomic ranks to the phenon scale, since it would lose its point and its flexibility. This is not to say that ranks might not by agreement be equated with the phenon scale in a particular named taxonomic study.

The consequences to taxonomic rank of adding or removing taxa from a study would, we believe, not prove a serious problem, provided that only a small proportion of the OTU's were involved. The coefficients of affinity themselves should be little affected if the recommendations in Chapter 6 are followed. The methods of cluster analysis employed (see Section 7.3.2) will themselves have some influence on the ranks, since these methods summarize the affinity matrix in slightly different ways. In general we expect this effect will be as great as that produced by omitting a small proportion of OTU's.

As work proceeds on the higher ranks there are sure to be changes in the relative ranks of some taxa. For example, it might become apparent when a thorough comparative taxonomy of all insect orders was made that the Blattaria, for example, which had been treated initially as an order, were only of familial rank. For this reason some new ranks might have to be intercalated to express this, or possibly a revision of the system might be forced. This should be a pressing reason for comparative work at various hierarchic levels to be attempted as soon as possible. In this connection, such techniques as comparative serology may have a valuable part to play. Whatever the growth of numerical taxonomy may be, there should be great efforts to build it up by coordinated work between different specialities, calling for much more cooperation than has occurred in the past. To make an imperfect but legitimate analogy with map making, a number of reference points over wide areas will be of as great value in systematics as surveyor's bench marks are in cartography.

Do we have enough ranks to handle the number of taxa which exist among living organisms? The use of numerical taxonomy may lead to a need for finer gradations of rank, with appropriate names for the new ranks. It is therefore of some interest to ask whether the existing ranks will be adequate for this task. Two separate questions arise. (1) Is the present hierarchy adequate to handle the taxa of living creatures if it only aims at giving a schematic and convenient system? (2) Is it adequate if it tries to reflect accurately the values for rank which numerical taxonomy may provide?

The first question is easy to answer if we confine ourselves to species and higher taxa. The number of species of living creatures is probably between $1.5 \times 10^6$ and $2.0 \times 10^6$, a majority of these being insects. Allowing for fossil species, it is unlikely that systematists will study more than $10^7$ species, even though the number of such fossil species over geological time may have been in total several powers of ten greater than this. The seven conventional ranks of kingdom, phylum (in zoology) or division (in botany), class, order, family, genus, and species would then be adequate if, on the average, each rank contained ten taxa of the rank below. In some instances the taxon would contain more than ten of the next subordinate taxa, but if they did not exceed one hundred the system would still be workable, especially with the help of the intermediate ranks such as subfamily, tribe, and others. The addition of subspecies and variety would also allow for ample scope at infraspecific levels.

The second question is not so easy to answer, for we cannot foresee sufficiently the scope of numerical taxonomy. In theory, at least, the present system of ranks would be quite inadequate. Consider those organisms with $10^9$ bits of genetic information (see Section 5.3.1). This would allow $2^{1,000,000,000}$ possible combinations of features, and if all combinations gave viable organisms this would allow the existence of about $10^{300,000,000}$ different forms of creatures. This is by no means the upper limit of the genetic potential of living creatures. In theory we might need to measure affinity coefficients sometimes between creatures which were identical, and sometimes between those which differed in $10^{300,000,000}$ respects. The few rank categories would be far too few to allow the flexibility needed. Several million ranks (each taxon of which contained some hundreds of the next lower taxa) would be barely adequate to express the numerical affinity coefficients in terms of rank. Yet in practice nothing as extreme could arise even if we were able to make numerical analyses of the size implied above. For if we consider only species, we have only $10^7$ of these. Even considering individuals will not lead to such fantastically large numbers, for if the number of protons and electrons in the observable universe is about $10^{80}$, and geological time is about $10^{17}$ seconds, it is clear that there could never have been on earth $10^{300,000,000}$ individual creatures even if each had lived for only one second. In addition, most of the possible combinations would have resulted in inviable organisms, though we cannot yet guess what percentage would be viable.

It is clear from the above example that most of the character hyperspace (which we can use to represent the relations of possible organisms) is empty. It seems likely that the present-day organisms are scattered somewhat unevenly through it because there are large tracts of it which appear to be unoccupied—for example, the enormous tracts which would hold the organisms intermediate between higher animals and higher plants, if such creatures could exist. Indeed, if we could visualize the phenetic position of all organisms past and present, we would expect them to represent a dendrogram in hyperspace outlining the phyletic tree of living creatures.

## 7.6. THE RELATION BETWEEN Q AND R TECHNIQUES IN NUMERICAL TAXONOMY

We have already briefly described differences between Q and R correlation matrices. Based on the same original data, the former represent correlations between subjects (in the case of numerical taxonomy between OTU's), while the latter represent correlations between characters. Since both sets of correlation matrices are obtained from the same $n \times t$ data matrix, it is obvious that the two are related to each other, and in fact they can in certain cases be transformed, one into the other (Thomson, 1951). Three aspects of R correlations are considered below.

The R correlations are important for their intrinsic interest. Little work on R correlations in taxonomic groups with OTU's as high or higher than the species level has been done. There are a number of studies in which OTU's represent individuals within populations or among populations (Hammond, 1957; Jolicoeur, 1959; Kraus and Choi, 1958; Sokal, 1959, 1962a; Sokal and Hunter, 1955; Sokal and Rinkel, 1963). However, we know only of the study by Stroud (1953) of R correlations using species as OTU's. Much of interest remains to be learned here. We would like to know how large correlations among characters are when different-sized groups are studied and whether different types of characters such as length and weight will correlate differently from meristic or qualitative characters. Correlations within larger taxa and among larger taxa are equally feasible and could be done by partitioning covariances, similar to the technique suggested by Sokal (1962a).

Since characters are correlated, the Q matrix of correlations between OTU's does not have a sampling distribution expected of ordinary correlation coefficients. This is because each reading for an OTU is not an independent sample from a common population but represents different characters. We have referred to this problem previously as that of the heterogeneity of column vectors. As we have seen, the problem of the reliability of correlation coefficients is somewhat alleviated by standardizing rows (standardizing the variates for each character). However, the problem of redundancy of information because of character correlations remains. We need to obtain more information on the magnitude of the effect of correlations among characters on the sampling distribution of correlations among taxa.

Work at present underway in Sokal's laboratory will investigate the relations between R matrices and Q matrices. One reason why no more has been done in this connection in numerical taxonomy is that in work done so far usually fewer OTU's than characters have been measured. It has been simpler, because of limited capacity of computers, to calculate correlations among OTU's than correlation among characters. As computational equipment gets better and faster, we shall be able to attack these problems more efficiently.

Factor analyses of R correlation matrices should be of great interest. Such analyses would presumably reduce the R correlation matrices to primary components, possibly orthogonal or deliberately orthogonal, by use of principal axes methods. This would mean that the correlations among $n$ characters could be analyzed into $k$ factors, where $n > k$. By reducing a character correlation matrix through factor analysis, we are isolating independent dimensions of variation of the R matrix, hoping thereby to remove redundancy from our studies. Studies of this sort have recently been carried out by Sokal (1962a), Sokal and Rinkel (1963), and Defayolle and Colobert (1962). This has interesting implications for numerical taxonomy. If there is redundancy in character information it might be possible to isolate the factors from an R correlation matrix and to calculate factor scores for each OTU on the factors obtained. We could then employ only those characters which provide independent information on the taxa concerned. This would reduce the number of character scores on the basis of which OTU's could be classified. It would, however, not reduce computational effort, owing to the tedium of factor analysis. It might be argued that after such an analysis characters would in fact be weighted in terms of the independent amount of information which they contain. This might open the door to a numerical taxonomy among OTU's based on weighted characters. These would, of course, not be weighted by their presumed phylogenetic importance but by the criteria mentioned above. Our thoughts in this connection should therefore not be misconstrued. Studies of this sort have not advanced beyond the programmatic stage. We have at the moment no idea how many common factors would be found in an R correlation matrix involving higher ranking OTU's. Studies of R matrices at the lowest taxonomic levels have generally not produced many factors (for a discussion of this point see Sokal and Rinkel, 1963).

## 7.7. THE PUBLICATION OF RESULTS

The publication of the results of numerical taxonomy may raise a number of problems. In many instances it would be desirable to publish the data on the characters together with the method of scoring them, and also the full affinity matrix. This information would be needed by workers who wish to re-examine the group by similar techniques. However, these data would take up a great deal of space, and it may be more convenient to arrange for microfilm records of the manuscript data to be made available to other workers. The original data matrix and the affinity matrix may be deposited in a library and the fact noted in the published work; for example, the Science Library in London has provision for the deposition of certain material of this kind. The data may also be stored in a form suitable for data processing, in punched card or tape format. Where it is possible to publish the lists of characters which were employed and their definitions, scaling, and coding, together with records of the material employed, this should be done; if the full details are too lengthy, they should be deposited with the data matrix. It would be valuable to publish, in addition to any diagnostic keys, a list of the most constant characters of the taxa which have been recognized, for these are of much practical value to subsequent workers.

Since the affinity matrix is of such importance (for the usual hierarchical tree is a gross oversimplification of it), it may be useful to publish it as a shaded diagram (Renkonen, 1938; Sneath, 1957b; Sneath and Cowan, 1958); see Figure 7-3. Not only does this take up less space, but the shading gives a clear visual impression of the affinities, provided that the OTU's have been arranged so as to bring together (as far as possible) the members of each taxon. The shaded diagram has some disadvantages: it is not easy to handle more than 8 or 10 different shades, so that the affinity values can only be represented to the nearest 10% or thereabouts, and this may be too coarse a spacing to allow for the best cluster analysis; it also must be converted back into numerical form if further analysis is attempted. Nevertheless, in many instances differences of much less than 10% may not be significant, so the loss of information may not in reality be very great.

The use of models (such as Anderson and Abbe, 1934; Lysenko and Sneath, 1959) may prove useful, but they are more helpful for obtaining a better idea of the relations while one is studying a group, or for teaching purposes, than they are for publication. For most purposes a dendrogram will be essential in any publication. It is important to specify what measures of affinity and clustering were employed. It may, in addition, be helpful to note the electronic computer and the program used, since other workers may greatly benefit if they can use programs which have already been prepared for these techniques.

## 7.8. THE INCORPORATION OF ADDITIONAL DATA INTO A CLASSIFICATION (INTERSTUDY COORDINATION)

After a numerical taxonomic study has been completed, two kinds of additional data are likely to be forthcoming. First, new study of the organisms may reveal characters other than those employed in the earlier work. Second, information may become available on OTU's which are related to those previously studied but which for one reason or another had not been included in the study before. The second problem may also arise when persons are studying similarities among a large number of organisms and are unable to process all the data simultaneously because of limitations of the computer. We shall take up these problems in turn.

Adding new characters will be warranted only if the new characters are quite numerous or if the earlier classification has been based on relatively few characters. If the hypothesis of the matches asymptote holds and a sufficient number of characters have been employed previously, the new characters should not change the arrangement of the taxa appreciably. We have so far no experience with situations of this sort and shall have to await work in this field before coming to definite conclusions on the number of characters which must be added before a revision of a group need be made. In such circumstances records of new characters should probably be deposited in some central agency (see in this connection our thoughts on the future of systematics, Section 10.5) until a sufficient number have accumulated in order to warrant revision of the group. It may also be that in future years there will be electronic files of taxonomic information available at certain central locations. This would permit the new characters to be added to the old. When taxonomic reprocessing of the data is indicated, all characters new and old would be considered. Consideration should also be given to studies of correlations of characters. It may be that newly studied characters will have to be correlated with characters that have already been established, and only new information in the sense of character variation not represented by the previously studied characters will be added to the eventual data matrix.

Related to the above problems are situations where two studies are made on the same material but using different samples of characters (even if partially overlapping). We expect that the similarity values would be very close in the two studies (provided the conditions mentioned in Section 5.4 are fulfilled, notably that the samples of characters are both large ones). As has been pointed out (Sneath, 1957b), the correspondence cannot always be expected to be close in actual affinity indices, but the *relative* values for given pairs will probably be more constant. If, for example, the similarity of sparrow to sparrow is 90% in one survey, but sparrow to duck is 50%, then a second study might yield the following results: sparrow to sparrow 95% and sparrow to duck 75%. We do not yet know very much about the mathematical properties

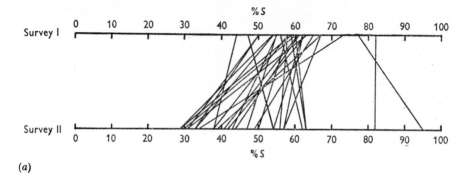

(a)

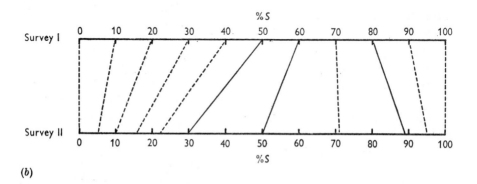

(b)

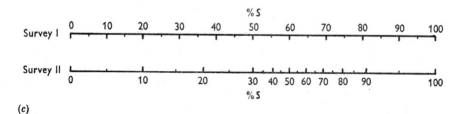

(c)

FIGURE  7-12

Calibration of one S value scale with another. [Sneath and Cowan (1958). Reproduced by permission of the Journal of General Microbiology.] (a) Method of calibration. A line is drawn from the S value found in one survey for the comparison of a particular pair of strains to the S value found in the other survey for the comparison of the same pair of strains. All the comparisons which were made in both surveys are similarly entered. (b) The approximate mean correspondence between the two scales of S is obtained by drawing lines from one scale to the other based on the mean slopes of the lines in figure (a). The S values of 0 and 100% are the same on both scales. Dashed lines are only presumptive, as they are not based on information in (a). (c) From (b) the two scales are calibrated against each other by distorting one of them.

of these relative values in different surveys. In the example given above the ratios of $1 - S$ are constant, but it would be hazardous to predict what relations will in fact be found to be the most usual.

It is possible to compare one study with another, so as to calibrate the two scales of rank. For a very simple example (Sneath and Cowan, 1958), see Figure 7-12. The mathematical treatment has not yet been developed, but it is likely that if the affinity values in the two studies are plotted as a scatter diagram, using a suitable transformation, the best-fitting line as given by a least squares statistic would be sufficient to allow us to calibrate the affinity value scale of one study in terms of the affinity value scale of the other study. If we employ affinity coefficients scaled to lie between 0 and 1 and plot the affinity values for two studies on the same pair of organisms, we can make a scatter diagram which illustrates the relation between the two scales. The points, if numerous enough and spaced throughout the whole range of affinity values, will lie with some scatter along a curved line, except in the unlikely event that the two scales are virtually identical. The ends of the curve will approach 0% at the lower ends of the two scales and 100% at the upper ends, and the intervening part of the curve may well be sigmoid. With correlation coefficients, the upper and lower limits will be $-1$ and $+1$, but similar relations will hold. This will mean that the curve will be of cubic or higher order, which will be difficult to fit to the scatter diagram without the use of an electronic computer. With the increased availability of electronic computing facilities it will be commonly practicable to fit the best-fitting higher-order curve to the scatter diagram, and this should prove to be sufficiently accurate for any ordinary work.

Even without curve fitting, we find two-way frequency distributions of similarity coefficients of great interest. Figure 7-13 shows such a scattergram for similarities between pairs of species (in males and females separately) of the 97 species of bees in the *Hoplitis* complex (Michener and Sokal, 1963). The similarity coefficients are correlation coefficients based on standardized characters. There is a clear positive correlation between the two variables ($r = 0.71$) although the scatter at the upper end of the distributions is quite wide. Thus when expressed in correlation coefficients there is considerable congruence between male and female similarity values.

Adding new OTU's to a study presents more serious problems. If many OTU's are added, it is obvious that a revision of the entire group is necessary. On the other hand, if only a single one or a few OTU's are added, the computation of the correlation coefficients between these new

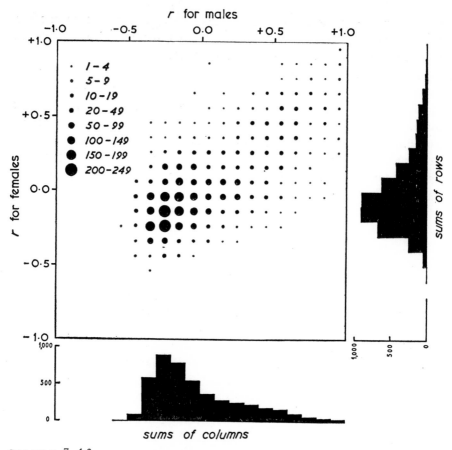

FIGURE 7-13

*Two-way frequency distribution of similarity coefficients (in this case* r) *for the comparison of similarity matrices based, respectively, on male and female characters in the* Hoplitis *complex. [Unpublished data from Michener and Sokal.] The abscissa and the ordinate indicate the magnitude of the correlation coefficient from males and females, respectively. The frequencies in each cell of the two-way frequency distribution are represented by solid circles. The size of each circle indicates the magnitude of the frequency according to the key shown in the upper left corner of the graph. The graph is based on 4,656 correlation coefficients. The correlation coefficient between the two variables is 0.71.*

OTU's and the others is relatively simply carried out. However, we are then faced with preparing a new dendrogram from the augmented similarity matrix. Such a procedure has two drawbacks. Having to recompute a cluster analysis of the similarity matrix is time consuming; second, since relationships would inevitably be changed to some degree, the advantage of the stability of an analysis is to some degree negated. It is therefore quite important to make efforts to obtain reasonably complete and representative taxonomic groups before undertaking a revisional study by numerical taxonomy.

Another approach may be to set up a series of standard OTU's, against which newcomers may be compared. Such a method would locate the newly added OTU's in hyperspace with respect to the standards but would not necessarily locate them with respect to each other nor with respect to other OTU's previously studied. This is therefore only a stopgap measure, which cannot take the place of a complete analysis.

CHAPTER **8**

# Phylogenetic
# Considerations

In developing the principles of numerical taxonomy, we have stressed repeatedly that phylogenetic considerations can have no part in taxonomy and in the classificatory process. Once a classification has been established, however, biologists will inevitably attempt to arrive at phylogenetic deductions from the evidence at hand. It will be our task in the present chapter to examine in some detail the nature of phylogenetic evidence and deductions. We shall, of course, restrict our efforts to phylogenetic considerations as they are related to numerical taxonomy; a comprehensive treatment of the subject of phylogeny is beyond the scope of this book.

## 8.1. THE RELATION BETWEEN PHENETIC AND PHYLOGENETIC EVIDENCE

### 8.1.1. The evolutionary basis of natural taxonomic groups

That evolution is responsible for the observed phenetic diversity of living creatures cannot be doubted. No other hypothesis can account for the organic world with the same cogency. The classificatory hierarchy was used by Darwin as one of his main arguments for natural selection (see Darwin, 1891, p. 340). The evolution of species (that is, genetic species) is intimately connected with mechanisms of genetic isolation, usually arising allopatrically, commonly culminating in the inability of the isolates to exchange genes even when sympatric. At this stage in their evolution, the isolated lineages are not necessarily natural taxa (in the sense in which this term is used by us in this book), since they may have almost identical sets of genes and may differ only in their genetic isolating mechanisms (Section 2.4.2). Many cryptic species, sibling species, and some allopatric species are presumably of this kind.

The genomes of the taxa become more different with time owing to the accumulation of genetic differences as the result of mutation and selection. As evolution progresses, the possible evolutionary patterns become further restricted. This is because the genotypes are highly integrated into a functional whole, and most of the possible changes would lead to poorer adaptation. For example, whales have not evolved into sharks, nor are they ever likely to do so, since changes from lung-breathing to gill-breathing (and in thousands of other functional systems) would disrupt the functional organization of whales. Even small changes in the direction of similarity to sharks would be disadvantageous; large changes would occur with vanishingly small probability. Reversal of evolution to any marked degree is therefore impossible (Dollo's law). There is consequently a constant trend toward evolutionary divergence, or increased phenetic difference. This trend is likely to be reversed only rarely and for a relatively few characters.

Natural taxonomic groups are formed by the restriction of evolution to certain regions of the phenetic hyperspace and the accumulation with time of genetic differences. The small stepwise nature of genetic changes suggests that most characters of descendants are the same as those of their immediate ancestors. The taxa may be polythetic, for there is no assurance that any given character of an ancestor will persist in all its descendants. They are in any event operationally polythetic, since constant characters may not be among those available for our study. We do not yet know fine genetic structure sufficiently to say how frequently and to what degree the OTU's in natural taxa are genetically alike, but it seems probable that appreciable parts of the genotype are constant in all members of many natural taxa, at least in taxa of lower rank, so that these taxa are probably not fully polythetic.

Most conceivable intermediates between actual organisms are likely to be nonviable. The successful organisms will therefore possess complexes of correlated characters, and these correlations allow the recognition of distinct taxa. In addition, the constant evolutionary divergence leads to overall phenetic divergence, though at different rates in different lineages. Hence forms that are distantly related phylogenetically will in general be phenetically distant, and vice versa. However, these two factors do not of themselves lead to the formation of the phenetic hierarchy. They might lead to the production of a large number of distinct forms all more or less equidistant from each other phenetically. Such a "cloud" of points could not be satisfactorily divided hierarchically on phenetic grounds (though it could form a cladistic hierarchy—see Section 8.1.2). To make a well-defined phenetic hierarchy, the forms must be clustered into compact groups, and these groups clustered into higher groups, and so on (see Section 7.1). The fact that the natural classification clearly shows this phenomenon (though its quantitative study will be a main field of inquiry for numerical taxonomy, as discussed in Section 8.2.3) implies more than the simple fact of evolution. The phenetic clustering may have arisen because some lineages die out; if so, some parts of phenetic space will remain unoccupied because they could only have been occupied by descendants of the extinct lineages, owing to the stringent requirements of evolutionary pathways mentioned above. If sharks became extinct today, the same sharks would never evolve again, either from ancestral groups (which are in any event also extinct) or from teleosts, crocodiles, or whales. Nor would *any* shark evolve again; that is, no organism would arise which we would classify with living sharks on phenetic grounds. Such apparent repetitions of evolution amounting to allochronous overall convergence do not, we believe, occur at higher ranks. Any resemblance between, for example, sharks, whales, and ichthyosaurs would be in a minority of characters related to their aquatic habitus. Such repetitions at lower levels, such as races and subspecies, are, however, more likely. Overall convergence or parallelism of marked degree is very unlikely. This is well expressed by Stebbins (1950, p. 542):

> Species differences are based largely on systems of multiple factors, which are built up by the occurrence and establishment of large numbers of genetically independent mutations. Hence, the probability that two isolated populations will evolve in exactly the same way in all of their characteristics is astronomically low, and the convergence in every respect of previously dissimilar organisms is even less probable.

Phenetic clustering may also have arisen because of different rates of evolution, especially if a lineage evolves rapidly without branching and then breaks up into a cluster of more slowly evolving lines (see Figure 8-1).

The phenetic gaps between contemporaneous forms are closed, as one goes back in time, by the succession of phenotypes leading from their common ancestor, but this point should not be misunderstood: there is

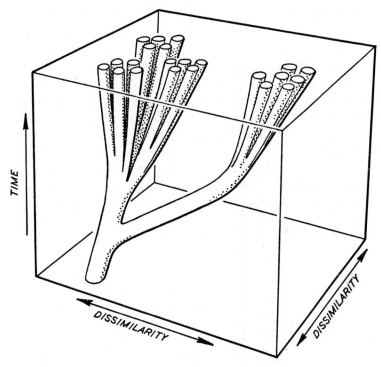

FIGURE  8-1

>    *Phenetic clustering due to changes in rate of evolution. The form on the right at first evolved rapidly and became phenetically very dissimilar from the remaining stocks; subsequently it broke into a cluster of slowly evolving lineages.*

no continuity between the phenotypes of the recent forms themselves. For example, the phenotypes of mammals and birds merge only through their lineages leading back to the early reptiles—that is, through a series of phenotypes by no means intermediate between existing birds and mammals. Chimeras, such as intermediates between mouse and sparrow, with an equal number of features of both, do not occur and never have occurred. The "intermediates" were reptiles, which were not phenetically intermediate between mice and sparrows.

Simpson (1961, p. 222) points out that most taxa arise as the result of the invasion of a new ecological niche. This is likely to be a main cause of a lineage's evolving rapidly for a time and hence yielding a new phenetic group. Though there may be some correspondence between the phenetic differentiation of such taxa and the degree of ecological difference between the niches, this correspondence is by no means strict. To explore these pathways of phyletics would require a way of measuring the ecological differences, which we do not at present have. Indeed, the concept of ecological niches has been distinctly vague; for example, a given habitat may be subdivided into a great many smaller habitats, using rather uncertain criteria, which turn in part on the phenotypes of the organisms themselves, since the organisms can change the habitat. Recent suggestions by Hutchinson (1957) to formulate ecological niches within the framework of a multidimensional system of environmental requirements may provide opportunities for fruitful development of an ecology-related phenetics. The concept of patterns in phenetic space evolving to fit configurations of ecological space suggests itself very readily.

### 8.1.2. The construction of phyletic classifications

Phenetic and phyletic classifications cannot be profitably compared until the meaning of phenetic and phyletic relationships has been made clear. Hennig (1957) and Cain and Harrison (1960b) have recently discussed this in some detail. Cain and Harrison divide relationship into phenetic and phyletic, and refer to phyletic relationship as "that which aims to show the course of evolution." They divide phyletic relationship into two kinds. First, two forms may be said to be closely related phyletically because they possess many characters which are derived from a common ancestor. They call the component of phyletic affinity which is due to such common ancestry (and not to convergence) *patristic* affinity. Second, the forms may be related closely through recency of common ancestry, without taking account of the number of characters derived from a common ancestor. This relationship in terms of phyletic lines is called by them *cladistic* (this is the type I phylogenetic relationship of Hennig, 1957). Cladistic relationship refers to the paths of the ancestral lineages and therefore describes the sequence of branching of the ancestral lines; it ignores evolutionary rates and therefore does not relate to phenetic similarity. This sequence of branching may be expressed by itself or in relation to time or number of generations.

While patristic affinity is a component of phyletic affinity, it is clear that our knowledge of it is likely to come from study of the phenetic affinities of the taxa concerned. In fact, patristic similarity comprises the major part of phenetic similarity, the other part being convergent similarity.

Since patristic and convergent relationships are both forms of phenetic relationship, they can be measured by numerical taxonomic methods. Patristic relationship may be estimated by those characters which have the same character state in the ancestor and in both descendants. On the other hand, by using only those characters which have been independently acquired by the descendants, one may estimate *convergent* or *homoplastic* similarity, to use the term suggested by Lankester to distinguish independently acquired characters from those derived from a common ancestor (homologous ones in the usual sense; see Haas and Simpson, 1946). Patristic similarity is based upon homologous characters only. It is therefore in general less than total phenetic similarity, since it consists of the latter minus the convergent (homoplastic) component.

It is evident that cladistic affinity has nothing to do with the above types of relationship. They are phenetic, and measure phenotypic similarities between the forms. Cladistic affinity is concerned simply with the way in which the lineages branched and not with the degree of difference. A genealogy or pedigree is an example of a cladistic scheme.

The relation between phenetic, patristic, and convergent affinity is shown below in an example, using two-state characters for simplicity and the simple matching coefficient $S_{SM}$. The characters may for convenience be grouped into classes responding identically for the three OTU's.

| Classes of Characters | Number of Characters in Each Class | OTU's | | |
|---|---|---|---|---|
| | | Ancestor | Descendants | |
| | | 1 | 2 | 3 |
| **A** | *a* | + | + | + |
| **B** | *b* | − | + | + |
| **C** | *c* | + | − | + |
| **D** | *d* | − | − | + |
| **E** | *e* | + | + | − |
| **F** | *f* | − | + | − |
| **G** | *g* | + | − | − |
| **H** | *h* | − | − | − |

The total number of characters is $n$.

Phenetic affinity between OTU's 2 and 3 is $(a + b + g + h)/n$, or the number of characters in classes **A**, **B**, **G** and **H** divided by the total number of characters, $n$. Patristic affinity between these two is given by the proportion of characters in classes **A** and **H**, convergent affinity by those in classes **B** and **G**; that is, by $(a + h)/n$ and $(b + g)/n$, respectively. It will be noticed that we could also estimate patristic affinity by $(a + h)/[n - (b + g)]$ and convergent affinity by $(b + g)/[n - (a + h)]$, depending on whether we completely disregarded convergent or homologous characters, a point which emphasizes the lack of precision in these apparently simple concepts. Cladistic affinity is expresssed not by the characters, but by the ancestor-descendant scheme—that is, the fact that 2 and 3 are both descendants of 1, whatever their phenotypes may be, and by any data on the time relations between them. We may summarize the above by the following statements about relationships:

Phenetic Relationship = Homologous (patristic)
                        + Homoplastic (convergent) Relationships

Phyletic Relationship presents two aspects:   (1) Patristic Relationship
                                              (2) Cladistic Relationship

The two aspects of phyletic relationship cannot be considered to be additive, as are the components of phenetic relationship, since they would have to be measured in different units. However, it is obvious that the close general correspondence between phenetic and phyletic relationships is caused by the almost invariable consideration of patristic affinity in judging phyletic affinity.

We do not know of any infallible criteria for overall phenetic convergence that may be obtained from a study of living forms of organisms alone. To detect convergence, we have to distinguish those features which do accurately reflect the phylogeny from those features which do not. This, however, is a question which can only be answered by knowing the phylogeny first. The problem therefore is insoluble within this logical framework, and one must have independent evidence (not derived from phenetic relations) in order to attack it. It can be seen from the example above that to distinguish patristic from convergent affinity we must be able to score the ancestor (OTU 1) for the characters we are studying; obviously we cannot score them if we only know the features of the descendants (OTU's 2 and 3). Cain and Harrison (1960b), in recommending the separation of convergent from patristic affinity, seem to us to gloss over the difficulties of deciding upon the status of the characters in question. They recommend that one should remove all enigmatic characters (those whose status is uncertain, unless it be so complex that this complexity suggests monophyly), to remove all but one of any complex of characters which are of necessity functionally or ecologically related, and to remove the characters which are convergent or are likely to be convergent. If this could be easily and accurately done, it would indeed give an estimate of patristic affinity. We question, however, the feasibility of this procedure. Cain and Harrison also suggest that to obtain cladistic information one should now discard the characters which give only patristic affinity, but it is not clear to us just what information would be left, since cladistic relationship does not bear any necessary relation to the phenotype.

Simpson (1961, pp. 132–135 and 187–201) includes phylogenetic considerations as criteria for higher ranks. He uses this term for the ranks of genus and above—that is, for taxa of two or more contemporaneous species or two or more successional species (successive stages in an evolving lineage). From the criteria used by him (pp. 165, 189) the contemporaneous are separate lineages composed of entities distinguished on either a genetic or phenetic basis, while the successional are of necessity phenetic entities. He would employ criteria based on diversity (defined by him as the sum of dissimilarities in all the characteristics studied, and presumably equivalent to phenetic difference), provided it was consistent with the phylogeny. More specifically, he would, given consistency with phylogeny, admit the degree of similarity in homologous and to some extent in parallel characters, but not in others, as a secondary criterion for establishing higher categories. We have pointed out in many places in this book that there is no way of distinguishing homologous from homoplastic characters without knowing both the phylogeny (the branching of the lineages) and the phenotype of the ancestors. After mentioning that phenetic difference and recency of ancestry are usually proportional (in which case we would, of course, have no problem), Simpson (1961, p. 194) continues: "Having measured or estimated degrees of resemblance and sizes of gaps, the taxonomist should then bring into the picture qualitative judgment of homology, convergence and the like." This again assumes that the phylogeny is already known. He says that higher taxa should be monophyletic, at least in the broader definition of monophyly, which we have shown in Section 5.5.1 to be an unsatisfactory concept. Furthermore, we cannot deduce monophyly in contemporaneous forms except from their phenetic relations, since homologies as such are unrecognizable. Even fossil evidence is interpreted phenetically to yield the presumed phyletic lineages. The phylogenist cannot deny that phenetic similarity is generally a good indication of cladistic relationship, since he must use this principle to construct phylogenetic trees, though the time sequence of the fossils gives him assistance in this. The common occurrence of allopolyploidy in plants (Stebbins, 1950, p. 365) also makes monophyly difficult to apply as a general taxonomic criterion. Geographical data may sometimes give evidence that certain groups are monophyletic or polyphyletic, but again such evidence is available in only a minority of instances. Introduction of Huxley's concept of grades (Huxley, 1958) seems to us not to be helpful, as this is a somewhat vague idea of morphological or ecological advance, which need not reflect the whole phenotype and which we do not know how to measure.

Remane (1956) believes that the natural system is based upon the recognition of true homologies, though he does not use this term strictly in the phylogenetic sense. His main criteria for homology are morphological correspondence (including very detailed correspondences) and the occurrence of chains of intermediate forms of an organ in phenetically similar taxa. Other criteria are the greater constancy of homologous characters in taxonomic groups and the increased likelihood that simple structures will be homologous as we descend the taxonomic ranks. However, apart from morphological correspondence, which is measured phenetically, all these criteria require the prior recognition of taxonomic groups and therefore cannot be used for constructing such groups. His suggested method for recognizing cladistic relationships is to employ homologies. Remane's methods therefore cannot separate phenetic from cladistic relationship.

Hennig (1950, 1957) notes that the central problem is to distinguish cladistic relations from phenetic ones (although he does not employ this terminology). He argues that incongruence between larval and adult classifications shows that the cladistic relationships cannot be exactly proportional to the phenetic relationships, since the cladistic relationships of adults and larvae of the same species must be identical, while the phenetic relationships need not be. This statement is true, but the converse is not necessarily true; that is, congruence does not prove the exact correspondence of phenetic and cladistic relationships because both larval and adult features might have both undergone convergence to an equal degree, although this is unlikely.

Hennig (1957) bases the recognition of monophyletic taxa and the distinction between phenetic and cladistic relations very largely on recognition of original and derived states of characters. By implication these may be equated to ancestral and descendent states. He does not, however, give convincing arguments on how to recognize them (Figure 8-2).

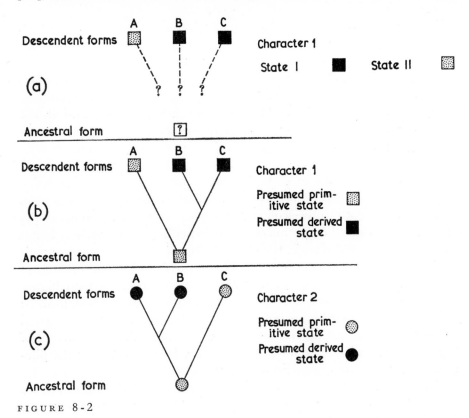

FIGURE 8-2

*A diagrammatic critical reexamination of Hennig's (1957) criteria for cladistic rela-*
*tionships. (a) Two states of the first character are found, but it is not known which is*
*the ancestral state. (b) State II of character 1 has been recognized as the ancestral one;*
*forms B and C show the derived state. The cladistic relationships are then deduced as*
*shown. (c) In a second character it is A and B which show what is believed to be the*
*derived state. This would imply a different cladistic relationship from (b).*

Even if we were able to recognize the ancestral state, shown as uncertain
in Figure 8-2(a), we would be unable to accept the method he uses
thereafter. Hennig would say that two forms possessing a derived (non-
primitive) state were more closely related cladistically, as shown in Figure 8-2(b). However, it is common on examining another character, 2,
to find that a different pair of forms possess the derived state—Figure
8-2(c)—giving a different cladistic scheme. To change our opinion about
which state of character 2 is primitive means that our end result depends
on which character we happened to study first. It is not clear to us how
Hennig would handle contradictory data of this kind. If one counted the

characters indicating one phyletic arrangement and those indicating another and took the verdict of the majority, this would be in effect employing phenetic affinities to indicate phyletic relations.

Where fossils are few, the practical difficulty of making classifications based on phylogeny is acute. Stresemann (1959), in an illuminating article, points out that there has been little advance since 1888 in the classification of orders of birds, and the prospects for an improvement are not bright. This is despite the fact that there is little argument about the genera, which are presumably based mainly on phenetic criteria, since there can be even less phyletic evidence at this taxonomic level. The logical conclusion, that orders as well as genera should be phenetic taxa, is presumably unwelcome. Even when fossils are abundant the difficulty remains. For instance, Pichi-Sermolli (1959) concluded that the deplorable confusion in the classification of vascular cryptogams is chiefly due to the fact that the classification of ferns is based upon fossil plants rather than living ones. A similar problem exists with higher vertebrates, as Bigelow (1956) pointed out. Crocodiles are thought to be more closely related by ancestry (cladistically) to birds than to lizards or turtles, yet crocodiles are not classified with birds as the criterion of monophyly requires, but with other reptiles. It is evident that the phenetic groupings are too useful to be abandoned.

Even if we could make use of phylogeny to create classifications, we may still ask whether this is necessarily desirable. To do so would discard much important and interesting phenetic information. An allopolyploid might originate repeatedly, giving rise to phenetically identical new species each time. In some groups phyletic classifications might prove chaotic—for example in viruses and especially in bacteriophages. Recent work (see Morse et al., 1956; Jacob and Wollman, 1959; Lederberg, 1960) suggests that bacteriophages are being constantly derived from bacteria as genetic entities that acquire the properties of autonomy and parasitism. This work not only implies that bacteriophages that are identical (or almost so) may be polyphyletic, but, even more disconcerting, it suggests that they may be of composite origin. They are able to transfer genes from one bacterial form to another and to incorporate such genes into their own genomes; it is therefore possible that they derive some of their own genes from one host and some from another. Other viruses may be similar in these respects to bacteriophages, and this raises the disturbing possibility that, for example, an arthropod-borne virus may be part insect, part mammal, and part bird. The only way to bring order into such a system is by a phenetic classification. Such classifications are now being attempted (Andrewes and Sneath, 1958; Sneath, 1962). While the phenomena discussed above do not really affect the taxonomy of most organisms, we feel that they are of considerable theoretical interest. There may also be borderline groups, such as the Rickettsiae, where the validity of a phylogenetic classification, even if possible, may be in serious doubt.

Cain and Harrison (1960b) pointed out that the principal disadvantage of phenetic classification is that some convergence and parallelisms may go unrecognized and that polyphyletic groups might be mistaken for monophyletic ones. However, the recognition of monophyly can scarcely be thought to be the only worthwhile or even the pre-eminent activity of systematists. If convergence is extreme, so that the convergent forms are practically identical, the phyletic classification only shows the fact that convergence had occurred, which could be expressed without the formal apparatus of a taxonomic and nomenclatural scheme.

### 8.1.3. What phylogenetic deductions can be made from a table of affinities?

Having made a phenetic classification, we will wish to know what deductions we may legitimately make about the phylogeny of the taxa. If the affinities are based on living organisms alone, we can only speculate on the phylogeny; to check our speculations we must have fossil evidence. Yet there are some conclusions which are more probable than others. We believe that these are as follows. (1) Phenetic clusters based on living organisms are more likely than not to be monophyletic. Thus phenetically adjacent taxa represent phyletic "twigs" which usually originate from the same branch; in other words, overall convergence is unlikely. (2) In the absence of direct evidence our best estimate of the attributes of a common ancestor of a cluster must be derived from the properties of the cluster itself. Whether this estimate should be based on a centroid or on a midrange value is a complicated problem (discussed in greater detail in connection with typology by Sokal, 1962b). In short, if we have no fossil evidence, the existing pattern is our best guide to the past history—though this may often be wrong. An argument similar to the first argument in favor of equal weighting of characters (Section 5.7) applies here: if we have no evidence that evolutionary rates differed, we must assume these to have been constant and equal in all the phyletic lines studied. If the reader thinks of a cross section through the top of a shrub with the vertical dimension representing time and the horizontal representing phenetic dissimilarity, he will have a ready, though some-what inadequate, simile for the situation.

The two points mentioned can then be illustrated as follows. (1) Ad-jacent twigs will generally arise from the same branch. Admittedly it will be very difficult to detect overall convergence near the tips of the branches, and this may have occurred quite commonly, together with some reticulate evolution due to the fusing of phyletic lines; yet gross degrees of overall convergence between the tips of main branches will be very much less likely, and its improbability will increase with the taxonomic difference between the branches below the plane of section. (2) In the main, the branches from which the twigs arise will lie more or less directly below the twigs; but we will have no way of telling whether the twigs arose almost vertically or whether they came off at a pro-nounced slant, for we can have no confidence that the twigs will fill the phenetic space evenly in the way in which the branches of an actual shrub do in order to obtain adequate sunlight.

The above deductions on the phylogeny (which are made from organ-isms belonging to one point in time) cannot give any estimate of the rates of evolutionary change, which may have differed in different phyletic lines. To estimate rates we must have data from several points in time.

If we have a matrix of affinities which includes OTU's from different geological periods, we can attempt to measure rates of evolution (dis-cussed in more detail in Section 8.2.1). However, we must first decide how the forms are related by ancestry (that is, cladistically) if we are to study the rate of change of one form into another. We shall sometimes have very adequate sequences of the evolutionary successions about which no reasonable doubt could arise. More often we will be faced with determining which form was the ancestor of which, or more prob-ably (since the ancestral line itself may well be unrepresented and we may have only members of its side branches), which form was closest to the ancestral line. This must be solved on the same principles as those mentioned above: in the absence of other evidence, phenetic resemblance is the best indication of cladistic relationships.

The above guide line will hold only in a simple form where one or two geological levels are represented. When there are more than two, we will commonly be faced with the question: have rates of evolution been con-stant over the whole period? For example (see Figure 8-3), we may have an extant form **A** which is more similar to a slightly earlier form **B** than it is to a much earlier form **C**, though **B** and **C** are more similar. Did, then, **A** evolve recently from **B** (the more similar) or more slowly and

directly from **C** (the less similar)? In the absence of other evidence, such as geographical isolation or a fuller fossil record, no certain decision can be taken even in such a simple case.
It is very easy to find cases which are more complex than the example given above. One lineage, for example, may evolve rapidly and another slowly, and it may be impossible or implausible to draw a phyletic tree in which all the lineages evolve at the same rate throughout the period. A diagram of the phenetic relations (expressed in one or two dimensions) *versus* time will usually make clear the degree to which we can safely reconstruct the phyletic tree, and where we must indicate by dotted and queried lines our uncertainty as to the course of the descent.

We have seen that one cannot derive evolutionary rates from similarity coefficients among recent forms. This is shown by the "pregroup-exgroup problem" discussed by Michener and Sokal (1957). Is it possible to distinguish whether an aberrant member of a cluster of forms was derived phyletically from one of the members of the cluster, or from the

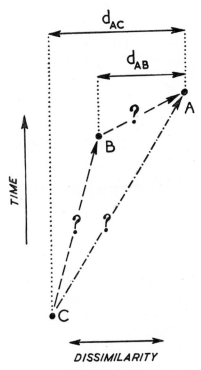

FIGURE 8-3

*The time-rate problem. Organism* C *is the ancestor of both* A *and* B. *With only the data shown one cannot tell whether* A *arose directly from* C *or via* B.

ancestral stem below the point at which the rest of the cluster arose (see Figure 8-4)? These authors suggested that if the aberrant member, **X**, showed approximately the same affinity to all the members of the cluster it was most likely "pregroup," or derived from the common stem; see Figure 8-4(a). If, however, the affinity with one member of the cluster was much greater than the mean of the affinities with the cluster, then the aberrant member, **Y**, was likely to be "exgroup," or derived from the member it most closely resembles—**D** in Figure 8-4(b). It is nevertheless possible to account for the observed affinities in the figure by means of a number of cladistic schemes, if the evolutionary rates differ in the lineages. At the time they wrote their paper, Michener and Sokal

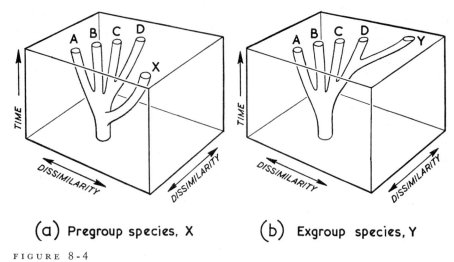

(a) Pregroup species, X          (b) Exgroup species, Y

FIGURE 8-4

*The pregroup-exgroup problem (for explanation, see text).*

(1957) were still attempting to establish phylogenetic classifications. Only subsequently did they realize (see also Michener, 1957) that the only classifications with claims to consistency and objectivity are phenetic ones. Therefore, for classificatory purposes the pregroup-exgroup problem is of no consequence, and we would not now recommend modifying dendrograms to attach exgroup species to their presumed cladistic relatives, as was done by Michener and Sokal (1957).

### 8.1.4. "Primitive" characters and forms

A number of workers have proposed indices of primitiveness or advancement based on characters of living organisms. There is much confusion over the precise meaning of terms such as "primitive character" and "primitive form," as Sporne (1956) has shown. The term "primitive character" must be qualified to avoid ambiguity. Since at some sufficiently early stage the character will not yet have appeared, in practice we mean by "primitive character" a character complex in the early stages of its evolution. It is thus necessary to specify what stage we mean or the geological time of occurrence of the organism thought to possess it. It is also important to point out the taxonomic level relative to which a character is considered primitive. A thysanuran leg is a specialized arthropod appendage but a primitive insect leg.

Whether we mean by "primitive" the character state as it was when it first appeared in the group concerned or as it was at the bifurcation of the lineages under study is seldom made clear. It is misleading to suggest that a structural or physiological simplicity is the essence of a primitive character. Evidence from a variety of groups (see, for example, Michener, 1949) points to structures appearing to be fully developed in ancestral or "primitive" forms and evolving by loss or reduction in number or size of constituent parts. Simplicity due to reduction is common in parasitism. It is also unjustified to assume that one or the other extreme of a series is necessarily primitive. It may happen that an organ evolves so as to become larger in one phyletic line and smaller in another.

Hennig (1950, pp. 172 et seq.) uses the occurrence of a given character state in a large proportion of the species of a taxon as his principal criterion for recognizing a character as ancestral. This however, implies the prior grouping of these species into the taxon. A second criterion is that agreement among members of a taxon in Bauplan of a complex structure is a good indication of monophyly, even if there are many simple characters which are inconsistent with the postulated phylogeny. However, we should point out that such a Bauplan is itself made up of a large number of characters. The decision will then depend on degree of correspondence among these characters, a procedure similar to numerical taxonomy.

The concept of the "primitive organism" is even more vague in most instances. "A primitive monocotyledon" may imply a plant either cladistically or phenetically close to the ancestor of the presumed monophyletic group *Monocotyledones*. A group is likely to be "primitive" in only some features. Furthermore, these features may be "advanced" with respect to a higher category. For example, a family of parasites might be "advanced" as a family with respect to mode of life, yet parasitism would be "primitive" within the family if some secondarily free-living species had later arisen within it. Thus the concept of primitiveness is relative.

"Overall primitiveness" would be the phenetic similarity between a given form and a specified (though possibly hypothetical) ancestor; and "overall advancement" would be the corresponding phenetic dissimilarity. Numerical taxonomy may be able to clarify some of these problems.

Frost (1930) and Sporne (1948) have developed numerical methods for estimating primitiveness. These are based on the hypothesis that, in general, features that are highly correlated in living forms are either all advanced or all primitive. If one can obtain from other sources an indication of the state in the ancestor of one of these characters, one can deduce which set of features is primitive and which advanced. Recently

Lowe (1961) has made a similar study of primitive and advanced features of monocotyledons, using Sporne's methods. Since fossil evidence is scanty, the studies of Frost on primitive features of woody tissues were employed to decide which characters were primitive. Bell (1956) has developed this idea further. He assumes that features common to large numbers of species within a genus are more likely to have been found in the ancestor of that genus than those features which occur in but few forms. The difficulty of this approach is that its validity depends on whether this assumption is correct in each instance and on the taxonomic validity of the taxa and how one decides their rank.

Another phylogenetic hypothesis is the "age and area" hypothesis of Willis (1922). This assumes that the age of a monophyletic group from the time of the common ancestor is proportional to the number of living taxa belonging to it and also is proportional to its present-day distributional area. There are so many obvious exceptions that this hypothesis is now generally discarded (see Stebbins, 1950, p. 531). The data of Willis, however, are of interest in connection with the branching pattern of dendrograms (see Section 8.2.3). A number of other generalizations— the center of origin hypothesis, trends in karotypes, Dollo's law, von Baer's law, Haeckel's biogenetic law, and others—are also very uncertain. They are well discussed by Stebbins (1950, pp. 445 ff., 448 ff., 532 ff.).

### 8.1.5. Can ancestral forms be included in phenetic classifications, and what is their rank?

It is plain that any division of continuous lineages is to some extent arbitrary. When two taxa ranked as classes are separated at a given line, the species on either side of this line, though both genetically and phenetically closely related, will be grouped in different classes. Remane (1956), in discussing this problem, points out that in lineages such as that in Figure 8-5 (representing the phylogeny of a family) the organisms **H** and **I** have a dual and partly contradictory relationship. They are very similar both in properties and closeness of ancestry and should therefore be placed in one genus. They are also ancestors respectively of the genus **A**, **B**, **C**, **D** and the genus **E**, **F**, **G**. Again, on their closeness of phenetic and phyletic relationship, they could legitimately be included in these two genera to give the genus **A**, **B**, **C**, **D**, **H** and the genus **E**, **F**, **G**, **I**.

This problem occurs wherever the dividing line is drawn. Some taxon-

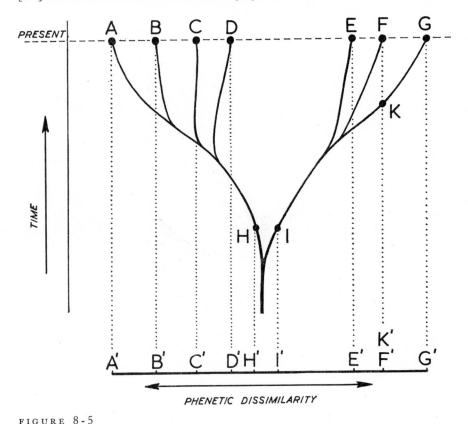

FIGURE 8-5

*A phylogenetic tree as commonly represented, with a time dimension and one phenetic dimension (for explanation, see text).*

omists would divide the lineages to give monophyletic groups wherever possible, since this would involve the least number of such arbitrary divisions. Similarly, when we employ phenetic criteria for classification, we would divide the genera (or other OTU's) so as to give the most cohesive clusters. In general the phenetic divisions would, we believe, be mainly monophyletic, but they would be based on observation of creatures and their characters, rather than on more or less speculative phylogenies inferred from phenetic data.

One misleading point about figures, such as Figure 8-5, is that they do not represent the phenetic relations at all accurately. In Figure 8-5, for example, the organism **K** is directly below **F**; it is, however, exceedingly unlikely that it would be phenetically identical with **F**. The phenetic relations of the forms in this diagram are their relations in the

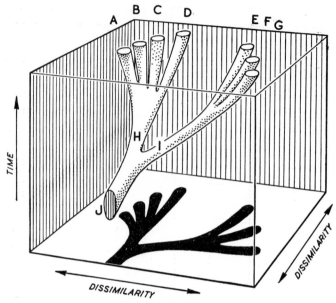

FIGURE 8-6

*A phylogenetic tree in three dimensions, one of time and two of phenetic dissimilarity. The "shadow" of the tree on the base indicates the purely phenetic relationships (for explanation, see text).*

horizontal plane, as would be shown by throwing a shadow of them onto the base line. This is equivalent to making projections of all the points on the dendrogram onto the abscissa, as is shown for a few points in Figure 8-5. It must be added that, of course, a single dimension is in principle insufficient for representing phenetic relationships but is employed here to convey understanding of relations which are equally applicable to multidimensional models. In this figure these projections would form a single line from the point **A'** to the point **G'**. The phenetic relations are better represented (though still inadequately) in Figure 8-6, where a three-dimensional model of a substantially similar diagram is shown. Here the horizontal plane shows phenetic dissimilarity in two dimensions, while the vertical dimension represents time, as before. The phenetic relations would then be shown by the shadow of the phylogenetic "tree" projected onto the base plate. This shadow is shown again in Figure 8-7(a). It is a fronded figure in which the organisms of all time periods are shown without overlapping one another (on this scale of taxonomic discrimination). If we wished to divide it phenetically, we would divide it into two main groups, genera perhaps, roughly as shown. The exact place of the division line could be determined mathematically, if we wished, though for most purposes a division at the point of branching would suffice. We would, however, rarely have enough fossil data to have a complete shadow; we would be more likely to have an incomplete set of organisms, giving a shadow such as in Figure 8-7(b), and in most cases we would be lucky to get this amount of information. The exact position of the dividing line would then be not worth much argument.

We might have had some subsidiary branches (say, **L** and **M**) near the common ancestor, as shown in Figure 8-7(c). If so, one would, on phenetic grounds, divide it more or less as shown into the three genera **U**, **V**, and **W**. Note that in all cases the phenetic divisions—divisions made on the basis of the shadows—are, as we would expect, fairly close approximations of monophyletic groups or single lineages, though divergent clusters of branches may be excluded from the basal taxon. This seems to us the only honest thing to do, since we believe that phylogenies are deduced substantially from the phenetic relations. In addition, the shadows in this model are not as unsubstantial as they may seem. They represent a great many attributes of the organism. If convergence should give phenetic groupings that are not monophyletic, the groups nevertheless would contain far more information than the monophyletic groups and would be far more useful and "natural" to everyone except the phylogenist. What is likely to be troublesome, we believe, is not so much discrepancies between the phyletic and phenetic arrangements as discrepancies between taxonomies based on different sets of characters or on alternative methods of cluster analysis (see Chapters 5 and 7).

## 8.2. POSSIBLE CONTRIBUTIONS OF NUMERICAL TAXONOMY TO PHYLOGENETIC, GENETIC, AND PALEONTOLOGICAL PROBLEMS

In the discussion that follows, such contributions have been arranged under these headings: (1) rates of evolution; (2) studies of speciation, and the correlation of phenetic groups with genetic relations among the organisms; (3) the pattern of branching of taxonomic dendrograms; (4) paleontological problems.

In Section 8.1.2 we discussed the problems of deducing from phenetic classifications which fossil organisms are the most probable ancestors of others and of reconstructing the most probable phylogenetic lineages. If monophyly and phenetic affinity are in fact largely overlapping if not coincident properties, affinity values will determine very largely the form of the phylogenetic trees by showing which fossil organisms are the most probable ancestors of other organisms, as judged by their overall resemblance. This will aid taxonomists in deciding between alternative choices for the ancestor of a taxon.

Although the concept of the direction of evolutionary change has been repeatedly used by students of evolution, particularly in hypotheses such as orthogenesis and parallel evolution, it has never been clearly defined or measured. If the organisms at successive periods of an evolving lineage are treated as points in a phenetic hyperspace, it is in principle possible to draw lines through this hyperspace from each organism to its descendant. The directions of these lines, their curvature and the convolutions which they display can then be evaluated by standard methods of analytical geometry. In Euclidean hyperspace a straight line from point $A$ to $C$ is one such that for any intermediate point on this line, $B$, the equation $AB + BC = AC$ holds, or, in the convention used for taxonomic distance,

$$\sqrt{d^2_{AB}} + \sqrt{d^2_{BC}} = \sqrt{d^2_{AC}}.$$

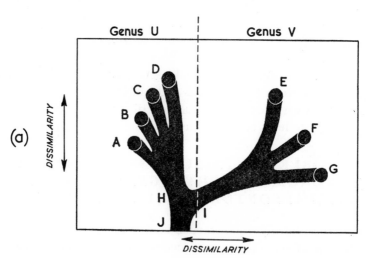

FIGURE 8-7

The "shadow" from Figure 8-6. The phenetic relationships are represented as shadows on the horizontal plane. (a) The shadow from Figure 8-6 with a dashed line dividing it into two phenetic taxa, such as two genera. (b) A patchy shadow. This is a more realistic representation because of the usual scarcity of fossils. (c) Division into three phenetic taxa (such as genera) when branches L and M have been added.

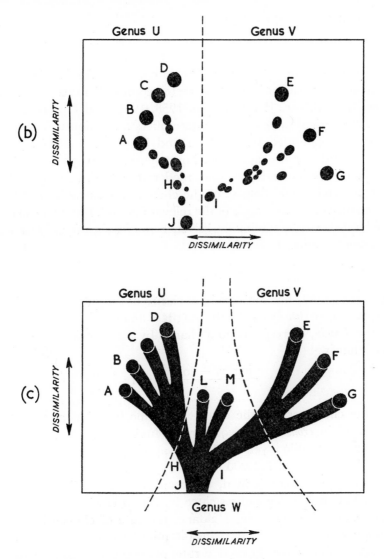

For any profitable work of this kind, a considerable number of fossil specimens from many time horizons and offering many characters for analysis will, of course, be necessary.

### 8.2.1. Rates of evolution

When it is possible to study fossil material and thus obtain data from several known points of time, the affinity coefficients will allow estimates of overall evolutionary rates. The dissimilarity between ancestral and descendant forms will be the measure of the overall evolution which has occurred in the intervening period. Simpson (1944) has discussed the great advantages of measuring the overall rate of evolution (what he calls the "organism rate"), as well as the rate of evolution in one or a few characters ("character" and "character complex" rates such as those studied by Haldane, 1949; Kurtén, 1958, 1959; and Buzzati-Traverso, 1959). Numerical taxonomy therefore offers a solution to many of the problems propounded by Simpson and by Huxley (1957). Simpson (1944) uses the terms tachytelic, horotelic, and bradytelic to describe rates which are respectively rapid, moderate, and slow. Little is known about tachytelic evolution, since the changes are so rapid that there is small chance of finding fossils of the relevant period. Bradytelic evolution is the kind shown by "living fossils" such as *Lingula, Gingko, Metasequoia,* and the coelacanth, *Latimeria.*

### 8.2.1.1. Character rates

Haldane (1949) has suggested a measure of the rate of evolution of a single character (for example, the length of an organ), such that the unit rate, the *darwin*, corresponds to a change by a factor of *e* in one million years—that is,

$$\frac{\log_e x_t - \log_e x_0}{t} = 1,$$

when the character has the value $x_0$ at time 0 and $x_t$ at time $t$, with $t$ measured in *crons*. [The word *cron* (Huxley, 1957) is a convenient term for one million years.] This is approximately equivalent to a change by a factor of 1/1,000 in 1,000 years. If the allometry equation $\log y = \log a + b \log x$ is used, the constant $b$ should be used without transformation into logarithms since it is itself effectively a logarithm. In the examples studied by Haldane, the rate of change in horotelic evolution was around 0.04 darwins (40 millidarwins), but he noted that domestic animals have changed at rates of kilodarwins, so that increased selection can evidently greatly increase the usual rate of evolution.

In a recent study of fossil horses, Downs (1961) found rates of 12.3 to 124.3 millidarwins for tooth characters, their mean being about 57 millidarwins. These rates seem fairly typical of horotelic evolution, though Simpson (1953) notes that there is considerable variation in horotelic lines. The rate may, of course, vary within any one line as well. It may be that in the work to date there has been a tendency to select for measurement the more rapidly changing characters.

The darwin cannot be thought of as an absolute measure of evolution, since its value depends on the manner of scaling of the character. If a bacterium, for instance, is selected for drug resistance, the resistance may increase (by successive mutations and selection) by a factor of one thousand in the course of a few days, and the precise rate in darwins will depend on how the character is measured, whether in terms of the inhibitory concentration of the drug or, as is common, in terms of the logarithm of the concentration. The rates in microorganisms can be very great, as in this instance, where it is of the order of $10^8$ darwins.

Boyden and Gemeroy (1950) have suggested that some serological characters, notably those of serum globulins, have changed at a slower rate than those of serum albumins, and quantitative data are available here. However, there are, of course, no data on the proteins of ancestral forms, and these findings could be attributed to the different antigenicity of some classes of proteins as compared with others.

### 8.2.1.2. Organism rates

When we come to a discussion of evolutionary rates in organisms, we enter a subject fraught with many pitfalls. In a simple, superficial sense it seems quite clear that different groups have evolved at different rates. For example, the statement that coelacanths have evolved more slowly than horses since the Eocene appears self-evident and is not likely to be challenged. However, when we attempt to analyze in detail the meaning of statements such as these, we run into considerable difficulty. Should we measure overall change of all the characters of each organism? Or should we only use those characters known to have changed within the forms during the periods under study? If we use only characters that change, we face a problem if we analyze groups in which only a small proportion of the characters have changed. These changes might appear quite appreciable. They might equal the changes in another lineage where most of the observed characters had changed but where the change per character was on the average the same as that of the changing characters of the first lineage. Yet we would intuitively feel that the first lineage was evolving more slowly.

We think that we can make two definite statements. First, no group should be investigated from the point of view of absolute evolutionary rates until its characters and phenetic resemblances have been investigated and evaluated with relation to the higher ranking groups to which they belong and also to neighboring taxa. If this has not been done, we cannot be sure that the taxonomic group under study is really a natural taxon. We cannot define a taxon as natural unless all possible contenders for affiliation have been examined and included or rejected. Once such a group has been established, the relative changes within it can be measured with consistency. How such relative changes are to be compared among groups remains problematical.

Second, a paleontologist, in comparing the rates of evolution of coelacanths and horses, has in the back of his mind an idea of the range of characters within vertebrates which have to his knowledge changed and the kinds and degrees of change which have happened in all the vertebrate classes. He is evaluating the changes in the coelacanths, and in horses, against this unexpressed standard. In this connection a possible mode of evaluation may be the following: once a large group, such as the mammals, for instance, has been sufficiently studied by means of numerical taxonomy, a series of marker taxa may be chosen, with which evolutionary change can be compared. Thus a single representative of each order of mammals might be appropriately included in the matrix of affinities and serve to furnish the proper scale for a group such as the horses, for example. A fairly comprehensive standard set of taxa of this sort would comprise a reasonably stable standard of comparison.

An advantage of organism rates is that they are likely to be more steady than character rates, since bursts of rapid change in individual characters will tend to be smoothed out. Simpson (1944) has estimated organism rates (the "taxonomic rates" of Kurtén, 1959) by measuring the time for a phyletic lineage to change morphologically (phenetically) from one genus to another. From the data of Simpson (1944, 1961) and Kurtén (1959) and a consideration of the time of appearance of different taxa in vertebrate evolution, we may estimate that the time corresponding to change in rank in horotelic evolution in vertebrates is approximately as follows: morphospecies, 0.5 crons; genus, 7 crons; family, 20 crons; order, 45 crons; class, 80 crons. Myers (1960) discusses the rate of evolution of fishes after their introduction into lakes. With the exception of one lake in the Philippines (where very rapid evolution of several genera may have occurred in as little as 10,000 years), the usual pattern is the evolution of a few new species and subspecies after about 1/10 cron, many new species and some new genera after 1/2 cron, and many new genera and some new families after 1 to 2 crons. These rates are somewhat faster than those given above.

The rates appear to be much slower in some other phyla, such as many lines of molluscs. In flowering plants, Stebbins (1950, pp. 529, 547 ff.) states that there has been little change during the Tertiary period; many genera of woody plants have evolved new species in the last 50 crons, and a few families have evolved new genera. Many genera and species of tropical trees have been almost unchanged for 20 crons. Herbaceous plants have evolved at about the same rate as trees, though there has been more rapid evolution of some groups during the Pleistocene, with new species arising within 1 cron, including some arising in historic times.

Westoll (1949) tried to estimate by a simple arithmetic technique the overall evolutionary rate in the lungfishes. Few characters were used and these were chosen to show regular trends; they were thus not representative of all the characters available, which were unfortunately rather few in number.

It should be made clear that by the phenetic change corresponding to a genus (for example), we mean the minimum phenetic difference between two forms which would just necessitate the placing of the two forms in different but closely similar genera instead of placing both in one genus (according to the criteria established by the investigator).

Kurtén (1958) suggested that the percentage of significantly differing allometric growth gradients between two populations could be used as a measure of the organism rate. He calls this the "differentiation index." The index increases as a geometric series, with the limit value of 100; for example, the steps from 0 to 50, from 50 to 75, and from 75 to 87.5 are all equivalent. It runs parallel with taxonomic (phenetic) change but has the disadvantage of not taking into account the magnitude of the differences in the gradients (except so far as the magnitudes make the differences statistically significant). In most instances in mammals the rate of change was about 0.2% per thousand years, but periods of more rapid evolution also occurred. He found that the morphological difference between two subspecies was equivalent to an index of about 50% and that between two species was about 75% (Kurtén, 1959). It is clear from the context that Kurtén here uses subspecies to indicate a major morphological subdivision of a species rather than a trivial variant, and that by species he means a category approximating a morphospecies.

We should emphasize that all the above considerations are based on conventional judgments of taxonomic rank and are only as precise as these evaluations. Lacking better ones, we cite them to give a general indication of the nature of the problem. It should be evident that the methods of numerical taxonomy will have a considerable contribution to make to this field. Present techniques in numerical taxonomy will yield affinity values between chronologically successive organisms, which can be used as measures of evolutionary rate. Over small ranges the change in the affinity values compared with time will be satisfactory expressions of the rate. Over larger ranges this may be unsatisfactory since the affinity values may be in a scale (such as the index of Kurtén, described above) in which equal affinity differences do not have equal significance with regard to taxonomic rank at all parts of the affinity-value scale. For the present, therefore, it may be wisest in such cases to divide the affinity-value scale to define different ranks (see Section 7.5) and to express the evolutionary rate as the time taken for a phyletic line to pass through the degrees of affinity values applicable to these ranks, as Simpson suggested. Sneath (1964) has speculated on the relations between phenetic change and genetic change in evolution, particularly with respect to changes in DNA.

Should we attempt to express organism rates in darwins? In principle it would be possible to measure the mean of a large number of character rates expressed in darwins, which would approximate to measuring organism rates in darwins. We feel that the use of this term would be confusing, in view of the conceptual difference between similarity in a single character and overall phenetic similarity, and we therefore suggest that other terms should be employed when necessary.

### 8.2.2. Speciation and the correlation of numerical taxonomy with genetic relations

Little has yet been done with numerical taxonomic methods in studies of the formation of species and of the correspondence between genetic relationships and phenetic groupings. Ehrlich (1961c) recently made a start on the problem of finding whether phenetic similarity is concordant with the currently accepted taxonomies in certain species of butterflies. He did not find a very close correspondence; in fact his work suggests that there may be many phenetic groupings of low rank (possibly of the nature of subspecies or local races) that can be recognized by numerical taxonomic methods. Some of these phenetic groups, while keying out to certain species by the usual identification methods, appear to be different from those species with which they are commonly identified. Such work may lead to considerable revision of the detailed classification of certain genera and species. In the material studied by Ehrlich, not many data were available on the genetic relationships among the populations, but this will obviously become one important aspect of such studies, together with geographical and phenetic investigations. Morishima and Oka (1960) found reasonable agreement between phenetic relations and the ease of hybridization. For example, the species of the "sativa" cluster of rice are all easily crossed. Soria and Heiser (1961) found similar agreement in *Solanum* species.

It must be remembered that at low taxonomic levels, such as the species and below, there is a sharp distinction between phenetic groupings and genetic groupings. This has been discussed in Section 2.4.2; it was there pointed out that if a sterility barrier arose within a phenetic group, there would be for a period of time two distinct genetic groups within a single phenetic group. Phenetic, genetic, and geographical groupings cannot always be equated with one another. The point of interest is how far these different ways of grouping the organisms are concordant and how far they are not, and why this is so. We believe that phenetically distinct groups based on numerical taxonomy will usually be found to be genetically distinct, just as the experience of conventional taxonomy shows.

Heincke (1898) investigated the distribution of individuals of races of herrings in what was in effect a taxonomic character space and obtained results giving the following generalizations for any one homogeneous race: if the mean of each character is calculated and a hypothetical individual is postulated whose characters have these mean values, one obtains a sort of "average individual," analogous to the "average man" of anthropologists. In a homogeneous population such as this, we would expect the several characters of the race to be distributed approximately normally. The sum of the squares of deviations of all characters from this "average individual" is, according to Heincke, approximately the same for every member of the race. He formulated this as a law, sometimes called "Heincke's law." Zarapkin (1934), however, has reservations on the validity of this concept.

Little additional data are yet available in numerical taxonomy to test "Heincke's law," but it may be noted that the similarity values found by Sneath (1957b) for strains of each of two species of bacteria, considered in turn, showed approximately a normal distribution. Smirnov (1925) did not expect the "law" to hold at levels higher than the race, and our knowledge of quantitative genetics and speciation would support his views.

The pattern of speciation emerging from numerical taxonomic studies in microorganisms is one of many slightly different forms (usually clones) grouped into rather ill-defined "series" or "species-groups" (see Sneath, 1962, for details). This pattern seems to be common, if one may accept orthodox and intuitive taxonomic studies in groups which are largely apomictic, as is well illustrated by many plants (for example, dandelions, blackberries, and many of the fungi). It is not confined to plants, similar phenomena seeming to occur among the annelid worms, for instance. This pattern is also found among the protozoa, as discussed in an excellent review by Sonneborn (1957). The pattern may be likened to an ill-made brush, in which the clones are represented by the bristles, and the bristles are clustered erratically into tufts of various shapes and sizes and various degrees of compactness. The phenetic differences are represented by horizontal distances and time by vertical distances among the bristles. The pattern in sexually reproducing organisms is more like a bundle of ropes, where each rope represents a single and well-defined sexual species, within which the fibers represent the interwoven lineages. These two phenetic patterns presumably depend on different genetic patterns; in bisexual species the lineages are continually meeting and blending in a reticulate fashion and it is the rope as a whole which is the main unit of evolutionary change. Sometimes two such ropes will fuse wholly or partially, as when hybridization occurs between these sexual species, from time to time, in nature.

Clonal reproduction, however, will produce many minor variants, as mutations occur in the stocks, and most of these variants will in all probability die out. But a few of them persist and may undergo rare sexual recombination with other clones, leading to new bursts of variation due to reassortment of the genes of the parental clones (and not simply to their content of mutants). The bristles representing the clones will form a diffuse array within any tuft, and adjacent tufts will often be connected by intermediates. Sometimes the tufts will be tightly clustered into masses of bristles, and sometimes they will be straggly and widely spaced. The smallest practicable unit of taxonomic nomenclature will often be the tuft or perhaps the whole brush, although for certain special purposes it may be useful to label the bristles with some number or other designation. Numerical taxonomy, by locating the bristles in the horizontal plane which represents the phenetic resemblance in our analogy, will help systematists to recognize these tufts and will assist in their description. It will also help the student of evolution to see whether sexual recombination occurs between adjacent (phenetically similar) bristles or between bristles which are further apart (more dissimilar) and thus to gain some understanding of the relation between phenotype and the ability to hybridize.

Intermediate patterns may be met with in fungi, where Pontecorvo and his colleagues have shown the occurrence of another mechanism of gene exchange known as the parasexual cycle, operating through hetero-karyons and rare diploids with occasional segregation of genes (Ponte-corvo, 1956). Heterokaryosis is just as efficient in storing genetic variation as the normal diploid sexual condition, but genetic recombination will generally be less frequent than with sexual reproduction. It is beginning to be recognized that some means of gene recombination is almost uni-versal in living creatures, and in this sense the analogue of the sexual species may be seen in most groups of organisms. However, the mechan-isms are so unlike the well-known sexual mechanisms that it is no easy matter to define and delimit the populations which are undergoing gene exchange. Heslop-Harrison (1962) has discussed this at some length and has suggested some reasons for these taxonomic patterns.

### 8.2.3. The branching of dendrograms

Willis (1922) noted that in many families of animals and plants a histogram recording the number of genera containing respectively one, two, three species (and so on) gave a "hollow curve"; that is, there was a marked excess over expectation of monotypic genera and also an excess of genera containing a great many species. Willis and Yule (1922) found that plotting the logarithm of frequency against the logarithm of the number of species these genera contained yielded straight lines with slopes close to 1.5. At high species numbers the number of genera fell off (possibly because taxonomists tend to subdivide large, unwieldy gen-era into several genera). A similar pattern was found in higher ranks, as when the number of genera per family was studied. The interpretation of these curves has been much debated (see Wright, 1941; Stebbins, 1950, pp. 531–532), but in the absence of objective criteria for what should be a family or a genus, and so on, the problem has been difficult to study, and the regularities have never been satisfactorily explained.

Recently Walters (1961) has pointed out that historical factors may partly explain these curves. With the development of numerical taxon-omy, objective tests of the number of subgroups extant per phenon will become possible, together with a study of the mode of branching of the dendrograms. It should be remembered, however, that the dendrograms are not phylogenies. They only indicate phenetic relations existing among forms and do not indicate how many forms have become extinct. Since they do not have simple evolutionary interpretations, the mathe-matical study of Yule (1924) does not seem applicable.

If the branching in the dendrograms—not of the phylogenies—occurs at random (so that there is an equal chance of every stem giving off one or more side branches in a given interval of the phenon scale), the number of side branches per stem in a given interval will obey a Poisson distribution (the number of OTU's being the total number of side branches plus one).

The data of Michener and Sokal (1957) on bees show that there is, at most levels, an excess over expectation (on the basis of the Poisson distribution) of stems which do not branch and also of stems which branch many times. This gives an excess of phenons with only one species and of phenons with many species. For example, at the 80-phenon level (800 level in the original paper) the distribution of the numbers of branches (which are always one less than the number of OTU's in the phenon) are as follows: phenons with 0 branches, 16; with 1 branch, 4; with 2 branches, 1; with 3 branches, 2; and 6 phenons with, respectively, 4, 5, 7, 8, 12, and 20 branches each. The variance, 19.06, is much greater than the mean number of branches per phenon, 2.31, and the expected number with no branch (monotypic phenons) is 3.8 instead of the observed 16. Only a few other studies have been made which include a good cross section of the species of one taxon, but a similar if less marked pattern is seen in the dendrograms of species of *Oryza* (Morishima and Oka, 1960) and *Bacillus* (Sneath, 1962).

The general form of the "hollow curves" is a clustered distribution, in which the variance is higher than that expected for a random distribution. This has a bearing on the construction of hierarchies, as has been discussed in Section 7.1, and it offers an explanation for the validity and usefulness of hierarchic classifications in systematics.

### 8.2.4. Paleontological problems

The most obvious application of numerical taxonomy in paleontology is to fairly complete and well-preserved fossil material, in which the hypothesis of nonspecificity is likely to hold well enough for us to obtain reasonably good estimates of overall phenetic similarity. In paleontological studies, the importance of exact and numerical methods is even greater than it is with living material, since in extinct forms there can be no appeal to genetic data, and unsuspected heterogeneities may complicate what at first sight seem to be single phyletic lines. Robinson's method (1951) may assist in determining chronological sequences in phyletic lines. It would therefore be difficult to overestimate the importance of numerical taxonomy in paleontology.

It is of great importance in paleontological work to make use of allometry, where this is possible (see Section 5.3.7). This is because one may have no way of knowing (or estimating) the age of the specimens at death, and the crude character sizes or ratios will sometimes be partly dependent on age and other factors. This has recently been well discussed by Joysey (1956). In many instances a fossil form is known from only a single specimen, which may represent a young or an old individual, and it may then be very difficult to know how to code its characters. The same problem, of course, occurs in orthodox taxonomic studies

An example of the application of numerical taxonomy to paleontology, which raises points that are too often glossed over in paleontological taxonomy, was given by Sneath (1961). Four samples of the fossil fish, *Knightia* (from the Paleocene and Eocene), which probably represent one phyletic line, were studied, using data given by Olson and Miller (1958). The number of features, fourteen, was unfortunately small—fewer than we would like to employ—but they could each be scored for many states, and as a pilot study it proved of some interest. It was noted that some individuals were more similar phenetically to individuals from different strata than they were to their contemporaries in their own stratum, but in the main fishes from any one stratum were most similar. Several aberrant individuals were noticed in some of the samples. Two coefficients of affinity gave very similar results, and the fish were then roughly clustered in two dimensions. After adding a third dimension, to represent time, a schematic diagram of their possible evolution was drawn (see Figure 8-8). It may be noted that the comparison of individuals considered as geometric shapes was fairly straightforward; when, however, one wishes to draw conclusions about the populations to which the fishes belonged, many more data are required. Allometric transformations are needed, as well as some assurance that only one population is represented in each sample. These are severe limitations on the use of fossil material in numerical taxonomy. They are, however, equally severe for orthodox taxonomy.

Sneath's study also showed that the phenetic means did not indicate a regular displacement with the time sequence. This raised the question of whether there had been a small degree of reversal of evolution. Alternatively, the ancestors of each group might have been an unrepresentative section of their contemporaries, so that there had perhaps been

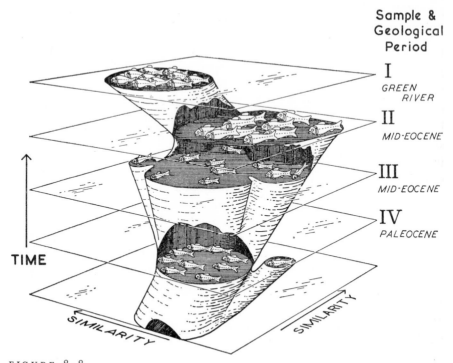

Sample &
Geological
Period

I

*GREEN
RIVER*

II

*MID-EOCENE*

III

*MID-EOCENE*

IV

*PALEOCENE*

TIME

FIGURE 8-8

*Schematic and speculative diagram of phylogeny in* Knightia. *The position in the horizontal plane indicates phenetic relationships among individual specimens. The time cuts are equally spaced although the actual time intervals are not equal. The axes labeled "similarity" approximate principal component factor axes. They should properly be labeled "dissimilarity." [From Sneath (1961). Reproduced by permission of the editors of* Systematic Zoology.]

repeated burgeonings of forms well adapted to the prevailing conditions but rapidly dying out and contributing little to the succeeding part of the phyletic line. This study was not suitable for estimating evolutionary rates.

It is perhaps worth noting that a large amount of the fossil record is based on fragmentary material—not merely on skeletal remains, but only on certain bones or teeth. Even complete fossil remains may yield very few characters because of the simplicity of their structure—for example mollusc and brachiopod shells and even the tests of echinoderms. It is especially unfortunate that many well-documented lineages showing gradual evolutionary changes are based on material of this kind (ammonites, oysters, sea urchins, and others), so that the interpretation of apparent convergence, parallelism, saltations, and the like is often in some doubt.

Stratigraphy is an activity on the periphery of systematics and might therefore be discussed in Section 10.6 with "other applications of numerical taxonomic methods." Thus study of the chemical similarities between strata, for example, would be such work. However, the comparison of fossils in different strata involves numerical taxonomy of the fossils, even though the results of the taxonomy may be intended to enable the strata to be identified in different localities, across geological faults, and so on. Such work is akin to ecological studies in that many different kinds of organisms may be included as components of one OTU (the OTU's would here be strata instead of organisms). Such studies would therefore involve a new element: strata would be similar or dissimilar not only in the number of species of fossils which they shared but also in the degree to which the fossils of one higher taxon were similar in the two rocks. For example, pertinent evidence on the degree of similarity between the strata $A$, $B$, and $C$ might be obtained from the degree of similarity between three species of a given genus, species **X**, **Y**, and **Z**, each characteristic, respectively, of strata $A$, $B$, and $C$.

# CHAPTER 9

# Problems of
# Nomenclature

We do not at present foresee that many changes in nomenclatural procedures will be brought about by numerical taxonomy in the near future. A few constructive proposals will be discussed below, together with suggestions of some of the lines along which nomenclature may develop. The student of numerical taxonomy may require a guide to the application of the present rules of nomenclature, and for his convenience we list in the bibliography the four International Codes of Nomenclature. For zoology a standard text of taxonomy has in the past been that of Schenk and McMasters (1956) or Mayr, Linsley, and Usinger (1953), and for botany Lawrence (1951) or Core (1955). In microbiology and mycology a concise guide is given in Appendix I in Ainsworth and Sneath (1962, pp. 454–463).

It is clear that one effect of numerical taxonomy on nomenclature will be through the taxonomic groups it creates. Obviously changes of rank will mean changes of names; simplification of the taxonomy will mean fewer names; increased detail, or the discovery of new taxa, will mean more names. These would be brought about by any method of taxonomic study that produced changes in established classifications. As Jahn (1962) points out, the use of computers in taxonomy will force some changes of nomenclature; the separation between the plant and animal kingdoms will be abandoned, with consequent alteration of many of the present Rules (especially those allowing homonymy between animals and plants).

## 9.1. NOMENCLATURAL CONSEQUENCES OF NUMERICAL TAXONOMY

### 9.1.1. The phenon nomenclature

One consequence of the application of numerical taxonomy may be the ease with which we are able to recognize small differences in rank. The traditional categories of rank, such as order, family, or genus, may not be numerous enough even when expanded by intermediate ranks produced by prefixing the terms sub-, super-, and infra-. Words such as "supersubfamily" would be ugly and prone to confusion. They could be avoided by citing the value which characterized the rank of the group in a numerical study, as described below.

The groups established by numerical taxonomy may, if desired, be equated with the usual rank categories such as genus, tribe, or family. However, these terms have evolutionary, nomenclatural, and other connotations which one may wish to avoid. We therefore prefer new expressions (Sneath and Sokal, 1962). We call the groups simply *phenons* and preface them with a number indicating the level of affinity at which they are formed. For example, an 80-phenon connotes a group affiliated at no lower than 80 on the similarity scale used in the analysis.

The terms are intended to be general ones to cover the groups produced by any form of cluster analysis or from any form of similarity coefficients. Their numerical values will vary with the coefficient, the type of cluster analysis and the sample of characters employed in the study. They are therefore comparable only within the limits of one analysis.

Phenons are groups which approach natural taxa more or less closely, and like the term taxon they can be of any hierarchic rank or of indeterminate rank. Since they are groups formed by numerical taxonomy, they are not synonymous with taxa; the term "taxon" is retained for its proper function, to indicate any sort of taxonomic group. The term phenon was employed in an entirely different sense by Camp and Gilly (1943). They used it for a division of a biological species which was divided by sterility barriers into phenotypically distinguishable segments. The word does not seem to have come into general usage, and since it appears appropriate, we have employed it in numerical taxonomy in a new sense.

An example of the delimitation of phenons can be seen in Figure 9-1.

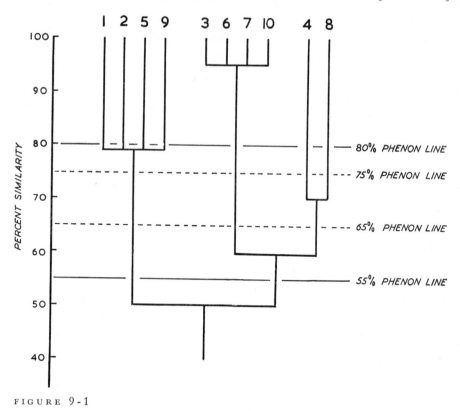

FIGURE 9-1

*Dendrogram to show the formation of phenons (for explanation, see text).*

Drawing a horizontal line across the dendrogram at a similarity value of 75% creates four 75-phenons, 1, 2, 5, 9; 3, 6, 7, 10; 4; and 8. We have found it convenient to refer to a given phenon by its first and last member. In the example above, we have 75-phenon (1 . . . 9). This is an informal system of nomenclature not based on types. The dots (ellipsis) do not indicate that the OTU's are necessarily in sequential, alphabetic, or numerical order, but merely that one or more are included between the terminal units. It is clear, of course, that such a label must refer to a given dendrogram and cannot easily be transferred to another study. If the original taxonomic units had been species, these phenons might be subgenera or genera. A second phenon line at 65% forms three 65-phenons. The advantage of phenons is that it is obvious that they are arbitrary and relative groups. This is not true of the Linnaean nomenclatural scheme. If some investigator felt that the taxa in Figure 9-1 should be divided into two instead of three groups, the phenon line would have to be drawn at a similarity value between 50% and 60%; or he might feel that the two phenon lines were too close together and did not summarize the main relations very fairly, as a result of which he might draw the first line at the 80% level. The designation of the phenons would then change to 55-phenons or to 80-phenons, respectively; however, the relationships among taxa in the dendrogram are quite unchanged. Phenons are primarily suggested for use with dendrograms but with suitable prefixes could be used for phenetic clusters defined on other than dendritic scales.

### 9.1.2. Stability of nomenclature

Stability is a matter of some practical consequence. It may be argued, as has been done by Gilmour (1961b), that numerical taxonomy may increase instability, and it must be admitted that it may do so, at least during the first studies on a taxonomic group. We believe, however, that numerical taxonomies will in the end be very stable. It is clear that one could, by raising or lowering the phenon level a little, produce considerable changes in the nomenclature. This we believe to be undesirable; the present hierarchic nomenclature cannot profitably employ ranks that are too numerous or finely graded. We would not recommend the rigorous application of phenon lines if this severely disturbed the nomenclature without making any positive taxonomic contribution. For example, if a second study showed that the phenon level of the majority of subgenera of the first study now fell just below the line chosen to indicate genera, we would not rename them all on this account. A third study might well shift them again into the subgeneric level. However, changes which in the opinion of the taxonomist are major and significant should involve renaming. For example, when what had been previously thought to be two aberrant species of one genus are shown by numerical taxonomy to be two monotypic genera of a new subfamily, new names are clearly in order. This is necessary if the nomenclature is to reflect reasonably well the "natural" taxonomic groupings. To do otherwise is to deny biologists the benefits of improved taxonomies. Eventually one would hope that a time would come when name changes were no longer permitted for reasons of priority, and author citations would become unnecessary.

Rohlf (1962) has pointed out that in successive studies the least disturbance of nomenclature would occur if the dendrograms are divided at points where the stems show the widest gaps between successive branchings. Sometimes these optimal levels would be easy to determine, but the temptation to make the rank lines wander up and down in their course across a single dendrogram would introduce an element of personal prejudice that is at variance with our hope for objective representation of the relationships.

## 9.2. NUMERICAL TAXONOMY AND NOMENCLATURAL PROBLEMS

### 9.2.1. Limits of taxa

It is now generally recognized that modern nomenclature does not concern itself with the limits of taxa but only with reference points to the taxonomic names. What is to be included in a taxon is left to the decision of the taxonomist. Bradley (1939) expressed this as follows. "Nomenclature is concerned with the nuclei of groups, never with their limits. Taxonomy is concerned with the limits of groups, not their nuclei. The limits are debatable, subjective, forever changeable, not amenable to decision by authority. The nuclei can be fixed by common consent, for they are objective, utilitarian, permanent." Numerical taxonomy may here prove of value, for it will in principle be possible to delimit the boundaries of taxa by exact estimation of affinities, so that what organisms should be placed in a taxon will no longer be simply a matter of opinion. The limits then, as well as the nuclei, may also be objective, utilitarian, permanent, and fixed by common consent.

### 9.2.2. Terminology of intermediate forms

If numerical taxonomy reveals intermediate forms between taxa we can employ mathematical methods of the type of discriminant functions to show where it is best to draw the dividing line, and the nomenclature of the groups will follow this decision. The forms close to the dividing line may need a special terminology similar to that already used for hybrids and for intermediate forms in phylogenies, such as "$X. y$ - $X. z$ intermediates," or "$X. y$ inter. $X. z$." This might even take numerical form when an entity $E$ is at a known taxonomic distance between two other entities, such as, 20 $X. y$ - 80 $X. z$ for an entity which in taxonomic hyperspace is 20% of the way from $X. y$ to $X. z$. To avoid confusion, the standard conventions for hybrids,

$$X.\,y \times X.\,z \qquad \text{or} \qquad \frac{X.\,y}{X.\,z},$$

should not be used. This simple situation occurs only when the inter-mediate form $E$ lies on what may be envisaged as the direct line in taxonomic space between $X.\,y$ and $X.\,z$. If it lies off this line, so to speak, the sum of the distances $X.\,y$ to $E$ and $X.\,z$ to $E$ will be greater than the distance $X.\,y$ to $X.\,z$. An intermediate could then be a "50 $X.\,y$ - 70 $X.\,z$ intermediate," where $X.\,y$ to $X.\,z$ is 100, and $X.\,y$ to $E$ is 50, and $X.\,z$ to $E$ is 70 (see Figure 9-2). The excess over 100 of the sum $X.\,y$ to $E$ and $X.\,z$ to $E$ (50 plus 70 in this instance) gives an idea of how far $E$ deviates from the straight line joining $X.\,y$ to $X.\,z$ (it does not, of course, indicate in which direction $E$ lies off the line). This raises the question of whether it should be considered an intermediate at all. Possibly $X.\,y$, $X.\,z$, and $E$ should be

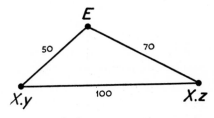

FIGURE 9-2

*Nomenclature of intermediate forms (for ex-planation, see text).*

combined into one taxon or $E$ should be given independent existence as a taxon. A rule-of-thumb would be that the sum of the distances $E$ to $X.\,y$ and $E$ to $X.\,z$ should not be more than 1.5 times the distance $X.\,y$ to $X.\,z$, if the convention is to be meaningful. It should also be noted that $X.\,y$ and $X.\,z$ may be represented either by their most central or most typical members or by their nomenclatural types (which may not be central or typical), and this must be made clear.

Similar occasions may occur in phylogenetic studies, and it may be possible to devise a terminology to suit this. One might, for example, re-cord either the estimated cladistic or phenetic position of a form interme-diate between two established and named points of a lineage, such as "40 $X.\,y$ - 60 $X.\,z$." While cladistic relations must total 100%, the phe-netic relations need not do so. Phyletic relations would be conveniently distinguished by using the term "transient" instead of "intermediate" for the form between the named points.

A new development would be a nomenclature based on the volume occupied by a taxon in taxonomic hyperspace. Whether it would have advantages remains to be seen, but the principle would be to define a volume of a certain size as a generic volume, and so on, and to name the taxa within the corresponding volumes accordingly.

### 9.2.3. Choice of new nomenclatural types

Numerical taxonomy will sometimes be applied to groups where there is no significant earlier taxonomy, or it may cause extensive revision of an existing taxonomy. In such cases it may be necessary to set up types for the names of the new taxa. Such types need not be phenetically typical of the taxon. Their function is expressed better by the term "nomenifer," or name bearer, suggested by Schopf (1960) than by the term "type," implying typicality (Simpson, 1940, has suggested "onomatophore"). Nevertheless, there are advantages in choosing a nomenifer which is also reasonably typical, and the taxonomist can choose a typical specimen for a species from the results of numerical analysis. Similarly, a typical species can be chosen as the type of a genus or higher category. In general we require an OTU which is central in a geometrical sense in a cluster of OTU's in taxonomic space; however, there may be practical considerations indicating the adoption of a noncentral OTU as the type of a taxon.

One simple method is to list for each character the character state which is the commonest among the OTU's of the phenon in question. An OTU which possesses these states, or almost all of them, will be acceptably close to the geometric center of the cluster. The typical member of a cluster is that OTU having the highest loading on a factor representing the cluster, when a factor analysis of the Q-matrix has been carried out (see Rohlf and Sokal, 1962). Another method, suggested by Silvestri et al. (1962), is to employ the technique of Rogers and Tanimoto (1960), and for each OTU in turn to calculate the product of the similarity coefficients between that OTU and all others in a cluster. The OTU for which this product is greatest will be the most central (the centrotype of Silvestri et al., 1962). Rogers and Tanimoto employ the $-\log_2$ of the similarity coefficients and take the OTU for which the sum is smallest.

These methods presuppose that the cluster is reasonably homogeneous and is a representative sample of the group in nature. Of course, if a number of OTU's are equidistant from the geometric center, the choice among them is arbitrary. The central form thus selected bears a certain relation to the artificial types of Smirnov and to Heincke's "average individual" (see Sokal, 1962b, where some other methods for delimiting phenetic types are also discussed).

In summary we may say that, all other considerations being equal, we ought to employ type OTU's near a central point for a taxon. It may

be asked why one should go to all this trouble for a purely nomenclatural device; however, the computation of typical values can usually
be easily obtained as by-products of the computer routines of numerical
taxonomy.

### 9.2.4. Data-processing machines

A new development in nomenclature is the use of card-sorting machines and computers to handle the "book-keeping" of taxonomic names,
keys, bibliographies, and so on, discussed in detail by Gould (1958) and
Jahn (1961). Although this is not part of numerical taxonomy as treated
here, it is a parallel development which merits notice.

Jahn (1961) points out that classificatory schemes are being increas-
ingly developed in many branches of science as an aid to efficient automatic processing of information. Such schemes when once established
are difficult to alter; it therefore behooves taxonomists to see that these
are of the sort they want, lest they find themselves faced with a *fait
accompli*. In such applications, the use of "unnatural" taxa may have
damaging consequences; once the schemes are compiled it is difficult to
disentangle the information pertaining to the different entities which
have been lumped together.

Several schemes for codifying names are now being developed. In
taxonomy the most ambitious of these is the International Plant Index
(IPIx) at the Connecticut Agricultural Experiment Station, New Haven,
Conn. Its outlines are described by Gould (1962). The generic names of
plants are being given code numbers, and bibliographic, biographic, and
distributional data are being collected and coded. The Index hopes to
issue in the near future mechanically prepared indices that are more
comprehensive than any available hitherto. Other schemes have been
suggested by Mullins and Nickerson (1951) and Denmark, Weems, and
Taylor (1958). The Chemical-Biological Coordinating Center has developed an elaborate coding system (Seitner, 1960; Seitner, Livingston,
and Williams, 1960).

These developments should be welcomed. The use of code numbers,
while highly convenient, may perhaps be modified by treating the name
itself as a code number written in a twenty-six-valued notation (one
value for each letter of the alphabet) to save the trouble of allocating
code numbers and to permit automatic checking of homonyms.

# CHAPTER 10

# Present Problems
# and Some Future
# Prospects

## 10.1. THE ACCOMPLISHMENTS OF NUMERICAL TAXONOMY TO DATE

It is not easy to evaluate the accomplishments of numerical taxonomy to date without a detailed knowledge of the organisms studied, and the range of these is too wide for us to present a competent critique of all the studies. The results in microbiology have been reviewed by Sneath (1962), and fields other than biological systematics are discussed in Section 10.6. The findings presented below are arranged in systematic order (Section 10.1.1) and by the type of problem to which they furnish an answer (Section 10.1.2).

### 10.1.1. Published applications of numerical taxonomy to different groups of organisms

So far there have been relatively few studies which employ numerical taxonomic methods of the kind we feel are necessary. In listing those of which we are aware at the time of writing, it is impressive to note the number of people who have independently undertaken such studies in the last few years and to see the wide range of organisms for which numerical methods have been successfully used.

In zoology, numerical taxonomy has been applied to the study of bees (Michener and Sokal, 1957; Sokal and Michener, 1958; Sokal, 1958; Rohlf and Sokal, 1961; and Rohlf and Sokal, 1962). These studies on 97 species of the *Hoplitis* complex (four genera of the family Megachilidae) have illustrated a number of points; the affinities and dendrograms were in good agreement with the previous orthodox taxonomy of the group, and in addition they gave interesting new information on the finer structure of the taxonomic hierarchy and on the systematic position of a number of aberrant species. Rohlf (1962) studied 48 species of the mosquito genus *Aedes*, developing a classification resembling those established by recent studies of the group. Ehrlich (1961c) studied butterflies (*Euphydras* species) and examined the correspondence between affinities based on characters from different parts of the body and also the relation between phenetic status and geographic location. A brief report has appeared on numerical taxonomy applied to man (Cain and Harrison, 1960a). Sokal (unpublished) has reanalyzed the data by Haltenorth (1937) on skulls of 8 species of cats. These data await suitable publication. Little (1963) has recently completed a numerical taxonomic study of the boring sponge genus *Cliona*, in which 103 species were clustered on the basis of 36 characters. The classification resulting from this work seemed to agree well with modern ideas on this group.

In botany numerical taxonomy has been applied to rice (*Oryza* species) by Morishima and Oka (1960), who found reasonable agreement with orthodox taxonomy and with genetic data, and to manioc plants (Rogers, in IBM, 1959; and Rogers and Tanimoto, 1960). Soria and Heiser (1961) studied species of *Solanum* and found rather close agreement with the earlier taxonomy and also some agreement with the relations as judged by the ease of hybridization between the species. Hamann (1961), in a numerical taxonomic study of the thirteen families of the "Farinosae" of Engler together with four other monocotyledonous families, found the resulting similarity coefficients agreeing well with newer opinions on relationships of these families (see Section 10.1.2.2).

These methods have also been applied in paleontology to fossil fish (Sneath, 1961) but only as an illustrative example.

In bacteria the methods are used more widely. Some studies have included a wide range of bacteria from different orders (e.g., Sneath and Cowan, 1958), and the methods seemed as successful as when applied to strains within one species. Several atypical forms, such as the plague bacillus, were correctly classified as judged by later and more detailed evidence on their position. Brisbane and Rovira (1961) have made a similar study of soil bacteria, but they used fewer characters and obtained less clear-cut results.

A great simplification of the confused taxonomy of the actinomycetes, particulary species of *Streptomyces*, together with some interesting correlations with the antibiotics they produce, is resulting from the work of Silvestri and his colleagues (Gilardi et al., 1960; Hill et al., 1961; Silvestri et al., 1962). Similar assistance has been given in the taxonomy of cocci (Hill, 1959; Pohja, 1960; Blondeau, 1961; Colobert and Blondeau, 1962), *Pasteurella* (Talbot and Sneath, 1960) and the pseudomonads (Liston, 1960; Liston and Colwell, 1960; Shewan, Hobbs, and Hodgkiss, 1960; Thornley, 1960; Colwell and Liston, 1961a, b, c, d; Rhodes, 1961; Lysenko, 1961). In some of these instances these workers were also able to distinguish subgroups within rather homogeneous collections of strains. In other instances the existing arrangements of species into genera were largely confirmed. A detailed study of one genus, *Chromobacterium*, was made by Sneath (1957b), and very good correspondence was found with the previous grouping of strains into "species" and with serological data (Sneath and Buckland, 1959; Sneath, 1960). Results on another genus, *Bacillus* (Sneath, 1962), were also fairly consistent with other data. Cheeseman and Berridge (1959) employed a restricted set of chemical attributes in a study of *Lactobacillus*, in which agreement with the current taxonomy was not very close; however, the current taxonomy of this genus is not very satisfactory (see Sneath, 1962).

The application of these methods to viruses (Andrewes and Sneath, 1958; Sneath, 1962) has shown that groups are formed which are very similar, with one exception, to those recognized and named informally by virologists, although the data are not yet sufficient to build a meaningful hierarchy for the groups. The application of numerical taxonomy to entities on the uncertain borderland between living organisms, genes, and chemical compounds is a severe test, and the results are therefore encouraging.

### 10.1.2. Assistance of numerical methods in some taxonomic problems

*10.1.2.1. Concordance between numerical taxonomic studies and established taxonomies*

The study of Michener and Sokal (1957) on bees showed quite good agreement with the established taxonomy. Morishima and Oka (1960) and Soria and Heiser (1961) likewise found good agreement with the established taxonomies of *Oryza* and *Solanum*, respectively. For example, the five species of the "Sativa" group of *Oryza* were clustered together, and the aberrant *O. subulata* was well separated from them. However, *O. granulata* did not occur in a separate section (as in the earlier taxonomy) but was part of the "Sativa" complex.

In bacteria the earlier taxonomies are widely recognized as often unsatisfactory, so that concordance with them is not an important issue. Nevertheless, most studies have shown reasonable agreement (for example, Hill, 1959; Liston, 1960; Sneath, 1962).

### 10.1.2.2. The naturalness of taxa

The testing of the naturalness of higher ranks is closely related to the question of agreement with previous taxonomies, but in addition it may involve transfer of major subgroups from one group to another. Michener and Sokal (1957), for example, found that most of the earlier subgenera were "natural," but the genera *Hoplitis* and *Proteriades* underwent some change by the transfer of two subgenera from the former to the latter.

Hamann (1961) found that the thirteen monocotyledonous families of the "Farinosae" of Engler were an unnatural assemblage. He regrouped them into four orders on the basis of a numerical taxonomic study. The Thurniaceae were placed in the order Juncales; the Pontederiaceae, Cyanastraceae, and Philydraceae were placed in the order Liliales; the Bromeliaceae were separated as an order Bromeliales; and the remaining families formed the Commelinales (divided into four suborders). It is not clear why Hamann did not take the logical steps of including the Cyperaceae in the Juncales, the Gramineae with the Restionineae, and adding the Bromeliaceae to the Liliales, as indicated by the affinity values he obtained. Possibly the number of features was not adequate for a thorough revision of the group, and the affinities do show some unusual properties when subjected to cluster analysis (Section 7.3.2.6).

In bacteria a number of studies have confirmed that many of the recognized genera are natural, such as *Pseudomonas, Aeromonas, Xanthomonas* (Liston, 1960; Thornley, 1960; Colwell and Liston, 1961c; Rhodes, 1961), while other genera, such as *Vibrio*, are very heterogeneous, as had been suspected (Colwell and Liston, 1961b). Among the higher groups certain families and orders were found to form natural taxa, such as, the Actinomycetales (Sneath and Cowan, 1958).

A pervasive problem in bacteriology is the initial grouping of individual strains into taxa of low rank, conventionally regarded as species.

There is often doubt whether strains bearing one specific name comprise one reasonably homogeneous taxon. Most of the numerical taxonomic studies in bacteriology deal in part with this problem. Sneath (1957b) made a thorough comparison of many strains of two species of *Chromobacterium* and found that they fell into the expected two groups, which were sharply separated from one another, as clearly shown by models (Lysenko and Sneath, 1959). Studies by Hill (1959), Pohja (1960), Talbot and Sneath (1960), and Blondeau (1961) showed that many of the earlier groupings were natural, though some were not. Silvestri et al. (1962), however, found one or two instances of variant strains which were not placed very close to their known parents, and one or two instances of bacteria which seemed to be seriously misplaced. These were only a small minority of the strains studied. Viruses fell into the groups generally recognized by virologists, with one notable exception, the pox viruses (Sneath, 1962), but the confidence bands in this study were quite broad because of the few characters available. Zarapkin (1939) noted good agreement between phenetic relationship and the recognized different geographic races of the coccinellid, *Epilachna*. Ehrlich (1961c), however, found that geographic variants of certain butterflies were not always concordant with established species groupings. Little (1963) was able to recover three species of the sponge genus *Cliona* when clustering 47 individual specimens.

Numerical taxonomy has been used to look for clusters within diffuse assemblages of very similar strains of bacteria and to get some idea of how distinct these clusters were. In addition to the papers cited above, the following studies were directed toward this: indistinct clusters were found in a species of *Streptococcus* by Defayolle and Colobert (1962); Rhodes (1961) was unable to find any distinct clusters in a collection of strains of *Pseudomonas*, which had earlier been found to be very homogeneous; and Brisbane and Rovira (1961) found somewhat indistinct divisions in a large collection of soil bacteria of several genera, perhaps because they employed rather few characters. Since there is considerable uncertainty about the extent to which bacteria form sharp groups and how far they merge together into an indistinct "spectrum" of intermediate forms (Cowan, 1955), these studies are of some importance in this field.

Bojalil and Cerbón (1961), Cerbón and Bojalil (1961), and Bojalil, Cerbón, and Trujillo (1962) discovered in the genus *Mycobacterium* some new taxa which had previously not been recognized. Pohja (1960), Blondeau (1961), and Colobert and Blondeau (1962) also found new and unnamed groups of cocci by numerical taxonomic analysis. Colwell and Liston (1961a, c) reported new subgroups within the genus *Xanthomonas*. As a consequence of their study on bees, Michener and Sokal (1957) established a new subgenus, *Isosmia*.

Numerical taxonomy has helped various workers to decide the "proper" taxonomic position of certain curious and puzzling organisms. In bees, Michener and Sokal (1957) were able to place satisfactorily several "difficult" species. Sneath and Cowan (1958) were able to classify satisfactorily *Jensenia*, *Corynebacterium pyogenes*, and the plague bacillus, which had puzzled taxonomists. Colwell and Liston (1961c, d) obtained interesting information on the aberrant plant pathogens, *Pseudomonas solanacearum* and *Xanthomonas stewarti*. Gilardi et al. (1960) were able to place satisfactorily several curious strains of actinomycetes.

Michener and Sokal (1957) and Morishima and Oka (1960) noted that the dendrograms obtained by numerical taxonomy gave increased discrimination between the forms they studied. This has the same effect as introducing rank categories intermediate between those usually employed and named. It seems to us that the phenon nomenclature is well suited for labeling such categories. In contrast, several bacteriological studies have led to a considerable simplification of taxonomies which had previously been confused, both at low ranks (for example, Blondeau, 1961) and medium ranks (for example, Hill, 1959; Thornley, 1960; Colwell and Liston, 1961a, c; Silvestri et al., 1962).

### 10.1.2.3. Concordance of numerical taxonomies with other properties of the organism

This problem has been mainly studied in bacteria. The host range of bacteriophages is closely associated with genetic similarity and ease of hybridization. Numerical taxonomic work to date agrees fairly well with bacteriophage studies (Sneath, 1964). The recent work on bacterial cell walls gives much the same generic groupings as numerical methods (see Cummins and Harris, 1956, 1958; Sneath and Cowan, 1958), which in some instances are not the same as the traditional taxa.

An important practical use of numerical taxonomy would be to allow one to predict the finding of new antibiotics in new streptomycetes. This might be possible if the clusters of streptomycetes were correlated with the class of antibiotic they produced. Little has yet been published in this connection, but the work of Silvestri et al. (1962) seems promising. Some correspondence was noted by Talbot and Sneath (1960) between the phenetics and the pathogenicity of the hemorrhagic septicemia bacillus (*Pasteurella septica*). They noted that all the strains from cats and from internal lesions in humans had high affinities with one another (unlike many of the strains from dogs), which suggested that most human internal infections involving the organism probably originate in cats.

### 10.1.2.4. The stability of numerical taxonomies

It is clearly too early to say much about the stability of taxonomies obtained by numerical methods. Comparisons of analyses on the same groups of microorganisms by different workers or using different sets of characters indicate that the taxonomies will probably be quite stable (compare the classifications of Liston, 1960, and Colwell and Liston, 1961b, with those of Shewan et al., 1960, Thornley, 1960, and Rhodes, 1961; also compare Hill, 1959, with Pohja, 1960; and Sneath, 1957b, with Sneath and Cowan, 1958).

One of the attractive properties of taxonomies based on large numbers of characters is their robustness under different statistical treatments. By this we mean that a given body of data, when analyzed by different similarity coefficients or by different cluster analyses, or both, usually yields remarkably similar dendrograms and hierarchies. This is undergoing intensive testing at the moment, but a few published findings may be cited. Sokal and Michener (1958) obtained very similar dendrograms from several different methods of cluster analysis. There is close agreement between association coefficients using negative matches and those which do not, as well as between cluster analyses by the weighted variable-group methods of Sokal and Michener (1958), the method of Rogers and Tanimoto (1960), and that of Sneath (1957b) (see Gilardi et al., 1960; Hill et al., 1961; and Silvestri et al., 1962). Sneath (1961) found very similar relative affinities, using the MCD of Cain and Harrison (1958) and correlation coefficients. Comparisons of a number of different statistics and methods are given by Sokal and Michener (1958), Sokal and Rohlf (1962), and Rohlf and Sokal (1962). Agreement between taxonomies based on these statistics is quite good.

## 10.2.  CRITICISMS OF NUMERICAL TAXONOMY

In presenting numerical taxonomy to the scientific public at meetings as well as in print we have met with repeated criticism based on a variety of grounds. Much of this has been constructive criticism which has been gratefully received and has led to modifications and, we hope, to improvements of our views. Other criticism is often based on a misunderstanding of our position. Many of the controversial issues have already been presented at appropriate places throughout the book. We have collected below various other criticisms not adequately discussed in earlier chapters. They are divided into those objecting to our philosophy or procedures on the basis of fundamental biological principles, those criticisms of numerical taxonomy based on considerations of convenience and practicality, and those comments deploring the advent of quantification and automation in taxonomy.

### 10.2.1. Objections on fundamental biological principles

One frequently voiced objection has been well stated by Hennig (1950) in a discussion actually antedating the recent development of numerical taxonomy. He argues that phenomena in the various disciplines subsumed under the general heading of systematics (taxonomy, ecology, zoogeography, behavior, and so on) can be unified only by the principle of descent with modification, as expressed by the phylogeny of the group. The validity of this viewpoint is self-evident. Hence, Hennig reasons that any taxonomy must be based on this unifying principle, and therefore phylogeny must be considered the primary principle of classification. We would agree with all but the last conclusion. Evolution is indeed an all-explanatory principle. It cannot, however, be used in classificatory procedures, since we mostly do not know (and in many cases cannot know) its true course.

The approach of numerical taxonomy has been called anti-evolutionary. It seems hardly necessary to disavow such attitudes, because of our own interest in evolution and our employment of evolutionary modes of thought. Only the principles and processes of classification are restricted to phenetic evidence, not the entire field of systematics.

It has been said that biological classifications have special characteristics which distinguish them from classifications of inanimate objects. Assuming that vitalistic principles are not invoked when such a statement is made, we can only believe that this assertion refers to the historical dimension of biological organisms—their phylogeny. However, even inanimate objects such as automobiles or nuts, bolts, and screws show evidence of their historical development, as discussed elsewhere. There appears to be no difference between empirical, phenetic classifications of living organisms and those of inanimate objects except that the hierarchies arrived at in classifications of inanimate objects do not necessarily reflect the course of descent with modification. Those who would now reverse this argument and say that because empirical, phenetic classification can be applied to inanimate objects it must not be applied to living objects seem to us to find a mystique in the latter, which unless demonstrated and defined would not warrant consideration.

It has been charged that the methods of numerical taxonomy are typological (Inger, 1958; Simpson, 1961). By this is surely meant that the procedures employed are allied to the now largely discredited views of typology and idealistic morphology. Sokal (1962b) has shown in an extensive review of this subject that the term typology as used in taxonomy implies procedures and philosophies of diverse meanings. While some aspects of typology are untenable in the context of modern biological theory (especially those related to Platonic idealism), others are reasonable and defensible in the light of present-day knowledge. Simpson's (1961) statement that typological theory is inextricably linked with philosophical idealism is not correct. Simpson himself has pointed out the empirical nature of some of the newer typological approaches and has stated that there is no necessary connection between the idealistic point of view and an empirical but nonphylogenetic method. Bloch (1956), in an extensive philosophical study of the nature of systematics, finds that it is not necessary to consider all nonphylogenetically oriented morphology and taxonomy as idealistic.

Simpson (1961, p. 50) also criticizes typology to the effect that "the concept of distinct and static patterns cannot meaningfully be applied to real groups of organisms, which are parts of an evolutionary continuum and which are always highly variable." It seems to us that these statements confuse the dynamism of evolution with the essentially static nature of the resemblances and differences on the basis of which we perceive evolutionary changes and their results in a group of organisms. To deny the validity of a static approach to classification is in effect to deny the validity of the bulk of the taxonomic work in existence today. The legitimacy of the coexistence of static classifications alongside the phylogenetic ones has been recognized by such eminent taxonomists as Hennig (1950) and Michener (1957). Typology is unacceptable when contaminated with idealistic, metaphysical concepts or when restricted only to morphological evidence and based on few characters. But when (1) it represents an empirical summation of the information available on a given taxon without phylogenetic value judgment of these characters, and (2) when it is performed on the basis of numerous characters of many kinds rather than few of a single kind, typology can serve as a yardstick of resemblance between taxa. This yardstick, when properly quantified, should yield important information on the results of evolutionary processes. It is the aim of numerical taxonomy to furnish such a yardstick. Problems of noncorrespondence between phenetic and phyletic relationships have been adequately discussed in Chapters 2 and 8.

Many people have criticized the Adansonian principle of allocating equal weight to all characters. We have already adequately covered this topic in earlier sections. Statements to the effect that one character may be much more useful in classifying a group of organisms than ten other characters are based on confusion between construction of taxa and identification of individuals. Unless and until a consistent, logically defensible system for weighting characters can be provided, weighting must remain equal. When such a weighting scheme has been devised, it is likely that the analysis would still be done on a computer, employing the logic furnished by the taxonomist.

In a recent paper Kiriakoff (1962) has criticized the neo-Adansonian school, though regrettably this was written before he had an opportunity to see the most recent papers on the theory of numerical taxonomy. It is interesting to see that he agrees with us on three points: (1) that most current systematic work is crypto-typological; (2) that similarity and blood relationship do not necessarily agree; (3) that the details of phylogeny cannot be known with certainty. On some points, however, he is under a misconception about numerical taxonomy. First, the work of Verheyen (which Kiriakoff cites as an argument against equal weighting) was not a numerical taxonomic study of the kind we advocate. Second, Kiriakoff writes: "I feel quite certain that any neo-Adansonian would classify two very different organisms together *if he had the positive evidence of their recent common ascendance* [his italics]. In failing to do so, he would expose himself to the loss of his scientific standing." We have clearly stated the very opposite in this book (see also, Sneath, 1961). Third, he states that numerical taxonomy is unable to use such factors as time and space, which is incorrect (see Sections 5.4.4, 8.2.2, 8.2.4). We do not think that Kiriakoff offers any constructive suggestions for an alternative method of taxonomy.

### 10.2.2. Considerations of convenience and practicality

There are numerous statements in the literature (for example, Hennig, 1950) that phenetic relations can in principle never be measured, or that at least the present techniques are inadequate for this. We believe, however, that taxonomists have always estimated phenetic relations intuitively and that the methods of numerical taxonomy are in general adequate for estimating them objectively. We are unaware of serious criticisms of the methodologies of coding and processing taxonomic information.

Persons skeptical of the method may claim that it takes too much work to describe such a large number of characters in a large group and then process it by procedures which are expensive and possibly time-consuming. Why is all this necessary when by previous methods, based on few characters and the intuitive assessment of resemblance, one could achieve reasonable taxonomies? We have pointed out in Chapter 2 why good taxonomies have been established by *repeated* revisions using earlier methods. Numerical taxonomy aims to reach a position of comparable stability *immediately*. This would clearly be of importance in little-studied groups. Even in the best worked out groups, relationships among the taxa are vague because they have not been quantified; in less studied groups such relationships are altogether missing. It is therefore inaccurate to say that the work done by the computer can be duplicated by taxonomists working on a few characters. On the contrary, computer processing should be superior to that done by the average taxonomist.

Gilmour (1961b), in discussing the mathematical approach to taxonomy, notes that it may help to decide between disputed classifications, but he warns against two dangers. The first is that the increased precision may not be worth the labor involved and may involve changes in nomenclature and consequent loss of stability in classification. We believe that the increased precision will be valuable and will require little extra effort. The confirmation of previous classifications will increase our confidence in systematics; the changes in previous classifications will lead to better ones. There is in any event much instability in nomenclature, and to insist on stability where major taxonomic revisions are proposed would deny biologists the possibility of improving their taxonomies, whether the improvements come from numerical, orthodox, or other studies.

The second danger, that one may imagine that one is achieving some sort of "objective reality," is quite real. This danger is indeed pertinent from a philosophic point of view. We do not claim that numerical taxonomies are "objective realities"; the fact that a number of slightly differing taxonomies may be obtained by different statistical methods is clear evidence that they are not. Nevertheless, having defined precisely what is pertinent to biological classification and what are the best statistics for achieving a given end, we can obtain taxonomies which fulfill the needs for which they are devised, in the same way that we can agree that the arithmetic mean is a valid measure of the central tendency of a frequency distribution, for a given purpose we have in mind.

With respect to the agreement between the results of numerical taxonomic work and previous taxonomies, we unfortunately become involved in a "damned-if-you-do" and "damned-if-you-don't" type of argument. If a classification by numerical taxonomy yields results similar to those previously shown by orthodox methods, it is argued that numerical taxonomy is unnecessary since the results are after all similar. If, on the other hand, numerical taxonomy yields radically different results, then the new method is "clearly wrong," because the results differ from the established ones, which "obviously" must be right. We believe this dilemma can be solved only by consistently basing classifications on numerical techniques.

Taxonomists may believe it is difficult to find 100 characters in their material; however, it is possible to find many more characters than have in the past been used for taxonomic work. This is certainly true in external morphology but clearly even more so when internal morphological, histological, cytological, histochemical, and similar characters are considered. An abundance of the classical type of morphological characters have been demonstrated in well-studied groups where they had hitherto been overlooked, as, for example, by Ehrlich (1961a), who described a great number of internal morphological characters in butterflies; by Rohlf (1962), who found a large number of previously undescribed characters on the legs of the well-known mosquito genus *Aedes;* and by Haltenorth (1937), who recorded 86 characters from only the skulls of cats, not even considering the teeth. Thus, lack of characters is due most probably to lack of appropriate methods of discovering these characters and to the taxonomists' satisfaction that a few are enough. The term character is often used by taxonomists in the sense of a feature differentiating one group from another in a given classification. Accordingly, variation in features within an accepted taxon is often considered as trivial by taxonomists and not recorded. Conversely, characters that do agree with an accepted classification are also ignored by some because they do not "add" to the present taxonomy.

The arguments that computational facilities are not available or that the techniques are too intricate are not realistic. There should be little difficulty today in obtaining computer facilities. Almost every university and many government institutions where active research is carried out have a computer installation. Taxonomists in government service or museums or research institutes can, if they wish, have access to these computers, frequently at very reasonable rates, if not gratis. It should be emphasized here that one need not be a master statistician or computer programmer in order to practice numerical taxonomy.

### 10.2.3. Objections to the quantification and automation of the taxonomic process (the "Man versus Machine" controversy)

At meetings of taxonomists where these ideas have been presented, the question has often been raised, openly or implicitly, whether techniques such as numerical taxonomy will not result in computers taking over the work of the taxonomist. At this stage of the development of computers and of numerical taxonomy, it is, of course, too early to forecast the relative roles of automated equipment and taxonomist by the end of this century. However, interesting thoughts about the symbiotic relations between scientists and computers have recently been expressed by Fein (1961) and Jahn (1961). At the moment it would appear that the job of the taxonomist will continue to be the collection of data for taxonomic research and, more importantly, evaluation both taxonomically and phylogenetically of the results of computer-processed taxonomic work. Only the estimate of similarity between taxa—tedious and difficult to perform—and the cluster analysis are done by the computer. The rest of the taxonomic task still needs the experience and judgment of the specialist in the field.

A misconception about the nature of computers is that machines can calculate and count, but not evaluate or analyze form and shape [such a comment, for example, was made by Illies (Appendix to Sokal, 1960)]. It is, of course, not correct that machines cannot evaluate or make logical decisions. These they can do if the thought processes of the taxonomist are exactly defined. The machine has the advantage of being faster than taxonomists; it is not easily influenced in an unpredictable fashion; and it can process more information simultaneously than the human mind. A major benefit of programming taxonomy for a machine is that the taxonomist has to think through the logic of the taxonomic process rather than simply follow his taxonomic "intuition."

Some colleagues have stated explicitly or at least implied that quantification is an inherently unsuitable procedure in biology, or at least in taxonomy. Kiriakoff (1962) says: "Neo-Adansonians may be right quantitatively or statistically (and even so with many qualifications); they are wrong biologically." From this it seems that he wishes to separate quantitative and statistical approaches from so-called biological ones (whatever the latter may mean). He also implies that the classical methods of taxonomy are adequate for present-day problems. We do not agree on either point and should take this opportunity to declare firmly that, as in other sciences, quantification is a desirable goal in taxonomy. Scientific processes cannot be thoroughly formulated or understood until they are quantified, and this holds true for biology as well as for any other science.

Mayr (1959) has stated that no electric computer has so far been able to surpass in the arrangement of higher categories the integrating power of the brain of an intelligent and experienced taxonomist; he says, "in the hands of our less gifted colleagues even the best computer would produce absurd systems." The facts are quite to the contrary. Not only do we hope to have shown that numerical taxonomy will yield results superior to those obtained by orthodox taxonomic work, but especially do we feel that it will give protection against poor taxonomic practices. It will permit a check on the nature of characters chosen. If the characters studied by the taxonomist are poorly defined and erroneously recorded, the evidence will be there for his peers to judge. Furthermore, if the characters have been correctly collected, the machine procedures would produce repeatable results clearly preferable to a classification established by "one of our less gifted colleagues."

It has been said that by employing numerical taxonomy we do not rely on the experience of the taxonomist, which would ordinarily be used in weighting characters. We have been asked whether an "intelligent ignoramus"—one possessing enough intelligence to find characters, but knowing nothing of a group—could by cataloguing the characters and then passing them through the procedures of numerical taxonomy arrive at a proper classification. It seems to us that this may be possible. If that were indeed so, the premium presently put on experience might be unwarranted. We hope to be able to test this particular aspect of numerical taxonomy in the future. Yet it is also clear that experience on the part of the investigator will result in better choice and description of characters.

## 10.3. SOME PRACTICAL CONSIDERATIONS

### 10.3.1. Material for numerical taxonomic studies

At present the field in which numerical taxonomy is most useful is in the middle and lower ranks, in the study of genera and species and perhaps of families. In bacteria, where there is great difficulty in establishing satisfactory lower taxa, it has been very useful when applied to individual strains, and there seems to be no reason why it should not be employed with individual specimens in other fields, particularly in paleontology and in some other applications mentioned below.

We believe that in the great majority of organisms it will be possible to find the necessary numbers of characters for analysis. In a few difficult groups there may be few available characters, which in itself would show that previous taxonomies must have been based on inadequate data; any improvement in the classification, therefore, must first require new methods of study.

How representative of the whole taxon should the OTU's be? It is obvious that the more representative the data, the more representative will be the results. Ideally one would study all the species of a genus and all genera of a family, and so on. Yet it is seldom that all such material is readily accessible, and it may be necessary to work with incomplete material. It will then be necessary to reanalyze the taxon with more data at a later time.

A more difficult problem is that of incomplete data for the characters in the OTU's of a study. This has already proved troublesome in studies on viruses (Sneath, 1962), where very few characters had been recorded for all the viruses under study. It is also a problem in current studies on higher categories in animals and plants. For example, the best described species of an order may never have been examined by newer techniques, while for other members of the order it may be mainly the newer data that are recorded. This commonly happens when different organisms are used as the representative of the order in different laboratories, because of availability, personal interest, and the like. It would clearly be unjustifiable to score the characters of one organism on the assumption that they are the same as these characters in another organism without checking the specimens concerned. In consequence it may be necessary to undertake extensive studies to obtain the missing data. Although this is in a formal sense a limitation of numerical taxonomy, it is equally a limitation of orthodox taxonomy, since a great many assumptions of this kind may have been unconsciously made during the description of higher ranking taxa.

We may look forward to the application of numerical taxonomy to higher ranks, such as orders and classes. The problems of choosing taxa and suitable characters will be somewhat different from those in the studies carried out to date. However, the application of numerical taxonomy to a range of bacteria which is conventionally considered to cover several different orders has given a reasonably satisfactory result (Sneath and Cowan, 1958), and there seems no reason to assume that the extension of numerical taxonomy to the higher ranks of other kinds of organisms will involve any basically different principles.

We discussed in Sections 5.1 and 5.8 the choice of entities intended to represent heterogeneous taxonomic groups, and there is no need to repeat this except to point out that one exemplar, however typical, cannot exhibit the range of variation of the whole taxon. Systematists must therefore choose sufficient exemplars to serve the purpose they have in mind. The choice of characters when studying the higher ranks is likely to be more difficult. It is at first sight not easy to know how we could select features for the comparison of an insect with an echinoderm. Much of the difficulty will lie in knowing whether it is legitimate to employ features which seem to have no relevance to one of the forms. Would it, for example, be allowable to mark the echinoderm as "wings absent," or should it be scored as "this feature does not apply?" We believe that the absence of wings is indeed a perfectly valid taxonomic difference between a winged insect and an echinoderm. It may be more debatable whether absence of wings in two echinoderms should score as a similarity in a study in which winged animals are also included. In other words, the validity of negative comparisons may be more doubtful as we analyze more widely differing creatures. Yet even in extreme cases like the one given above we can find some characters to serve for numerical studies—for instance, the composition of the integument, the form of symmetry, the forms of digestive organs, the composition of the tissue fluids, and so on. We may be forced to omit many features because of uncertainty on whether they can validly be considered "the same" in the two forms, even employing the concepts of operational homology (see Section 5.3.4). When we choose a less extreme example, such as a bird compared to a mammal, we can at once find a large range of characters for use, such as form of erythrocytes, structure of the heart and great vessels, form of the parts of the brain, and many others. We must only be on our guard against choosing solely those features which have been selected to prove a preconceived point or which have been accepted by tradition as significant, for to do so would bias the analysis from the start. This statement should not be interpreted to mean that no previously recognized characters can be employed. The study by Michener and Sokal (1957) was based entirely on previously recognized characters. However, previous taxonomic treatments of the same groups

had each made use of comparatively few characters, the sets of characters used differing from one study to the next; and for no one species
had bee taxonomists ever employed anywhere near the number of
characters which Michener and Sokal used.

## 10.3.2. Techniques of numerical analysis

Until the advent of electronic computers, numerical analysis of taxonomic data, if they were abundant, was quite impracticable. This is no
longer true. Computers now are widely available, and several centers
are able to process material for taxonomists who are at a distance from
such facilities. The cost is small, far smaller than that of either hand
computation or traditional rumination and revision, if the real cost of
maintaining departments of systematics is considered.

It is, of course, inevitable that some of the statistics will have to be
taken on trust. Few biologists have the interest in mathematics that
would lead them to familiarity with all the arguments involved here.
Nevertheless, they have a check on the statistics in their own shrewd
judgments on the worth of the results. How many biologists understand
all the statistical logic underlying such simple measures as the arithmetic
mean and the standard deviation, which so many of them employ? With
better experience it will become possible to advocate standard numerical
methods which are applicable with safety to most material, and thereafter the taxonomist, if he will take this on trust, need not consider the
details of the mathematics or of the computers. The basic concepts are
simple enough. In the Appendix many practical points of analysis are
discussed in some detail.

We may here add some comments on the likely advances in technique
in the future. It seems to us that these will occur in three main ways.
First, there will be better methods for assembling the crude data into a
state suitable for analysis. This may take the form of automatic standardization or character coding. Even more valuable would be methods for
converting drawings into matrices of character states, employing such
concepts as information theory, character recognition, and automatic
analysis of complex variables (for example, Rogoff, 1957). These would
have the effect of "streamlining" the work by eliminating much of the
laborious coding of characters and their states.

Second, the estimation of affinity and cluster analysis will become
more sophisticated and more generally applicable, with increased safe-
guards against ridiculous results and with provision for isolation of

pertinent factors such as overall size and shape. Third, automatic processing of the affinities and dendrograms will enable diagnostic keys, discriminant functions, and tests of significance to be made as a routine, together with information on Q-R relations and even on nomenclature.

The use of machines for automatic printing of distribution maps is another development (Walters, 1954). The day when a monograph can be prepared by computer may still be far off, but the way toward this is clear. Modern data processing machinery in centers for numerical taxonomy would here come into their own.

Advantages would accrue from close cooperation between different workers in the field. The exchange of data, affinity matrices, and computer programs would facilitate this. A step in this direction is the inception of the newsletter *Taxometrics* issued by the Progetto Sistematica Actinomiceti, Istituto P. Stazzi, Via Celoria 10, Milan, Italy. A central repository where copies of the data could be deposited might prove very useful.

## 10.4. THE EXTRACTION OF DISCRIMINATORY FEATURES AND THE PREPARATION OF KEYS

After a numerical taxonomic analysis has been carried to the point of drawing up the hierarchy of natural taxa, it may be necessary to inspect the original tables of data in order to find those characters which are the most useful for rapid identification of the taxa. From these characters a synoptic key can readily be made. Hill (1959) and Pohja (1960) made such keys by finding the features by inspection, and Sneath (1962) used a method of extracting the features by their relative constancy within and among the taxa. They were then tabulated as the characters which best separated the main sections of the genus studied, and those which best separated the species within each section. More sophisticated methods will doubtless be needed in the future. This aspect of numerical taxonomy has been relatively neglected, and in this section we will only point out a few of the possible lines of development.

It is important to remember that these methods can only be employed after the taxa have been constructed. They cannot, as a rule, be relied upon to yield the taxa themselves, since they are generally based on monothetic division (though combined methods for cluster analysis and discrimination may be developed in the future). Two contrasting situations may occur. First, there may be some character states that sharply distinguish two taxa; that is, they are present in all members of one taxon and absent in all members of the other. It is then only necessary to find these character states. Second, there may be no single states of this kind, but it may be possible to distinguish the taxa by using several character states which occur with different frequencies in the two taxa. This latter situation, phenetic overlapping (sometimes referred to as reticulation, as by Turrill, 1950, presumably because it has been attributed to reticulate evolution) is found in taxa that are fully polythetic (see Section 2.2). It has been studied mainly in botany (Anderson and Abbe, 1934; Anderson and Whitaker, 1934; Whitehead, 1954). Phenetic overlapping may occur extensively at lower taxonomic ranks (generic and below) but seems to be less common at higher ranks. Sharp discrimination without overlapping is produced by absolute correlation of two or more features, and one problem of cluster analysis is to find clusters that differ sharply in a few respects when there are many inconstant features present. A distinction must here be made between phenetic clusters (in which the inconstant features are treated equally with the correlated features) and the smallest groups showing character correlations. The latter are not necessarily phenetic taxa, though they may be of much taxonomic interest. The "Siamese" mutant of the domestic cat shows constant correlation of certain characters, but it is not certain that, phenetically, Siamese cats would form a phenon, since there are many other variable characters in both Siamese and other cats. The position is thus similar to that in genetic isolates; there may be several distinguishable entities within one phenetic taxon. The entities can be evaluated by the number of correlated features they possess, a field which has not yet been explored.

Similar considerations apply to groups distinguished by the "75 percent rule." The statistical difficulties of this have been discussed by Amadon (1949), Pimentel (1959), and Sokal and Rinkel (1963). More pertinent is the fact that the rule, or its variants, does not consider how to choose the characters for its application. If any variable feature is chosen it is plain, as Wilson and Brown (1953) and Pimentel (1958) have pointed out, that one may obtain from several characters a variety of different groupings which are not concordant. Such groupings may not even show two well-correlated characters.

The minimum number of characters for discrimination is easy to calculate. No more groups can be distinguished than the product of the numbers of character states. Thus three characters, two of three states and one of four states, allows at the most the distinction of

$3 \times 3 \times 4 = 36$ groups. In general, log (number of distinguishable groups) $\leqq \sum$ (log states). In practice many more characters are required than the theoretical minimum, since many do not discriminate between the taxa. A more advanced treatment of this topic is given by Ledley and Lusted (1959a).

Where there is phenetic overlapping, one needs to find for the taxa studied those characters that best discriminate taxa. For two-state characters the algebraic difference, $G$, between the frequencies of a given state in two taxa may be used (Sneath, 1962): the most discriminatory characters have the highest values of $G$ (positive or negative). Nonadditive scoring (see Section 5.3.6) causes difficulty in this method. The classificatory method of Lockhart and Hartman (1963) also extracts discriminatory characters, while Möller (1962) obtains in addition the probability of misidentification. Another simple statistic is the Hybrid Index (Anderson, 1936; Gay, 1960). In general the best discrimination is given by discriminant analysis (Fisher, 1936), in which each character is given a loading such that there is the least probability of misidentifying an individual taken at random. A worked example is given by Whitehead (1954). Related work is that of Rescigno and Maccacaro (1960) and Birnbaum and Maxwell (1961).

We do not propose to discuss at length the making of keys; for practical details we refer to the reader to the articles of Ainsworth (1941), Voss (1952), Metcalf (1954), Stearn (1956), and Cowan and Steel (1960). For a mathematical approach, see Maccacaro (1958). One will use where possible the features that are easiest to observe accurately, and the use of several characters at each fork may help with damaged or aberrant material.

The decision has first to be taken whether the most efficient and probably quite artificial system is to be used or whether the key is to be based on the taxonomy established by the numerical program. In the first case the steps to be taken are relatively quite simple. They consist in eliminating initially all those characters which are unsuitable for identification on the conventional specimen (which is commonly a preserved adult), such as, physiological and ethological characters. Then a methodical search is made by the machine for specific character states unique to the basic taxonomic entities in the study. The machine then works out the smallest number of characters required in order to differentiate every taxon from every other one. This would be done under a system which would permit a stage in the key to have more than two alternatives. If it is deemed desirable that each stage in the key should have only two alternatives, the machine can be programmed to search for the character states which will differentiate the taxa. All those taxa that cannot be characterized by a single character state are identified by unique combinations of two or more character states.

When a natural key is desired it is simple to sort out and segregate the various taxa in the original data and then to determine the constant character states for each taxon. Among these constant characters we again eliminate those unsuitable for conventional specimens and then proceed as with the artificial key. The above methods may be described as rather pedestrian, but they are well suited to the type of routine and repetitive operation which electronic computers carry out. Key construction, however, is a field where more sophisticated approaches— information theory, for example—can produce more elegant and efficient procedures (see Maccacaro, 1958; Rescigno and Maccacaro, 1960; Möller, 1962; Hill and Silvestri, 1962).

Taxonomists may feel that keys based on single characters are unsatisfactory, since damaged specimens may not yield information on the critical character. Furthermore, the person identifying a given specimen may not be certain about the interpretation of a given feature in a taxonomic key and may wish to confirm his decision by reference to a second (and even a third) characteristic. The methods outlined above would, of course, be quite adaptable to producing keys based on any number of characters, so long as differences did in fact exist between the taxa which had been erected.

## 10.5.  THE FUTURE OF SYSTEMATICS

Ehrlich (1961b) has made some predictions on the future of systematics which he refers to as unpopular. These include the prediction that data-processing equipment will be the most important tool of the taxonomist in 1970 and that a great simplification of nomenclature will take place. These predictions may be unpopular today, though whether they will prove so in the future is another matter. Fein (1961) predicts that by 1975 at least one botany department in a large university will offer a course in the application of computer techniques to taxonomic botany. Jahn (1961), in an extraordinarily interesting paper, has discussed a number of exciting possibilities. Among these he foresees machines which do not merely retrieve information, identify specimens, or give us their synonymies but which also will tell us if we have found a new organism ("Congratulations! You have discovered a new phylum"), suggest a suitable name, question the taxonomist's veracity, and learn by experience as new organisms are discovered and their particulars given to it. "Furthermore," Jahn says, "the goal to be achieved by intellectronics is not to copy human errors of thought, but to serve as an extension of man's intellect."

Jahn also suggests that diagnostic keys might be recorded on magnetic tape for use in computers, and "presumably these tapes would be available in suitable taxonomic units from any good biological supply house." We may even look forward to the day when the larger museums have a computer wholly employed as a machine for identification of specimens, to be fed with specified characters on punched cards. Even the isolated worker may have access to such facilities by mail or telegraphic lines. Such facilities are now available for information retrieval, abstracting services, and the like. In the systematics of thoroughly worked groups of organisms the use of these devices should not be unfeasible.

Jahn (1962) has in a recent paper advocated a rigidly logical approach to taxonomy. With large, fast computers, the universal coding of taxa, descriptions, and names may indeed become feasible. At present there are two main difficulties: (1) comprehensive, logical nomenclature and identification first require satisfactory and comprehensive taxonomies; (2) until these are available we must retain large coded descriptions for the OTU's (perhaps of a hundred decimal digits). Otherwise a later taxonomic revision might disrupt a logical nomenclature that employed ordinal, familial, generic, and species code numbers.

The flood of new data available to biologists will raise its own problems. Cain (1959c) has pointed out that the assimilation of new data is one of the main problems facing systematics today. The efficient understanding of the biological significance of the data will be a greater problem. This is clearly true of their ecological and evolutionary significance. In molecular biology and genetic fine structure this will be even more difficult. It was noted in Section 5.3.1 that the potential store of information in a mammalian nucleus is of the order of $10^{10}$ bits, and Jahn (1961) comments that it has been calculated that this would, if set in type, fill a thousand standard books, a feat of miniaturization far exceeding any that engineers can envisage today. The scale of this can be judged from the fact that the Library of Congress could be in theory comfortably encoded in the anther of a lily.

The natural history museum of the future will be very different from those of today. It will still contain many preserved specimens and some type material, but far more emphasis will be given to exhibitions of biochemical properties. A central feature will be a data-processing installation. Dusty files on nomenclature will be consigned to a limbo: in their place will be a few international indices which would provide immediate access to stored taxonomic data. As to the nomenclature itself, it might be mononominal (as Cain, 1959b, has suggested), with numerical additions to indicate the hierarchic relation, or it might possibly be wholly numerical.

Should there be a separate numerical taxonomy, parallel to but distinct from orthodox systematics? Some aspects of the latter, such as, nomenclature, may be relatively unconcerned with numerical methods. There is a great deal to be said for incorporating the findings of numerical taxonomy into orthodox taxonomy wherever this is possible, if only because the latter is an efficient system of information retrieval.

A more detailed essay on the future of systematics can be found in Sokal (1964).

Numerical taxonomy and genetics will together provide a bridge between the molecular and evolutionary views of biology. The first will relate genotype to phenotype and will measure the degree, rate, and direction of evolution. The second will relate the genotype to physico-chemical composition and to the mechanisms of evolution.

## 10.6. OTHER APPLICATIONS OF NUMERICAL TAXONOMY

The principles of numerical taxonomy can be applied to domains other than that of the classification of living organisms. Analogous methods, many of them anticipating the ones we have discussed, are already widely used in plant ecology for the study of types of vegetation, in which "taxa" such as woodland, prairie, or moorland can be distinguished and analyzed (see, for example, Sørensen, 1948; Goodall, 1953; Williams and Lambert, 1959; Harberd, 1960; and the detailed review of Dagnelie, 1960). These vegetation types may sometimes form hierarchies analogous to those in systematics. Sørensen employed both association coefficients and cluster analysis. Similar methods have been used to distinguish ecological associations of marine plankton (Williamson, 1961). Grieg-Smith (1957) and Dagnelie (1960) described many of the methods used in ecology, with a critical discussion of them. There is a growing dissatisfaction with many ecological concepts at present poorly defined (Ehrlich and Holm, 1962). An attempt to make some of these more rigorous was made by Hutchinson (1957).

Sneath has examined the ecological data on the Hoveton Great Broad (shallow lake), kindly provided by Dr. J. M. Lambert (Lambert and Jennings, 1951), consisting of 56 quadrats scored for 73 plant species. The data consisted of a series of quadrats forming a transect across a lake, bordered by reed swamp, fen, and carr (swampy willow thickets) on either side. The similarity coefficient was $S_{SM}$ and clustering was on single linkage of similarity values. The clustering analysis, as one would have expected, brought together reasonably well the quadrats from each vegetational association; for example, the reed swamp quadrats were, in the main, placed together, though spatially on opposite sides of the lake.

On comparing this polythetic method with the monothetic association analysis described by Williams and Lambert (1959), the following points were noted. The polythetic method was less sensitive to chance presence or absence in a quadrat of any single species. That is, in the monothetic method a quadrat may be occasionally removed from quadrats which are highly similar in overall floristic content because of the chance presence or absence of the species which served to define the monothetic group. However, if the full process of nodal analysis is carried out (Williams and Lambert, 1962), these quadrats would be normally picked out as distinct. As expected, it was often impossible with the polythetic method to find "indicator species" (single species diagnostic of the clusters of quadrats). Nevertheless the dendrograms given by the two methods were very similar in differentiating open water, fen, and reed swamp, but they showed some differences in the treatment of the carr.

Similar comparisons by the two methods of the "inverse" relations (R type analysis; the grouping of species according to the quadrats in which they occurred; see Williams and Lambert, 1961a, b) also gave generally concordant results, with findings similar to those in the "normal" analyses (Q type, discussed above).

An interesting application would be the difficult subject of the classification of soils (see Manil, 1959; Chenery, 1960). Leeper (1954) has discussed soil classification and strongly criticized those based on speculations on the origins of the soil rather than on their observed properties, a significant echo of the controversy over phylogenetic taxonomies in systematics. Hughes and Lindley (1955) applied Mahalonobis' $D^2$ statistic to soils but employed very few characteristics. The study of Hole and Hironaka (1960) is also related to distance.

Numerical taxonomic methods may also prove useful in investigating the degree to which the environment affects the phenotype, both as regards overall size (or its equivalent) and shape. It may also find some application in genetics, such as in blood groups or where large numbers of genes have been described for certain species and their mutants (see, for instance, Kelus and Lukaszewicz, 1953; Harland, 1936).

Ornstein (1960) has used the method of Rogers and Tanimoto (1960) in studying serum protein patterns. Numerical taxonomy could be applied to some classes of chemical substances, such as proteins, and possibly genes or their DNA sequences. Sneath is currently studying peptide structure by numerical taxonomic methods, in part along the lines suggested by Fox and Homeyer (1955). Some interesting reflections on the relation between classification and chemical structure of viruses are given by Pirie (1962).

Although numerical taxonomy has not been employed in anthropology in the rigorous manner which we feel is essential for valid results, there is, nevertheless, a considerable body of data of some interest which was obtained by rather similar methods, notably the Coefficient of Racial Likeness. Much of the earlier work is summarized in the reviews of Bielicki (1962) and Wierciński (1962; see also, Campbell, 1962). The study of the physical anthropology of race seems to be in urgent need of studies based on characteristics of individuals rather than speculative "original" races or ill-defined populations. This is evident from a comprehensive collection of essays on race (Count, 1950), in which few authors even touch on the question of how one recognizes a race by objective criteria. It seems scarcely credible that there should still be argument over this (Bielicki, 1962; Wierciński, 1962). Possibly the same criticism applies to social anthropology (Leach, 1962).

The techniques of numerical taxonomy may also prove of use in the field of medical diagnosis. Some attempts have been made to employ computers in this field (for example, Lipkin and Hardy, 1957; Lipkin et al., 1961; Tolles et al., 1961), but they have usually met with logical problems which are taxonomic in a wide sense of that word. In particular, the validity of the disease entities (the definitions of the diseases) may be questioned, for if these should prove to be unsound the diagnostic schemes will inevitably be unsatisfactory. The construction of disease entities (that is, disease taxa based on individual cases of disease) can be made by numerical taxonomic methods, and association analysis with clustering on single linkage (as suggested by Sneath, 1957a) has been successfully used in grouping cases of leukemia (Hayhoe, Doll, and Quaglino, report to be published). It is probable that most well-known disease entities are valid groupings, but there has been little study of this point: it is doubtful whether most of the obscure diseases have been satisfactorily classified. Possibly polythetic concepts would prove valuable here, despite the conventional emphasis on defining a disease by its etiology. Etiology, despite its great influence on treatment of diseases, may prove in medicine to be almost as unsatisfactory as phylogeny has been in biology as a general principle for defining taxa. Some clinical entities may have a varied etiology—for example, the great similarity of kinds of purulent meningitis caused by very different bacteria; conversely, one etiology may produce varied signs, symptoms, and pathology—for example, syphilis.

The construction of sound disease taxa would seem to be a necessary preliminary to full use of computers in diagnosis and prognosis. When this has been done, the correlation methods (Tolles et al., 1961) and matching methods (Lipkin et al., 1961) will prove of great value in the diagnostic process. A detailed logical study of diagnosis has been made by Ledley and Lusted (1959a, b) and Lusted (1960). The simple logical methods of Nash (1954, 1960) may also be applicable. In passing we may add that successful diagnostic techniques would seem to need provision for (1) deciding on what signs, symptoms, and diseases are pertinent (and conversely what is considered "normal" or "healthy"), (2) the satisfactory construction of disease entities, or the checking thereof, (3) the weighting of attributes for diagnosis and discrimination, (4) the questioning of the physician to confirm signs which may have been misread or overlooked, and (5) the correction of the disease entities by new data. There will be many opportunities for fruitful collaboration between those working on medical diagnosis and those working on taxonomic keys and identification methods.

We know of few applications of numerical taxonomy to fields outside biology. It may be of use in comparing and identifying rocks, for such purposes as detecting their position with regard to faults and other geological formations. It has been applied with some success to the classification of reaction facies in the study of oil-bearing strata. Whitten (1961a, b) has recently applied rather similar methods to the study of rocks. As in the studies of soils cited above, very few characteristics were studied. It should be remembered that while it is possible to compare the points of a single transect in a checkerboard of affinities, to compare the points of an area in this way would require four dimensions. This is also true of ecological, racial, and other geographic distributions. There is considerable literature on classificatory methods in psychology.

Numerical taxonomy has recently been applied to political science in a study of legislative behavior (Professor J. G. Grumm of the University of Kansas, personal communication). It was used to classify groups of legislators into clusters, as defined by their voting patterns. Less sophisticated methods of this general kind had been used as early as 1927 by Rice and later by Beyle (1931) and Truman (1959).

The close connections between taxonomy and information theory may be seen by reading the article of Good (1958). There is a discussion not only of clumps and how to measure them (equivalent in many ways to cluster analysis) but also of John Wisdom's cow. "A cow has four legs and gives milk," but it may have three legs and may not supply milk. No one property may be essential to its "cowness." Estrin, quoted by Good, suggests information retrieval by asking for $k$ out of $n$ index words before selecting a document. But the group "cows" is a polythetic taxon. So are Estrin's document clusters.

Numerical taxonomy may have a part to play in problems of pattern recognition (see Unger, 1959; Stearns, 1960; Bonner, 1962). Lusted (1960) refers to this as one of the challenging problems to be found in many fields of science, such as psychometry, radiography, mapping, and recognition of handwriting. Patterns may be polythetic, and different variants of one pattern would then form phenons, which would be difficult to distinguish by monothetic methods of classification.

Other fields which come to mind where numerical taxonomy may offer assistance are archeology (Clarke, 1962), astronomy, economics, mythology, oceanography, library classification, and the identification of the literary style of different authors. It has already been used in philology (Ross, 1950). Parker-Rhodes and his colleagues are now exploring its use in language translation research (Parker-Rhodes, 1961). Methods in cultural anthropology are quite similar (Driver, 1962). A modified method was used by Sneath to solve a simple jigsaw puzzle. Almost any field dealing with polythetic groupings may find numerical taxonomy useful.

## 10.7. LATE REFERENCES

In a rapidly developing field, such as numerical taxonomy, bibliographies are out of date before they are even printed. In preparing this book we have had to draw a deadline beyond which references could not be included for consideration in the general text. However, we would like to avail ourselves of the opportunity to present here references to papers which came to our attention by galley proof time. These are mostly recent publications related to numerical taxonomy. However, some of them are earlier papers which have been pointed out to us by colleagues and which we include for the sake of completeness. The publications are presented alphabetically by author in the form of an annotated bibliography.

Cavalli, L. L. 1949. Sulla correlazione media fra piú caratteri in relazione alla Biometria. *Metron*, **15**:1–16. This paper discusses Zarapkin's method of discriminating between populations and relates it to the "mean correlation coefficient," defined as the mean of the $n(n-1)/2$ correlation coefficients between pairs of $n$ characters. Cavalli also discusses the relation between this mean correlation coefficient and other such coefficients—as, for example, Gini's synthetic coefficient and the intraclass correlation coefficient. A reference to earlier work by Cavalli in this field is also given.

Clements, F. E. 1954. Use of cluster analysis with anthropological data. *Amer. Anthropologist*, **56**:180–199. An example of the use of Holzinger's coefficient of belonging and Tryon's cluster analysis.

Downe, A. E. R. 1963. Mosquitoes: comparative serology of four species of *Aedes* (*Ochlerotatus*). *Science*, **139**:1286–1287. The four species compared serologically in this study were also included in the numerical taxonomic study by Rohlf (1962). The serological findings show *A. communis* closely related to *A. punctor*, with *A. trichurus* related more closely to those two than is the fourth species, *A. excrucians*. These findings are duplicated by Rohlf's analysis of distance coefficients based on adults; however, his analysis of data based on adults and larvae pooled places *A. excrucians* closer to *A. communis* and *A. punctor* than to *A. trichurus* and in fact he has put *A. trichurus* in a separate species group of the subgenus *Ochlerotatus*. This is so because *A. trichurus* has several unusual larval characteristics. Thus the serology of adults is quite congruent with a numerical taxonomy of adults. It would be interesting to learn whether the serology of the larvae would be congruent with adult serology or would agree more with the rather different relations found in the numerical taxonomic study of larvae. We find here further support for the nonspecificity hypothesis, in that relationships based on morphological characteristics are paralleled by relationships based on protein structure.

Driver, H. E. 1963. Survey of numerical classification in anthropology.

In Hymes, D. H. (ed.), *The Use of Computers in Anthropology.* Mouton, The Hague (in press). We have been privileged to see the manuscript copy of this article. It will be an invaluable source for persons interested in problems of numerical taxonomy as they relate to the field of anthropology, both physical and cultural.

Driver, H. E. and A. L. Kroeber. 1932. Quantitative expression of cultural relationships. *Univ. Calif. Publ. Amer. Archaeol. Ethnol.*, **31**:211–256. An early attempt to quantify cultural relationships in an attempt to make natural classifications. They discuss a number of association coefficients and show that, as a rule, these give closely concordant results.

Ellegård, A. 1959. Statistical measurement of linguistic relationship. *Language*, **35**:131–156. Discusses previous work and, at some length, the significance of negatives (absence of a word or language feature). He concludes that inclusion of negative matches may be misleading in some circumstances. The inclusion of negative matches, as in *phi*, measures interdependence, or interinfluence (positive or negative), while omitting negative matches measures similarity. *Phi* = zero can indicate either no similarity at all or else no interinfluence in related languages. He concludes with some notes on significance tests, with formulas.

Floodgate, G. D. 1962. Some comments on the Adansonian taxonomic method. *International Bulletin of Bacteriological Nomenclature and Taxonomy*, **12**:171–179. Floodgate discusses the meaning of the term "feature" and reaches conclusions very similar to our own, in that he distinguishes between characters that are permissible in taxonomy from those which are not because they are redundant, invariable, or inapplicable. He also shows by an example the close agreement between several different ways of estimating similarity.

Floodgate, G. D. and P. R. Hayes. 1963. The Adansonian taxonomy of some yellow pigmented marine bacteria. *J. Gen. Microbiol.*, **30**:237–244. Another study, principally covering strains that probably belong to the genera *Flavobacterium* and *Cytophaga*, in which two main phenons and some smaller groups were found, in good concordance with other work on these bacteria.

Günther, K. 1962. Systematik und Stammesgeschichte der Tiere 1954–1959. *Fortschritte der Zoologie*, **14**:267–547. This is a useful and comprehensive summary of systematics during the years indicated. It presents a critique of the early work in numerical taxonomy but not of the more recent work.

Klimek, S. 1935. Culture element distributions. I. The structure of Californian Indian culture. *Univ. Calif. Publ. Amer. Archaeol. Ethnol.*,

**35:**1–70. Klimek uses a sine transformation of the four-point correlation coefficient *phi*, such that $Q_6$ = sine of $\frac{1}{2}\phi\pi$ radians. Illustrated by a Q type and R type analysis of the same body of data, showing correlated clusters of both tribes and of culture traits. The method seems to come from Czekanowski in 1911.

Kroeber, A. L. 1960. Statistics, Indo-European, and Taxonomy. *Language*, **36:**1–21. Discusses the paper of Ellegård (see above) on classification of languages, and a number of association coefficients, with some interesting comments on biological classification and the phylogenetic problem in linguistics.

Lubischew, A. A. 1962. On the use of discriminant functions in taxonomy. *Biometrics*, **18:**455–477. In this paper, and in an earlier paper in Russian, Lubischew works out a coefficient of discrimination which is a type of distance based on a single character. Lubischew's techniques are of interest also because they can be carried out with simple computational devices, including the use of nomograms.

McQuitty, L. L. We would like to draw attention to numerous papers by this author published in *Educational and Psychological Measurement* between the years 1957 and 1962. McQuitty develops a number of relatively simple methods for cluster analysis. Whether such methods can be of use in numerical taxonomy remains to be investigated.

Michener, C. D. 1964. Some future developments in taxonomy. *Systematic Zool.* (in press). This important contribution takes up several issues intimately connected with numerical taxonomy. It holds that current classifications (whether made in the traditional manner or by numerical taxonomy) are not as natural as they could be, partly because of the tradition of mutually exclusive taxa, reinforced by the present system of nomenclature in which the genus name is part of the classification and at the same time part of the name of the organism being classified. Michener recommends a system of uninominal nomenclature for which certain advantages are claimed—simplicity of rules and relatively great stability, in addition to the major one of liberating classification from the restrictions of nomenclature.

If taxonomy is to progress to best advantage on earth or be ready to provide a basis for systematic work on foreign biotas when exobiology becomes a reality, it must, of course, take advantage of instruments for automatic discovery and recording of characters and of systems for storage and retrieval of data. In connection with information retrieval systems, some suggestions are made for the development of an appropriate numbering system for organisms. There should be a unique designation for each species that incorporates nothing of the classification; the latter can be indicated by a prefixed number, subject to change as the classification changes with improved knowledge.

Emphasis is placed on the idea that even investigators as different in their approaches and objectives as numerical taxonomists and New Systematists can each contribute important information to a systematic study. Numerical taxonomy can contribute at all taxonomic levels except perhaps the highest, while contributions of New Systematics are largely limited to lower levels, especially the specific level and below.

Some of the reforms suggested by Michener require work by numbers of biologists, or discussion and action by appropriate international commisions on nomenclature, or even a costly international center for the storage and retrieval of taxonomic and related data, and such recommendations have been made by him.

Pohja, M. S. and H. G. Gyllenberg. 1962. Numerical taxonomy of micrococci of fermented meat origin. *J. Appl. Bacteriol.*, **25**:341–351. Several different statistical methods were used, including clustering by single linkage and central clustering of Rogers and Tanimoto, and the data were compared with previous numerical taxonomy of these organisms. There was close agreement between all the dendrograms. A brief reference, without details, is made to a clustering method based on the number of mismatches that is statistically significant in an association coefficient.

Proctor, J. R. and W. B. Kendrick. 1963. Unequal weighting in numerical taxonomy. *Nature*, **197**:716–717. The authors defend unequal weighting for the avowed purpose of making "form genera" (and other artificial taxa) in fungi, which they do not claim to be natural taxa (these they consider impracticable). They divide characters into primary (such as presence of some organ) and secondary—that is, characters that qualify a primary character (such as color of the organ). A primary character is given an additional weight equal to the number of secondary characters in the study that qualify it. We do not see how one can consistently distinguish primary from secondary characters. "Spores showing spines" could be a primary character, "spines (on the spores)," or a secondary one, "spores spiny." The details of scoring are not given, but one gathers that the effect will often be that of scoring inapplicable character states as being applicable. It is not clear why the authors consider a natural taxonomy to be impracticable.

Shepard, R. N. 1962. The analysis of proximities: multidimensional scaling with an unknown distance function. I and II. *Psychometrika*,

27:125–140 and 219–246. These papers describe a novel method by which the rank order of a series of some function of distances between $N$ points in multidimensional space controls the collapse of the configuration into the smallest number of dimensions consistent with monotonicity. It has been programmed for a computer. In addition, the underlying function of distance can usually be obtained.

Smirnov, E. S. 1926. Über die Phylogenese der Kongregationen. *Biologia Generalis*, 2:1–17. Another earlier paper on numerical taxonomy.

Smirnov, E. S. 1938. Species construction from a taxonomic point of view [in Russian, English summary], *Zoologicheskii Zhurnal*, 17:387–418. This is an earlier paper by Smirnov which we had overlooked. In it he developed a method ("the principle of exhaustive characteristics") for reducing the number of characters on which an evaluation of similarity is to be based. The author states that once such characters are detected and utilized, all other properties of individuals will be either tautological or will distort the real aspect of similarity. This method thus appears to be similar in aim to the use of factor analysis for removing the redundancy in character correlations which we have speculated upon earlier.

Smirnov, E. S. 1962. On the structure of a three-membered genus. In Serguiev et al. (eds.), *Problems of General Zoology and Medical Parasitology*, pp. 229–255. State Medical Publishing House, Moscow (in Russian). This paper expands the formulas of Smirnov (1960) as applied to a genus containing only three species.

Wagner, W. H., Jr. 1963. Biosystematics and taxonomic categories in lower vascular plants. *Regnum Vegetabile*, 27:63–71. Wagner questions the validity of conventional biosystematic information in botany based on few characters thought to be important as compared with the great abundance of characters employed in numerical taxonomy for classification of plants. Attention should also be drawn to Wagner's method for expressing phylogenetic deductions, which permits quantification of the data. An example can be found in Mickel, J. T. 1962. A monographic study of the fern genus *Anemia*, subgenus *Ceratophyllum*. *Iowa State Univ. J. Sci.*, 36:349–482.

Williams, W. T. and M. B. Dale. 1962. Partition correlation matrices for heterogeneous quantitative data. *Nature*, 196:602. If a data matrix such as an $n \times t$ table contains many zeros, this makes the mean to variance relationship approximate to that of a qualitative $(0, 1)$ distribution. The authors suggest a method for partitioning the data into qualitative and quantitative elements. This indicates how the populations may be subdivided into more homogeneous subdivisions.

# APPENDIX

# Computational Methods for Numerical Taxonomy

For the benefit of the reader interested in familiarizing himself with the computational details of the various techniques discussed in Chapters 6 and 7, the Appendix shows some of the most common computations in numerical taxonomy. While all computational steps will be illustrated, we cannot, of course, explain the fundamentals of statistical procedure in this section. Readers lacking any statistical background should refer to one of the numerous books on the subject (for example, Simpson, Roe, and Lewontin, 1960, or Steel and Torrie, 1960, for biological statistics). All the necessary formulas have already been given in the previous sections; presented below are small illustrative examples which bring out some of the problems involved in doing the actual computations and which may help those readers who are not too facile with mathematical computations to visualize what is happening. Indeed, since much of the work will in the future be done on computers, the present examples will serve to show what is going on "behind the scenes." In Section A.1 we shall briefly review how characters may be coded and scaled in order to present them in a data matrix. We shall then discuss the computation of various estimates of affinity or similarity in Section A.2. This is followed by a discussion of methods of clustering in Section A.3. In Section A.4 some of the ancillary methods, such as studies of frequency distributions of similarity coefficients and computation of cophenetic correlations, are illustrated, and the final section makes brief mention of the problems of computer programming for numerical taxonomy.

## A.1. Choice and coding of characters

Detailed techniques for coding characters have already been discussed in Sections 5.2 and 5.3 and need not be repeated here. Table A-1 shows an $n \times t$

**Table A-1.** *Original Data Matrix*

| Characters | OTU's | | | | | | Mean | S.D. |
|---|---|---|---|---|---|---|---|---|
| | **A** | **B** | **C** | **D** | **E** | **F** | | |
| 1 | 1 | 8 | 1 | 7 | 2 | 5 | 4.000 | 3.098 |
| 2 | 1 | 6 | 1 | 6 | 1 | 3 | 3.000 | 2.449 |
| 3 | 6 | 1 | 5 | 1 | 4 | 2 | 3.167 | 2.137 |
| 4 | 1 | 0 | 1 | 0 | 1 | 4 | 1.167 | 1.472 |
| 5 | NC | 6 | 3 | 6 | NC | 1 | 4.000 | 2.449 |
| 6 | NC | 2 | NC | 3 | 1 | 1 | 1.750 | 0.957 |
| 7 | 8 | 2 | 7 | 2 | 5 | 5 | 4.833 | 2.483 |
| 8 | 1 | 6 | 1 | 6 | 3 | 4 | 3.500 | 2.258 |
| 9 | 1 | 8 | 1 | 8 | 2 | 4 | 4.000 | 3.286 |
| 10 | 6 | 1 | 6 | 1 | 5 | 2 | 3.500 | 2.429 |
| 11 | 3 | 3 | 3 | 3 | 3 | 3 | 3.000 | 0.000 |

data matrix for six OTU's labeled **A** through **F** and eleven characters numbered one through eleven.

It should be pointed out immediately that the example here is entirely for
illustrative purposes. A numerical taxonomic study should not be based on
eleven characters alone. However, so far as computational details are concerned, the smaller the example the easier it will be to present. Also, it is not
customary to label OTU's by letter in computational work. In larger studies,
and especially when digital computers are employed, referring to the OTU's
by number is essential. The characters considered in this entirely hypothetical
example are multistate characters varying in their range from three states for
character 6 to eight states for characters 1 and 9. Most of the characters presented here have been coded with "1" as the lowest class. However, since the
characters will eventually be standardized, the numerical value of the lowest
character state is immaterial. All sets of characters can have a constant subtracted from them without changing their standard deviation or their standardized character state codes. Thus, for example, character 7 has the character
state codes 8, 2, 7, 2, 5, 5 which could be recoded to read 7, 1, 6, 1, 4, 4 by
subtraction of 1. The standard deviation of these characters would be the same
regardless of whether the 1 had been subtracted or not; hence the standardization would give identical results. All possible character states may be shown
in a data matrix, as for example the three-state character 6, where states 1, 2,
and 3 all occur. On the other hand, some of the intermediate states may not
exist in a given data matrix, as is the case with most of the other characters
in the matrix of Table A-1. This could be so for three reasons. (1) The character
state codes may actually refer to counts of certain structures, such as number of

COMPUTATIONAL METHODS [APP.]

bristles or segments in an insect, number of leaflets in a plant, or number of tentacles in an animal possessing these, or they may refer to the concentration of a certain substance in an arithmetic scale or in a logarithmic scale when such seems appropriate. Thus, for example, character 4 may represent the characteristic of the logarithm of the concentration of a given substance $X$ in the blood of the organisms with which we are working. In such a scheme, character state code 0 would represent that the substance is undetectable—for example, less than 10 micrograms per unit volume; character state code 1 would then represent up to 100 micrograms per unit volume, and character state code 4 would represent from 10,000 to 100,000 micrograms per unit volume. (2) A second reason why all character states are not present may be that we are working only with a section of a larger study. However, in such a case it may be argued that the standardization employed should be based on all the characters rather than only on the sample used here.

(3) A third reason could be that the taxonomist working on the group may know from his experience and comparative knowledge of other groups that there are in fact intermediate states between the extremes that he is examining at the moment. Thus, for example, in character 1 the states are coded from 1 to 8, yet character state codes 3, 4, and 6 are missing. It may well be that the taxonomist knows that according to his scheme of coding such character state codes occur in other OTU's but not in the ones in the present study. Therefore he may feel that to code as shown here is more appropriate than to use a coding scheme limited entirely to the character states in the OTU's he is at present studying.

Two further points of interest in the original data matrix should be noted. Character 11 has the identical character state code for all the OTU's in the example. This is therefore a character that is not admissible in a numerical taxonomic study (see Section 5.3.3.4). It should not have been included at all. Its presence is immediately obvious in this small study; however, in a large study invariant characters may not be noticed during the preparation of the data matrix (this may quite easily happen if the data are processed by automatic data-processing equipment). In such a case the next step, standardization of characters, would automatically remove character 11 from consideration. This is so because its standard deviation is zero, and it will be impossible to compute standardized character state codes for this character since such a procedure would necessitate division by zero.

Second, characters 5 and 6 show the letters NC in place of character state codes for certain OTU's. NC stands for "no comparison." Such a score is indicated when data are missing because of damaged specimens or when characters or organs are missing and some property of these can therefore not be measured or evaluated. The wing veins in wingless insects or some chemical attribute of chlorophyll in plants that do not possess chlorophyll would be cases in point. This whole subject has been discussed in detail in Section 6.5, "Unwarranted Comparisons." No comparison or calculation is made regarding the resemblance between two OTU's for any particular character when one or both of the OTU's involved are scored NC. Thus in comparing **A** and **B**, two NC's are involved—one for character 5, the other for character 6—and the total number of valid comparisons is only 8 (remember that character 11 is omitted from the study altogether). The OTU's **C** and **E** also have eight valid comparisons. OTU's **B** and **D** on the other hand, can be compared in all ten characters, while **E** and **F** can be compared in 9 characters. It should be noted that the number of NC's should not be excessive, to ensure the relevance of a comparison (the percentage of valid comparisons over the total number of characters involved in a study) remaining fairly high. In the present study the lowest relevance is between **A** and the other OTU's and between **C** and **E**, where eight out of ten possible comparisons can be made, or a relevance of 0.8. The other comparisons in the present example have relevances of 0.9 or 1.0.

Some hesitation may be felt on how to score OTU's which seem to be intermediate between two arbitrarily assigned character state codes. Thus, having erected a scale, say, from 1 to 6, one may find a specimen which seems to be more or less intermediate between 4 and 5. How should it be scored? Twice in published criticisms of numerical taxonomy this issue has been raised as an apparent example of a lack of objectivity in numerical taxonomy equal to that of classical systematics. This is not so! When a specimen is truly intermediate, so that it should fall on the borderline between 4 and 5, arbitrary assignment to one or the other of these groups does not result in a large degree of distortion of the similarity coefficients computed from such data. This is a well-accepted and proven principle of statistics, and only through ignorance or misunderstanding of statistical procedures would this issue have been raised in the first place. Furthermore, if a digital computer is employed, where character state codes do not have to be a fixed number of digits, it is perfectly acceptable to record the character as 4.5 in the best judgment of the taxonomist and have the machine compute a more exact value of the similarity coefficient. However, a little experimenting with numbers along this line will convince anyone that the differences are very minor indeed between the similarity coefficients obtained by such a procedure and those based on characters arbitrarily grouped into one of the two neighboring states.

The next step in processing the data for further computation of correlation or distance coefficients is the standardization of the characters, discussed in Section 6.2.2. To do this we calculate the mean and standard deviation of each character—that is, of each row of the data matrix. Before we proceed to do this we should review the symbolism which we have adopted for a data matrix. This is shown in Table A-2, where the entries are of the form $X_{ij}$, which stands for the character state value of character $i$ in the OTU $j$. There are $t$ OTU's and $n$ characters in a study. In the example of Table A-1, $t = 6$ and $n$ (after the elimination of the invariant character) $= 10$.

**Table A-2.**  *Symbolism of a Data Matrix*

|            |           | OTU's     |           |         |           |
| :--------: | :-------: | :-------: | :-------: | :-----: | :-------: |
| Characters | 1         | 2         | 3         |  ...    | $t$       |
| 1          | $X_{1,1}$ | $X_{1,2}$ | $X_{1,3}$ |  ...    | $X_{1,t}$ |
| 2          | $X_{2,1}$ | $X_{2,2}$ | $X_{2,3}$ |  ...    | $X_{2,t}$ |
| 3          | $X_{3,1}$ | $X_{3,2}$ | $X_{3,3}$ |  ...    | $X_{3,t}$ |
| .          | .         | .         | .         |         | .         |
| .          | .         | .         | .         |         | .         |
| .          | .         | .         | .         |         | .         |
| $n$        | $X_{n,1}$ | $X_{n,2}$ | $X_{n,3}$ |  ...    | $X_{n,t}$ |

The first step in standardizing the characters is the computation of the mean and standard deviation of each character of the data matrix as shown in Table A-1. The mean of character 1, given in the next to last column of Table A-1, is calculated as

$$\frac{1}{t} \sum_{j=1}^{t} X_{1j} = \overline{X}_1.$$

This formula signifies the addition of all $t$ scores for the first row, the sum being divided by $t$. Numerically, it is

$$\frac{1 + 8 + 1 + 7 + 2 + 5}{6} = \frac{24}{6} = 4.00.$$

The standard deviation is calculated as follows:

$$s_1 = \left\{ \frac{1}{t-1} \left[ \sum_{j=1}^{t} X_{1j}^2 - \frac{\left( \sum_{j=1}^{t} X_{1j} \right)^2}{t} \right] \right\}^{1/2},$$

where $\sum_{j=1}^{t} X_{1j}^2$ represents every score squared and summed; for example, in the first row we would have $1^2 + 8^2 + 1^2 + 7^2 + 2^2 + 5^2 = 144$. From this we subtract the so-called correction term, which is the square of the sum of the scores (found above for the computation of the mean) divided by $t$. This results in the "sum of squares," which is then divided by $t - 1$ to yield the variance, the square root of which is the standard deviation. Hence the standard deviation for character 1 equals

$$\left\{ \frac{1}{5} \left( 144 - \frac{(24)^2}{6} \right) \right\}^{1/2} = 3.098.$$

In cases where NC's occur in a character, the summation is, of course, not over $t$ scores, but over $t$ scores minus the number of NC's. This applies both to the mean and to the standard deviation. Similarly, division in such a case is by $t$

minus the number of NC's for the mean and by $t -$ (number of NC's $+ 1$) for the variance.

Standardized character states are computed as

$$X'_{ij} = \frac{X_{ij} - \overline{X}_{i\cdot}}{s_i},$$

where $X'_{ij}$ is the standardized character state code for character $i$ and OTU $j$, while $X_{ij}$ is the raw score for this character state, and $\overline{X}_{i\cdot}$ and $s_i$ are the mean and standard deviation of character $i$, respectively. Thus, for instance, the first character state for OTU 1 is a "1". Since the mean and standard deviation for character 1 are 4.000 and 3.098, respectively, the first standardized character state code is

$$\frac{1.000 - 4.000}{3.098} = -0.97.$$

The mean and standard deviation of standardized character state codes are 0 and 1, respectively. Table A-3 lists the data matrix with all characters standardized. Since the mean is 0, it is obvious that some standardized character state codes will be negative. When calculations are carried out on a computer, negative values and positive values are handled with equal facility. However, for desk calculator operations negative values are to be avoided as much as possible. Therefore, since the present example was to be processed on a desk calculator, the character state codes were transformed into positive values by addition of a constant, 5.00. These transformed character state codes are shown in Table A-4. For the purposes of computing correlation coefficients or distance coefficients the addition of this constant is of no consequence and will automatically cancel itself.

**Table A-3.** *Data Matrix with Characters Standardized*

| | OTU's | | | | | |
|---|---|---|---|---|---|---|
| Characters | A | B | C | D | E | F |
| 1 | −.97 | 1.29 | −.97 | .97 | −.65 | .32 |
| 2 | −.82 | 1.22 | −.82 | 1.22 | −.82 | .00 |
| 3 | 1.33 | −1.01 | .86 | −1.01 | .39 | −.55 |
| 4 | −.11 | −.79 | −.11 | −.79 | −.11 | 1.92 |
| 5 | NC | .82 | −.41 | .82 | NC | −1.22 |
| 6 | NC | .26 | NC | 1.31 | −.78 | −.78 |
| 7 | 1.28 | −1.14 | .87 | −1.14 | .07 | .07 |
| 8 | −1.11 | 1.11 | −1.11 | 1.11 | −.22 | .22 |
| 9 | −.91 | 1.22 | −.91 | 1.22 | −.61 | .00 |
| 10 | 1.03 | −1.03 | 1.03 | −1.03 | .62 | −.62 |

**Table A-4.**  *Data Matrix with Characters Standardized*
(*5.00 added to remove negative numbers*)

|            | OTU's |      |      |      |      |      |
|------------|-------|------|------|------|------|------|
| Characters | A     | B    | C    | D    | E    | F    |
| 1          | 4.03  | 6.29 | 4.03 | 5.97 | 4.35 | 5.32 |
| 2          | 4.18  | 6.22 | 4.18 | 6.22 | 4.18 | 5.00 |
| 3          | 6.33  | 3.99 | 5.86 | 3.99 | 5.39 | 4.45 |
| 4          | 4.89  | 4.21 | 4.89 | 4.21 | 4.89 | 6.92 |
| 5          | NC    | 5.82 | 4.59 | 5.82 | NC   | 3.78 |
| 6          | NC    | 5.26 | NC   | 6.31 | 4.22 | 4.22 |
| 7          | 6.28  | 3.86 | 5.87 | 3.86 | 5.07 | 5.07 |
| 8          | 3.89  | 6.11 | 3.89 | 6.11 | 4.78 | 5.22 |
| 9          | 4.09  | 6.22 | 4.09 | 6.22 | 4.39 | 5.00 |
| 10         | 6.03  | 3.97 | 6.03 | 3.97 | 5.62 | 4.38 |

## A.2. The computation of coefficients of resemblance

We shall first discuss the computation of correlation and distance coefficients and subsequently proceed to a discussion of the calculation of association coefficients. We do this because the first two coefficients are usually based on standardized multistate characters, as discussed in the previous section, while association coefficients are somewhat different in nature.

*Correlation coefficients* are conveniently computed by the computational formula

$$r_{jk} = \frac{\sum_{i=1}^{n} X_{ij}X_{ik} - \frac{1}{n}\left(\sum_{i=1}^{n} X_{ij}\right)\left(\sum_{i=1}^{n} X_{ik}\right)}{\left\{\left[\sum_{i=1}^{n} X_{ij}^2 - \frac{1}{n}\left(\sum_{i=1}^{n} X_{ij}\right)^2\right]\left[\sum_{i=1}^{n} X_{ik}^2 - \frac{1}{n}\left(\sum_{i=1}^{n} X_{ik}\right)^2\right]\right\}^{1/2}},$$

which is exactly equal to the formula

$$r_{jk} = \frac{\sum_{i=1}^{n} (X_{ij} - \bar{X}_j)(X_{ik} - \bar{X}_k)}{\left\{\sum_{i=1}^{n} (X_{ij} - \bar{X}_j)^2 \sum_{i=1}^{n} (X_{ik} - \bar{X}_k)^2\right\}^{1/2}}$$

given in Section 6.2.2 for the Pearson product-moment correlation coefficient. By way of illustration we shall calculate below the correlation between OTU's **B** and **C** by the computational formula. The formula may be broken down into the following steps. We need to find the sum of the character state codes for OTU $j$ and similarly for OTU $k$, or quantities $\sum_{i=1}^{n} X_{ij}$ and $\sum_{i=1}^{n} X_{ik}$. We need then to find the sum of the squares of these character state codes ($\sum_{i=1}^{n} X_{ij}^2$ and $\sum_{i=1}^{n} X_{ik}^2$) and finally the sum of the products of the character state codes of the two OTU'S ($\sum_{i=1}^{n} X_{ij}X_{ik}$). These terms and $n$ are all that we need to evaluate the correlation coefficient. Table A-5 shows the computational steps for finding the correlation between OTU's **B** and **C**. The standardized character state codes for **B** are shown followed by their squares. In the next column are the standardized character state codes for **C** followed by their squares, and in the final column we find the products between **B** and **C**. In an actual computation on a desk calculator, individual items and their squares would not be shown; they would be accumulated as running totals. Most modern desk calculators provide facilities for computing the five quantities simultaneously; however, when these are computed simultaneously it may not be possible to carry as many decimal places as shown in this example. It should be clear that when one (or both) of the OTU's has an NC code for one of the characters, as in the present case, the summation is carried out only for those characters recorded in both OTU's. Thus $n$ for this example necessarily reduces to 9. The remaining computational

**Table A-5.** *Computational Steps for Obtaining Correlation Coefficients*

| | | OTU's **B** and **C** | | |
|---|---|---|---|---|
| **B** | **B²** | **C** | **C²** | **BC** |
| 6.29 | 39.5641 | 4.03 | 16.2409 | 25.3487 |
| 6.22 | 38.6884 | 4.18 | 17.4724 | 25.9996 |
| 3.99 | 15.9201 | 5.86 | 34.3396 | 23.3814 |
| 4.21 | 17.7241 | 4.89 | 23.9121 | 20.5869 |
| 5.82 | 33.8724 | 4.59 | 21.0681 | 26.7138 |
| (5.26) | — | NC | — | — |
| 3.86 | 14.8996 | 5.87 | 34.4569 | 22.6582 |
| 6.11 | 37.3321 | 3.89 | 15.1321 | 23.7679 |
| 6.22 | 38.6884 | 4.09 | 16.7281 | 25.4398 |
| 3.97 | 15.7609 | 6.03 | 36.3609 | 23.9391 |
| 46.69 | 252.4501 | 43.43 | 215.7111 | 217.8354 |

$$r_{BC} = \frac{217.8354 - \dfrac{(46.69)(43.43)}{9}}{\left\{\left[252.4501 - \dfrac{(46.69)^2}{9}\right]\left[215.7111 - \dfrac{(43.43)^2}{9}\right]\right\}^{1/2}}$$

$$= \frac{217.8354 - 225.3052}{[(252.4501 - 242.2173)(215.7111 - 209.5739)]^{1/2}}$$

$$= \frac{-7.4698}{[(10.2328)(6.1372)]^{1/2}}$$

$$= \frac{-7.4698}{7.9247} = -0.943$$

steps are quite simple, according to the formula, and are shown in the lower half of Table A-5.

In a similar manner the other correlations between all pairs of OTU's are computed. The coefficients are then conventionally placed into a matrix, usually a half matrix with the correlation coefficients placed below the principal diagonal of the matrix; Table A-6 shows the arrangement for all pairs of OTU's in our illustrative example.

**Table A-6.** *Product-moment Correlation Coefficients Between All Pairs of OTU's Computed by the Method of Table A-5*

| | | OTU's | | | | | |
|---|---|---|---|---|---|---|---|
| | | A | B | C | D | E | F |
| | A | X | | | | | |
| | B | −.934 | X | | | | |
| OTU's | C | .990 | −.943 | X | | | |
| | D | −.933 | .946 | −.939 | X | | |
| | E | .854 | −.819 | .882 | −.884 | X | |
| | F | −.338 | −.100 | −.213 | −.201 | −.095 | X |

When the OTU's are based on the same number of characters (where there are no NC codes in a data matrix), the sums of squares (the expressions under the square root in the denominator of the correlation coefficient) remain constant for each column of the correlation matrix. Similarly, the sums of $X$'s employed in the numerator of the correlation coefficient are constant for each column of the data. Desk calculator operators should then set up the flow of the computation in such a way as to take advantage of this fact. Thus on one sheet is assembled a matrix of the products of two variables (we shall call it matrix 1). In another matrix (2) on a second sheet, the sums of $X$'s divided by $\sqrt{n}$ are placed around the margin (both at the left of the rows and at the heads of the columns), and the appropriate product of the marginal terms is subtracted from the product of the two variables in matrix 1, the difference being entered in matrix 2. Thus matrix 2 represents the numerator of the correlation term. The denominator is computed as the product of the square roots of the sums of squares (again conveniently entered at the margins of a third sheet) and entered into matrix 3. Finally, in a fourth matrix are entered the quotients of the corresponding terms of matrices 2 and 3; that is, the numerator of the correlation coefficient expression divided by its denominator. Thus matrix 4 is the correlation coefficient matrix.

Readers wishing to practice the computations in this example are cautioned against expecting their results to agree to the last decimal place with those presented here. These data have been computed carrying four decimal places

**Table A-7.** *Product-moment Correlation Coefficients Between All Pairs of OTU's Computed with the Sums of the Character State Codes and Their Squares and Products Rounded to One Decimal Place Only*

| | | A | B | C | D | E | F |
|---|---|---|---|---|---|---|---|
| | | | | OTU's | | | |
| | A | X | | | | | |
| | B | −.933 | X | | | | |
| OTU's | C | .990 | −.941 | X | | | |
| | D | −.933 | .946 | −.938 | X | | |
| | E | .855 | −.818 | .882 | −.884 | X | |
| | F | −.338 | −.101 | −.213 | −.202 | −.094 | X |

throughout, and if the data are treated in this manner the results should be very close to ours. However, the number of decimal places carried and rounding off at various stages during the computational cycle will affect the final values of the correlation coefficients. Thus, rounding off to one decimal place during the calculations produced the matrix shown in Table A-7. As can be seen by comparing this table with Table A-6, the differences are not appreciable. All other considerations being equal, it is, of course, preferable to keep as many places during the computation as possible and to round off figures after the correlation coefficients have been computed. Those persons using computers should also be aware that the output of a machine will vary depending on the precision with which the computations are carried on inside the machine. As an example we show Table A-8, which reproduces the output of a computation carried out on the IBM 650 digital computer, using floating decimal points and eight significant figures for all computations, including the initial computation of the standardized character state codes. Assuming that the data in Table A-8

**Table A-8.** *Copy of Output of Computer Program (COR-DIST on IBM 650 Computer) Showing the Correlation Coefficients Between All Pairs of OTU's Computed on the Basis of Eight Significant Figures*

| | | A | B | C | D | E | F |
|---|---|---|---|---|---|---|---|
| | | | | OTU's | | | |
| | A | X | | | | | |
| | B | −.93391829 | X | | | | |
| OTU's | C | .99014559 | −.94198138 | X | | | |
| | D | −.93274176 | .94611327 | −.93848123 | X | | |
| | E | .85499380 | −.81824288 | .88234334 | −.88400459 | X | |
| | F | −.33844704 | −.10110804 | −.21292392 | −.20196453 | −.093913755 | X |

are closest to the true but unobtainable values based on an infinitely precise arithmetic, we note that the figures in Table A-6 based on four decimal places are not always closer to the figures of Table A-8 than are those of Table A-7, based on one decimal place. However, none of the matrices is appreciably different from the others.

We take up next the computation of *taxonomic distance*, computed as $d_{jk}$, which is the average distance in its square root form, as described in Section 6.2.3.2. The formula used for this computation is

$$d_{jk} = \left( \frac{\sum\limits_{i=1}^{n} X_{ij}^2 + \sum\limits_{i=1}^{n} X_{ik}^2 - 2 \sum\limits_{i=1}^{n} X_{ij}X_{ik}}{n} \right)^{1/2},$$

which is the convenient computational formula for the mathematically identical expression

$$d_{jk} = \left[ \frac{\sum\limits_{i=1}^{n} (X_{ij} - X_{ik})^2}{n} \right]^{1/2} = \left( \frac{\Delta_{jk}^2}{n} \right)^{1/2},$$

which was shown in Section 6.2.3.2. It will be noted that the expressions in the computational formula are the very same ones employed in the computation of the correlation coefficient. It is therefore quite convenient to compute correlations and distances simultaneously. Once the computationally tedious portions of the operations have been completed, the final computation of both correlations and distances is simple and probably worthwhile. The computer program employed in the laboratory at the University of Kansas carries out the computation of correlations and distances simultaneously. Using the intermediate results obtained in Table A-5, we can compute the average distance between OTU's **B** and **C** as follows:

$$d_{BC} = \left( \frac{252.4501 + 215.7111 - 2(217.8354)}{9} \right)^{1/2} = (3.6100)^{1/2} = 1.900.$$

The average distances and their squares computed in this manner (again carrying four decimal places during our computations) are shown in Table A-9. Readers will remember that distances indicate the opposite of correlation coefficients; thus the greater the distance between any two OTU's, the less their phenetic relationship.

As an example of the computation of an *association coefficient* we shall present the simplest of these, the simple matching coefficient of Sokal and Michener. It will be remembered that association coefficients are based on character states coded "zero" and "one" only. These could be attributes, "zero" standing for absence and "one" for presence, or these two states may represent two attributes which cannot be linearly ordered, such as black and red. However, two-state coding can also be applied to linearly ordered measurements which are arbitrarily divided into two classes. This is what we have done here (Table

**Table A-9.** *Average Distance Coefficients Between All Pairs of OTU's**

|  |  | A | B | C | D | E | F |
|---|---|---|---|---|---|---|---|
|  |  | OTU's | | | | | |
| OTU's | A | $X$ | 4.347 | 0.049 | 4.178 | 0.437 | 2.097 |
|  | B | 2.085 | $X$ | 3.610 | 0.120 | 2.304 | 1.915 |
|  | C | 0.221 | 1.900 | $X$ | 3.460 | 0.252 | 1.674 |
|  | D | 2.044 | 0.347 | 1.860 | $X$ | 2.541 | 2.190 |
|  | E | 0.661 | 1.518 | 0.502 | 1.594 | $X$ | 0.968 |
|  | F | 1.448 | 1.384 | 1.294 | 1.480 | 0.984 | $X$ |

\* $d_{jk}^2$ above principal diagonal, $d_{jk}$ below.

A-10) by way of an example. We have taken the standardized data matrix from Table A-3 and have coded them in such a way that all scores equal to or less than zero have been given a "zero" score. All scores larger than zero have been given a "one" score. Such a division does not always have to be made at a given fixed point, however, but can lie at any place between the extremes of the range of the character states. To illustrate this, character 4 has been coded "zero" only for those standardized character states less than $-0.11$ and has been coded "one" for $-0.11$ and all higher states. The main reason for converting multistate characters into two-state characters in the present example is an illustrative one, so that data already obtained could be proc-

**Table A-10.** *Standardized Character State Codes of Table A-3 Converted into Two-state Characters by Calling All Scores $\leq 0$ Equal to "Zero" and All Scores $> 0$ Equal to "1"* *

| Characters | OTU's | | | | | |
|---|---|---|---|---|---|---|
|  | A | B | C | D | E | F |
| 1 | 0 | 1 | 0 | 1 | 0 | 1 |
| 2 | 0 | 1 | 0 | 1 | 0 | 0 |
| 3 | 1 | 0 | 1 | 0 | 1 | 0 |
| 4 | 1 | 0 | 1 | 0 | 1 | 1 |
| 5 | NC | 1 | 0 | 1 | NC | 0 |
| 6 | NC | 1 | NC | 1 | 0 | 0 |
| 7 | 1 | 0 | 1 | 0 | 1 | 1 |
| 8 | 0 | 1 | 0 | 1 | 0 | 1 |
| 9 | 0 | 1 | 0 | 1 | 0 | 0 |
| 10 | 1 | 0 | 1 | 0 | 1 | 0 |

\* Character 4 was coded "zero for scores $< -.11$ and "1" for scores $\geq -.11$

essed. Ordinarily one would not wish to carry out such coding, since it would lose information. If association coefficients are computed by preference, a method of converting multistate characters into two-state characters should be used, so as not to lose information, as suggested in Section 5.3.6.

The more common reason for employing two-state characters is that only two states are available for study, often without any logical linear order. Such characters are frequently employed in microbiology, and the hypothetical data treated below may be thought of in this framework.

The data of Table A-3, recoded into two-state characters as indicated above, are presented in Table A-10. Character state codes for which no comparison is possible are again labeled NC. Reference to Section 6.2.1 will show the arrangement of data for computation of a coefficient of association.

OTU $j$

|  |  | $+$ | $-$ |  |
|---|---|---|---|---|
| OTU $k$ | $+$ | $n_{JK}$ | $n_{jK}$ | $n_K$ |
|  | $-$ | $n_{Jk}$ | $n_{jk}$ | $n_k$ |
|  |  | $n_J$ | $n_j$ | $n$ |

The data consist of $n$ scores for two OTU's labeled $j$ and $k$. They are subdivided

**Table A-11.** *The Data of Table A-10 Arranged in 2 × 2 Tables for Computation of Coefficients of Association Between All Pairs of OTU's*

|  |  | A | B | C | D | E | F |
|---|---|---|---|---|---|---|---|
|  | **A** | $X$ | | | | | |
| | **B** | 0 4<br>4 0 | $X$ | | | | |
| | **C** | 4 0<br>0 4 | 0 5<br>4 0 | $X$ | | | |
| OTU's | **D** | 0 4<br>4 0 | 6 0<br>0 4 | 0 4<br>5 0 | $X$ | | |
| | **E** | 4 0<br>0 4 | 0 5<br>4 0 | 4 0<br>0 4 | 0 5<br>4 0 | $X$ | |
| | **F** | 2 2<br>2 2 | 2 4<br>2 2 | 2 2<br>2 3 | 2 4<br>2 2 | 2 2<br>2 3 | $X$ |

OTU's

**Table A-12.** *Necessary Quantities for Computation of Coefficients of Association Between All Pairs of OTU's\**

| | | | OTU Pairs | | | | | | | | | | | | |
|---|---|---|---|---|---|---|---|---|---|---|---|---|---|---|---|
| | AB | AC | AD | AE | AF | BC | BD | BE | BF | CD | CE | CF | DE | DF | EF |
| $n_{JK}$ | 0 | 4 | 0 | 4 | 2 | 0 | 6 | 0 | 2 | 0 | 4 | 2 | 0 | 2 | 2 |
| $n_{Jk}$ | 4 | 0 | 4 | 0 | 2 | 4 | 0 | 4 | 2 | 5 | 0 | 2 | 4 | 2 | 2 |
| $n_{jK}$ | 4 | 0 | 4 | 0 | 2 | 5 | 0 | 5 | 4 | 4 | 0 | 2 | 5 | 4 | 2 |
| $n_{jk}$ | 0 | 4 | 0 | 4 | 2 | 0 | 4 | 0 | 2 | 0 | 4 | 3 | 0 | 2 | 3 |
| $n_J$ | 4 | 4 | 4 | 4 | 4 | 4 | 6 | 4 | 4 | 5 | 4 | 4 | 4 | 4 | 4 |
| $n_j$ | 4 | 4 | 4 | 4 | 4 | 5 | 4 | 5 | 6 | 4 | 4 | 5 | 5 | 6 | 5 |
| $n_K$ | 4 | 4 | 4 | 4 | 4 | 5 | 6 | 5 | 6 | 4 | 4 | 4 | 5 | 6 | 4 |
| $n_k$ | 4 | 4 | 4 | 4 | 4 | 4 | 4 | 4 | 4 | 5 | 4 | 5 | 4 | 4 | 5 |
| $m$ | 0 | 8 | 0 | 8 | 4 | 0 | 10 | 0 | 4 | 0 | 8 | 5 | 0 | 4 | 5 |
| $u$ | 8 | 0 | 8 | 0 | 4 | 9 | 0 | 9 | 6 | 9 | 0 | 4 | 9 | 6 | 4 |
| $n$ | 8 | 8 | 8 | 8 | 8 | 9 | 10 | 9 | 10 | 9 | 8 | 9 | 9 | 10 | 9 |

\* Data taken from Table A-11.

into positive and negative classes for each of the two operational taxonomic units. Capital subscripts indicate positive or "1" states and lower-case subscripts show negative or "0" states. We designate as $n_{JK}$ the number of characters in which both OTU's are positive and $n_{jk}$ as the number in which both are negative. The number of characters positive for one OTU and negative for the other are $n_{Jk}$ and $n_{jK}$, respectively. Marginal totals are $n_J$ and $n_K$ for positive characters of OTU $j$ and $k$, respectively; similarly, $n_j$ and $n_k$ are the marginal totals for the negative characters. The following symbolism was established for convenience in writing formulas:

$m = n_{JK} + n_{jk}$, the number of characters in "matched" cells;
$u = n_{Jk} + n_{jK}$, the number of characters in "unmatched" cells;
$n = m + u$.

Table A-11 shows the data of the two-state characters in Table A-10 arranged as $2 \times 2$ tables for the computation of coefficients of association of pairs of OTU's. The arrangement of the frequencies in these tables is as in the schematic example shown above. Marginal totals are not shown because of the simplicity of the tables, but in any real analysis these would probably be necessary in order to complete the computations. From Table A-11 it is obvious which pairs of OTU's show special association and which do not. Since the formula for the simple matching coefficient is $S_{SM} = m/n$, we can see from Table A-12 that, for example, the simple matching coefficient between OTU's **A** and **B** is zero.

**Table A-13.** *Coefficients of Association Listed in Tables 6-1 and 6-2 Computed from the Quantities in Table A-12*

| Coefficient | AB | AC | AD | AE | AF | BC | BD | BE | BF | CD | CE | CF | DE | DF | EF |
|---|---|---|---|---|---|---|---|---|---|---|---|---|---|---|---|
| SM | 0 | 1.00 | 0 | 1.00 | .50 | 0 | 1.00 | 0 | .40 | 0 | 1.00 | .56 | 0 | .40 | .56 |
| J | 0 | 1.00 | 0 | 1.00 | .33 | 0 | 1.00 | 0 | .25 | 0 | 1.00 | .33 | 0 | .25 | .33 |
| RR | 0 | .50 | 0 | .50 | .25 | 0 | .60 | 0 | .20 | 0 | .50 | .22 | 0 | .20 | .22 |
| D | 0 | 1.00 | 0 | 1.00 | .50 | 0 | 1.00 | 0 | .40 | 0 | 1.00 | .50 | 0 | .40 | .50 |
| $un_1$ | 0 | 1.00 | 0 | 1.00 | .67 | 0 | 1.00 | 0 | .57 | 0 | 1.00 | .71 | 0 | .57 | .71 |
| $un_2$ | 0 | 1.00 | 0 | 1.00 | .20 | 0 | 1.00 | 0 | .14 | 0 | 1.00 | .20 | 0 | .14 | .20 |
| RT | 0 | 1.00 | 0 | 1.00 | .33 | 0 | 1.00 | 0 | .25 | 0 | 1.00 | .38 | 0 | .25 | .38 |
| K1 | 0 | ∞ | 0 | ∞ | .50 | 0 | ∞ | 0 | .33 | 0 | ∞ | .50 | 0 | .33 | .50 |
| $un_3$ | 0 | ∞ | 0 | ∞ | 1.00 | 0 | ∞ | 0 | .67 | 0 | ∞ | 1.25 | 0 | .67 | 1.25 |
| K2 | 0 | 1.00 | 0 | 1.00 | .50 | 0 | 1.00 | 0 | .42 | 0 | 1.00 | .50 | 0 | .42 | .50 |
| $un_4$ | 0 | 1.00 | 0 | 1.00 | .50 | 0 | 1.00 | 0 | .42 | 0 | 1.00 | .55 | 0 | .42 | .55 |
| O | 0 | 1.00 | 0 | 1.00 | .50 | 0 | 1.00 | 0 | .41 | 0 | 1.00 | .50 | 0 | .41 | .50 |
| $un_5$ | 0 | 1.00 | 0 | 1.00 | .25 | 0 | 1.00 | 0 | .17 | 0 | 1.00 | .30 | 0 | .17 | .30 |
| H | −1.00 | 1.00 | −1.00 | 1.00 | 0 | −1.00 | 1.00 | −1.00 | −.20 | −1.00 | 1.00 | .11 | −1.00 | −.20 | .11 |
| Y | −1.00 | 1.00 | −1.00 | 1.00 | 0 | −1.00 | 1.00 | −1.00 | −.33 | −1.00 | 1.00 | .20 | −1.00 | −.33 | .20 |
| φ | −1.00 | 1.00 | −1.00 | 1.00 | 0 | −1.00 | 1.00 | −1.00 | −.17 | −1.00 | 1.00 | .10 | −1.00 | −.17 | .10 |

$un_1$, etc. stands for unnamed coefficients number 1, etc., numbered in the order of their presentation in Table 6-1.

For OTU's **A** and **C** it is 1, and so forth. In Table A-13 we have shown all the coefficients listed in Tables 6-1 and 6-2, using the quantities in Table A-12.

## A.3. Clustering methods

Numerous clustering methods have been applied in numerical taxonomy, but we do not propose to present all of them in detail here. A review of the methods has already been given in Section 7.3.2. We shall discuss only the most commonly used types; the others are only minor modifications thereof and are easily applied.

We first demonstrate the *weighted variable-group method*, using Spearman's sums of variables method for recomputing the correlation coefficients. The possibility of reversals in the coefficients on recalculating the correlation matrices after the initial clustering step has already been described in Section 7.3.2.4. When some of the coefficients are appreciably negative, as they generally are when characters have been standardized, the reversals become quite large. In the present example we have rather high negative correlations, brought about by the artificial nature of the matrix with which we are dealing. In real cases negative correlations of magnitude $-0.9$ would not be likely.

The first step in clustering—by any of the group methods—is to find the mutually highest correlations as central points of the clusters to be formed. By a mutually highest correlation we mean a correlation between any two OTU's which is higher than the correlation of these OTU's with any other OTU. When working with a desk calculator, it is convenient to represent the matrix of correlation coefficients in symmetrical form. This is shown in Table A-14, where the correlations of Table A-6 have been copied as a full (symmetric)

**Table A-14.** *The Correlation Coefficients of Table A-6 Copied as a Full (Symmetric) Matrix, with Decimal Points Omitted. The Highest Coefficient for Each Column Has Been Underlined*

|   | A | B | C | D | E | F |
|---|---|---|---|---|---|---|
| A | $X$ | $-934$ | <u>990</u> | $-933$ | 854 | $-338$ |
| B | $-934$ | $X$ | $-943$ | <u>946</u> | $-819$ | $-100$ |
| C | <u>990</u> | $-943$ | $X$ | $-939$ | <u>882</u> | $-213$ |
| D | $-933$ | <u>946</u> | $-939$ | $X$ | $-884$ | $-201$ |
| E | 854 | $-819$ | 882 | $-884$ | $X$ | <u>$-095$</u> |
| F | $-338$ | $-100$ | $-213$ | $-201$ | $-095$ | $X$ |

matrix, omitting decimal points, which are understood to be in front of the leading digit. Next we underline the highest correlation in the column of each OTU (see Table A-14). We find that OTU **A** is correlated at level 990 with

OTU **C** and that the highest correlation of **C** is also with **A**. Thus the correlation between **A** and **C** is a mutually highest correlation and OTU's **A** and **C** will therefore form a cluster. We note, however, that **E** is also most highly correlated with **C** (882). However, **C** has a higher correlation with **A** than it has with **E**. Therefore the correlation between **C** and **E** is not a mutually highest correlation and **E** does not initiate a cluster. The highest correlation of OTU **B** is with **D** (946), and conversely **D**'s highest correlation is with **B**. Therefore **B** and **D** form a cluster. **F**'s highest correlation is with **E**, but **E**'s highest correlation is with **C**. Therefore neither **E** nor **F** are included in the initial clustering process. Thus at the conclusion of the first clustering cycle we find the following clusters:

$$\mathbf{A + C,} \qquad \mathbf{B + D,} \qquad \mathbf{E,} \qquad \mathbf{F}$$

In any variable group method, more than two members are permitted to join a cluster during one clustering cycle. We therefore determine whether **E** or **F** should be permitted to join any of the present clusters. In a variable group method a criterion for cluster formation has to be furnished. If adding a new member to a cluster would produce an average correlation between the new-comer and the established cluster *lower than the previous level of junction by more than the criterion*, the prospective member is not admitted. In the initial study of Sokal and Michener (1958), the criterion value was set, somewhat arbitrarily, at 0.03; as it turned out, this was a satisfactory value for their study. If we accept this criterion in the present example, just for purposes of illustration, we first have to calculate the average correlation of prospective members with the clusters they are likely to join. The OTU **E** is highly correlated both with **A** and with **C** and it therefore appears to be a likely candidate for the already established cluster **A + C**. The average correlation of **E** with **A + C** is 0.868:

$$r_{AE} = 0.854, \qquad r_{CE} = 0.882,$$

$$\bar{S}_n = \frac{1}{2} (0.854 + 0.882) = 0.868.$$

Sokal and Michener (1958) used $\bar{L}_n$ as the symbol for the average correlation; we now prefer to call it $\bar{S}_n$. The difference from the correlation $r_{AC} = 0.990$ to $\bar{S}_n = 0.868$ is 0.122, considerably in excess of our criterion of 0.03. Thus during the first clustering cycle **E** does not join cluster **A + C**. It is obvious that **F** with its relatively low correlation with any other OTU will not join any of the established clusters during the present clustering cycle and thus the cycle can be concluded. In a more realistic example, involving more OTU's than the present one, a number of possible members may have to be examined and some of them may in fact join the cluster. In such a case, after three members have formed a cluster, one will have to calculate the average correlation of the three cluster members with a fourth possible member in order to decide whether the clustering should cease or whether the fourth member should be admitted into the cluster. It may even be that, in a group of four mutually highly correlated individuals, two initial clusters of two members would form, and the two clusters of two each would come together in a single cluster without lowering $\bar{S}_n$ appreciably:

At this stage we have to recalculate the correlation of all clusters and unclustered OTU's among themselves in preparation for the next clustering cycle. For this we use Spearman's sums of variables formula. This formula is

$$ r_{qQ} = \frac{\square qQ}{\sqrt{q + 2\Delta q}\ \sqrt{Q + 2\Delta Q}}, $$

where $\square qQ$ is the sum of all correlations between members of one group with the other group, $\Delta q$ is the sum of all correlations between members of the first group, $\Delta Q$ is a similar sum between members of the second group, $q$ is the number of OTU's in group 1, and $Q$ the number of OTU's in group 2. Whenever we have to calculate a correlation between a cluster and a single OTU, Spearman's formula reduces to

$$ r_{zq} = \frac{\sum r_{zq}}{\sqrt{q + 2\Delta q}}, $$

where the numerator refers to the sum of all the correlations of the single OTU with members of the cluster.

In recalculating the correlation matrix both these formulas will be employed. The computational steps are as follows:

$$ \square (A + C)(B + D) = r_{AB} + r_{AD} + r_{CB} + r_{CD} $$
$$ = -0.934 + (-0.933) + (-0.943) + (-0.939) $$
$$ = -3.749. $$

$$ \sqrt{2 + 2(r_{AC})} = 1.9950, $$
$$ \sqrt{2 + 2(r_{BD})} = 1.9728, $$

$$ r_{(A+C)(B+D)} = \frac{-3.749}{1.9950 \times 1.9728} = -0.953, $$

$$ r_{(A+C)E} = \frac{r_{AE} + r_{CE}}{\sqrt{2 + 2(r_{AC})}} = \frac{0.854 + 0.882}{1.9950} = 0.870. $$

Similarly,

$$ r_{(A+C)F} = -0.276, \qquad r_{(B+D)E} = -0.863, \qquad r_{(B+D)F} = -0.153. $$

The correlation between **E** and **F** is, of course, unchanged.

The correlations between the taxa at this clustering stage and for successive stages are shown in the lower part of Table A-15. One problem during this

**Table A-15.** *Successive Clustering of Correlation Matrix by WVGM, Using Spearman's Sums of Variables Method for Recalculating Correlations*

| | Matrix | | |
|---|---|---|---|
| 1* | 2 | 3 | 4 |

Matrix 2

| | A′ | B′ | E | F | |
|---|---|---|---|---|---|
| A′ | X | −953 | 870 | −276 | |
| B′ | −953 | X | −863 | −153 | |
| E | 870 | −863 | X | −095 | A′ = A + C |
| F | −276 | −153 | −095 | X | B′ = B + D |

Matrix 3

| | A″ | B′ | F | |
|---|---|---|---|---|
| A″ | X | −939 | −192 | |
| B′ | −939 | X | −153 | |
| F | −192 | −153 | X | A″ = A′ + E |

Matrix 4

| | A″ | B″ | |
|---|---|---|---|
| A″ | X | −869 | |
| B″ | −869 | X | B″ = B′ + F |

*Matrix 1 is Table A-14

procedure is the labeling of the new clusters. The system adopted here is quite simple and works well for small matrices. Cluster **A + C** is now called **A′** and is defined at the right margin of Table A-15. Similarly, **B + D** has become **B′**, and successive clusters including **A′** and **B′** will be called **A″** and **B″** as their composition changes. When a large number of variables is employed, prime notation becomes too unwieldy; a convenient notation for desk calculator operations has been to use the letter or number of the first (leftmost) OTU in the group being clustered, together with a superscript or subscript identifying the clustering cycle during which this group has been formed. Different workers have different schemes for keeping track of their clusters, and no uniformly accepted system has been developed. When clustering is carried out on a computer, a different method has to be adopted. In some existing computer programs groups are renumbered at each clustering cycle, and a record is kept in the machine identifying the code numbers of the taxa at each clustering cycle in terms of the previous cycle. This record is then punched out with the output and permits the investigator to identify the stems at each clustering cycle. We have found it very helpful to draw a schema as shown at the top of Table A-15. The criteria for successive clustering are the same as in the first clustering cycle, and the procedure can be easily followed by working through the example shown in Table A-15. The results of this clustering process can be represented in the dendrogram shown in Figure A-1.

We might now take time out to discuss the various modifications of this clustering procedure which have been suggested. The most common variant is the *weighted pair-group method*, which permits only the two most highly correlated stems to join at each clustering cycle. Thus this method needs no criterion for admitting further joiners during any one cycle. In the present instance, the pair-group method gives identical results with the weighted variable group methods because no more than two stems came together during one clustering cycle anyway. Another variation is an *unweighted group method*, which during each clustering cycle recomputes correlations based not on the previous matrix but on the initial matrix. Thus, in Table A-15, if we were to calculate one of the correlations shown in matrix 3 by an unweighted method, these would not be based on the correlation coefficients found

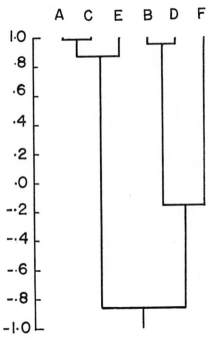

FIGURE A-1

*Dendrogram of the relations among six OTU's based on the WVGM clustering procedure of correlation coefficients shown in Table A-15. The ordinate is shown in correlation coefficient scale,* r.

in matrix 2, but, after considering which OTU's go to make up the two clusters which are joining in matrix 3, would be based directly on the original correlation coefficients of matrix 1. We shall evaluate the correlation between $\mathbf{A}''$ and $\mathbf{B}'$. $\mathbf{A}''$ consists of $\mathbf{A} + \mathbf{C} + \mathbf{E}$, and $\mathbf{B}'$ consists of $\mathbf{B} + \mathbf{D}$. By the unweighted method each OTU has equal weight within each group, while in the weighted method $\mathbf{E}$ has a weight equal to the stem $\mathbf{A} + \mathbf{C}$. The computations for the unweighted correlation between $\mathbf{A}''$ and $\mathbf{B}'$ are as follows (using Spearman's sums of variables method):

$$\Box(A + C + E)(B + D)$$
$$= r_{AB} + r_{AD} + r_{BC} + r_{CD} + r_{BE} + r_{DE}$$
$$= (-0.934) + (-0.933) + (-0.943) + (-0.939) + (-0.819) + (-0.884)$$
$$= -5.452,$$

$$\sqrt{3 + 2(r_{AC} + r_{AE} + r_{CE})} = \sqrt{8.452} = 2.9072,$$
$$\sqrt{2 + 2(r_{BD})} = 1.9728,$$

$$r_{(A+C+E)(B+D)} = \frac{-5.452}{2.9072 \times 1.9728} = -0.951.$$

This correlation of $-0.951$ is appreciably different from the $-0.939$ obtained by the weighted variable group method. This example also illustrates the "reversals" induced by Spearman's method. The average correlation is lower than any of its constituent correlations. Near the lower limit of $r$ this tendency can result in values of $r$ slightly less than $-1.0$. Thus unweighted $r_{(A+C+E)(B+D+F)} = -1.013$.

Finally, instead of Spearman's sums of variables method, *simple averages* could be used. This should not be done with correlation coefficients, since their variance depends on their magnitude, but can be done with transformations of correlation coefficients either to Fisher's $z$ or to angles which represent the arc cosines of the correlation coefficients. Such transformations can be looked up in conventional statistical or mathematical tables, or they are automatically generated on a computer. Thus the correlation 0.700 would be 0.867 when transformed to $z$ and 45.63° when transformed to an angle (arc cos $r$). A correlation coefficient of 0.0 corresponds to a $z$ of 0.0 and arc cos of 90°; $r = 1$ corresponds to $z = \infty$ and arc cos $r = 0°$. The transformed coefficients then can be averaged and retransformed to correlations if desired. The most common use for averages rather than Spearman's correlations would be in distance coefficients. Table A-16 shows a weighted pair-group method for clustering the distance coefficients. Since most clustering methods work from high coefficients to low ones and since the closest taxonomic units have smaller distances than less related taxonomic units, the complements of the distances are computed, generally the ten-complements ($= 10 -$ taxonomic distance). The successive matrices using this method are also shown in Table A-16. They were computed by the weighted pair-group method, so that no more than two stems joined at any one cluster. The new distances between clusters are always calculated as simple averages and thus correspond to the $\bar{S}_n$ values as described before. The interested reader should be able to reproduce easily for himself the figures

**Table A-16.**  *Ten-complements of Distance Coefficients Clustered Successively by*
WPGM, *Using Averages of Distance Coefficients to Form Successive Matrices**

| | OTU's | A | B | C | D | E | F |
|---|---|---|---|---|---|---|---|
| Matrix 1 | A | X | | | | | |
| | B | 7.915 | X | | | | |
| | C | 9.779 | 8.100 | X | | | |
| | D | 7.956 | 9.653 | 8.140 | X | | |
| | E | 9.339 | 8.482 | 9.498 | 8.406 | X | |
| | F | 8.552 | 8.616 | 8.706 | 8.520 | 9.016 | X |
| | | A' | B' | E | F | | |
| Matrix 2 | A' | X | | | | | |
| | B' | 8.028 | X | | | | |
| | E | 9.419 | 8.444 | X | | | |
| | F | 8.629 | 8.568 | 9.016 | X | | |
| | | A'' | B' | F | | A' = A + C | |
| Matrix 3 | A'' | X | | | | B' = B + D | |
| | B' | 8.236 | X | | | A'' = A' + E | |
| | F | 8.823 | 8.568 | X | | A''' = A'' + F | |
| | | A''' | B' | | | | |
| Matrix 4 | A''' | X | | | | | |
| | B' | 8.402 | X | | | | |

* Data taken from Table A-9.

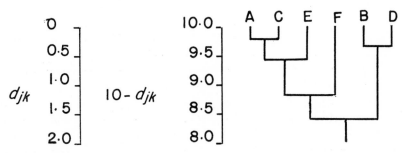

FIGURE  A-2

Dendrogram of the relations among six OTU's based on the WPGM clustering procedure using averages of distance coefficients shown in Table A-16. The ordinate is shown
in distance scale, d, as well as in the ten-complement scale ($10.0 - d$) in which the
computations had been carried out.

shown in Table A-16. The results of this clustering method are shown in Figure A-2.

## A.4. Miscellaneous techniques

The representation of taxonomic relationships in the form of dendrograms gives rise to problems. First, there is inevitable distortion of the relationships by trying to represent an essentially multidimensional relationship in two dimensions. Second, different relations can be obtained by using different similarity coefficients and methods of clustering. In order to measure the amount of distortion introduced by such techniques, the method of cophenetic relationships was developed (Section 7.4). This consists of drawing horizontal lines across a dendrogram, as shown in Figure A.3, which is the dendrogram based on Figure A.1 with the horizontal, so-called phenon lines drawn in at regular intervals across the figure. The cophenetic classes delimited by these phenon lines are coded "1" through "8," and the relationship between any pair of OTU's is assigned the cophenetic value of the cophenetic class in which the two OTU's connect. For instance, **A** and **C** have a cophenetic value of 8, since **A** and **C** connect in the cophenetic class 8. On the other hand, **B** and **F**

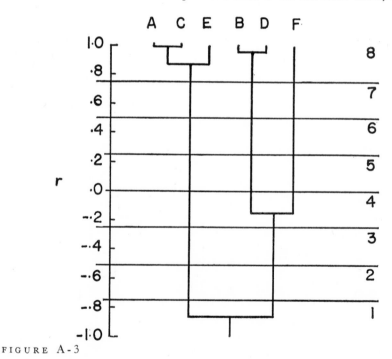

FIGURE A-3

*Dendrogram of Figure A-1 with phenon lines drawn in to illustrate the computation of cophenetic values.*

have a cophenetic value of 4 because they connect in the phenon class 4. The matrix of cophenetic relationships of the OTU's is shown in Table A-17.

**Table A-17.** *Cophenetic Values Between All Pairs of OTU's, Based on the Dendrogram of Figure A.3*

| | | A | B | C | D | E | F |
|---|---|---|---|---|---|---|---|
| | | | | OTU's | | | |
| | A | X | | | | | |
| | B | 1 | X | | | | |
| OTU's | C | 8 | 1 | X | | | |
| | D | 1 | 8 | 1 | X | | |
| | E | 8 | 1 | 8 | 1 | X | |
| | F | 1 | 4 | 1 | 4 | 1 | X |

Such a matrix can now be strung out in single file, first column followed by second column and so forth, and compared against either the original correlation coefficients or against a similarly strung out matrix of cophenetic values for a dendrogram obtained by another method. Such computations have not been carried out here because with so few OTU's the resulting correlation coefficient would be quite unreliable. The computation of correlations between such linearly arranged matrices follows exactly the same formula and procedures as have already been described.

If ranks are to be assigned to various taxa, phenon lines may also be used for this purpose. For instance, if the hypothetical OTU's in our present study are species and it is felt that they should all belong to one genus, then a phenon line might be drawn across Figure A.1 at $r = -0.500$ to represent the subgeneric level; then two subgenera [(−.5)–phenons] could be recognized: A + C + E and B + D + F. On the other hand, if one wished to raise this line to $r = -0.100$, three subgenera [(−.1)–phenons] could be delimited: A + C + E, B + D, and F.

Some remarks on the significance of coefficients of similarity are pertinent here. Section 6.2.4 discussed why the significance of such coefficients in a similarity matrix is not an important issue in numerical taxonomic work. The heterogeneity of the column vectors makes ordinary tests of significance inappropriate. However, lacking better ones we might employ the conventional tests as rough guide lines. Thus for a simple association coefficient, such as $S_{SM}$ or $S_J$, we can use the standard error of the binomial as an approximation. The standard error would then be

$$S.E._S = \sqrt{\frac{S(1-S)}{n}},$$

where $S$ is the association coefficient and $n$ is the number of characters. For example, an association coefficient of 0.30 based on 60 characters would have a standard error of $\sqrt{\dfrac{(0.30)(0.70)}{60}} = 0.0592$. This standard error can be used to set approximate confidence limits to the estimate of the association coefficients, using the normal distribution, in view of the large number of characters on which estimates are generally based in numerical taxonomy. Ninety-five percent confidence limits are calculated as

$$0.30 \pm (1.96)(0.0592) = 0.184 \longrightarrow 0.416.$$

For 99% confidence limits we would replace 1.96 by 2.58. More exact con-

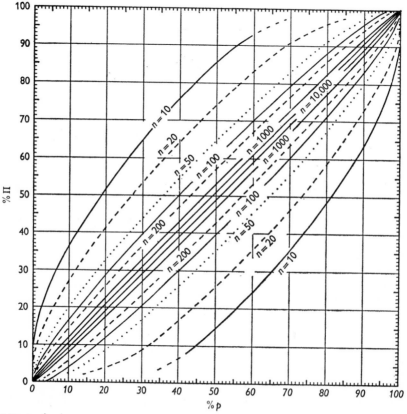

FIGURE A-4

*The 95% confidence limits of the binomial distribution for various values of n. For example, if the proportion, II, of positive values in a large population is 70% and one takes repeated samples of size n = 20, then in 95% of the cases the observed proportion of positives, p, will lie between 45.7% and 88.1%. [Reproduced with permission from the 12th Symposium of the Society for General Microbiology.]*

fidence limits can be obtained from Figure A-4, in which confidence bands based on various sample sizes, $n$, are shown, including values of $S$ close to 0 or 1.

To test whether the significance of the association coefficient is significantly different from zero, we test whether $S/\text{S.E.}_s$ is greater than 1.64 or 2.33 at the 5% or 1% level, respectively (this is a one-tail test, since $S$ cannot be negative). Thus for an association coefficient of 0.30 based on 60 characters, $0.30/0.0592 = 5.07$, which indicates significance at $P < 0.01$.

For the correlation coefficient, standard errors are best calculated after a transformation of the correlation coefficient to Fisher's $z$. This transformation is given in most sets of statistical tables and has already been discussed above. The standard error for $z$ is

$$\text{S.E.}_z = \sqrt{\frac{1}{N-3}}.$$

Thus for a correlation coefficient of 0.70 based on 60 characters we would compute 95% confidence limits as follows:

$$\text{S.E.}_z = \sqrt{\frac{1}{57}} = 0.132,$$

$r = 0.70$ corresponds to $z = 0.8673$.

Confidence limits: $0.8673 \pm (1.96)(0.132) = 0.6086 \longrightarrow 1.1260$.

These limits correspond to $0.54 \longrightarrow 0.81$ on the $r$ scale. Confidence limits of correlation coefficients can also be looked up from a graph shown in Table 15 of the *Biometrika Tables for Statisticians* (Pearson and Hartley, 1958).

The significance of correlation coefficients can be tested as $z/\text{S.E.}_z$ after they have been transformed to $z$ values. Thus the coefficient discussed above, 0.8673, is tested as follows:

$$\frac{0.8673}{0.132} = 6.57, \text{ which is greater than 2.58;}$$

therefore the coefficient is significantly different from zero at $P < 0.01$.

The computation of confidence limits for the distance $d$ is rather involved. Readers interested in the details are asked to consult Rohlf (1962) and Rohlf and Sokal (1963). Since the computations are involved, we have thought it better to tabulate expected values and upper and lower 95% bounds for the distance for four values of $n$, with $n = 20, 50, 100,$ and 200. The values of $n$ of interest to the reader are likely to be less than 200 and the bounds for a given value of $n$ can be found by interpolation. These values are presented in Table A-18. In the first and last columns of this table are given the expected value

**Table A-18.** *Expected Values, Limits Enclosing 95% of the Distances, and Approximate Standard Errors for Average Distance Coefficients at Four Sample Sizes* (n = *number of characters upon which coefficients are based*)

| | | 95% Limits | | |
| --- | --- | --- | --- | --- |
| $n$ | $\mathcal{E}(d)$ | Lower | Upper | S.E.$_d$ |
| 20 | 1.397 | 0.979 | 1.849 | 0.222 |
| 50 | 1.407 | 1.138 | 1.690 | 0.141 |
| 100 | 1.411 | 1.218 | 1.610 | 0.100 |
| 200 | 1.412 | 1.274 | 1.551 | 0.071 |

of $d$ and the standard error for $d$, $\sigma_d$, respectively. These are based on the formulas of Section 6.2.3.2:

$$\mathcal{E}(d) = \frac{(n-1)!}{\left[\left(\frac{n}{2}-1\right)!\right]^2 2^{n-2}} \sqrt{\frac{\pi}{n}},$$

$$\sigma_d^2 = 2 - [\mathcal{E}(d)]^2.$$

The limits shown in Table A-18 are not based on the standard error but on the more exact distribution of distances as derived by Rohlf (1962). However, the approximate standard errors shown here should be adequate for most users. These are computed as follows: for $n = 100$ characters, for example,

$$\log \mathcal{E}(d) = \log (n-1)! + \log \sqrt{\pi} - 2 \log \left[\left(\frac{n}{2}-1\right)!\right]$$

$$- (n-2) \log 2 - \frac{1}{2} \log n$$

$$= \log 99! + \log \sqrt{\pi} - 2 \log 49! - 98 \log 2 - \frac{1}{2} \log 100$$

$$= 155.970,0037 + 0.24858 - (2 \times 62.784,1049)$$

$$- (98 \times 0.30103) - \frac{1}{2} (2.00000)$$

$$= 0.14943,$$
$$\mathcal{E}(d) = 1.4107,$$
$$\sigma_d^2 = 2 - [1.4107]^2 = 0.00993,$$
$$\sigma_d = 0.100.$$

Thus, to test the significance of a distance value of 0.8 based on 100 characters, we could proceed as follows:

$$\frac{d_{jk} - \mathcal{E}(d)}{\text{S.E.}_d} = \frac{0.800 - 1.411}{0.100} = -6.11,$$

which is a highly significant difference (greater than 2.58, hence $P < 0.01$).

## A.5. Computer programming for numerical taxonomy

We shall not give detailed flow charts and programs for computer processing in numerical taxonomy, although these exist, because they change very rapidly as computer facilities improve and new methodologies are developed. Programs can be obtained from various sources, and the interested reader is referred to a newsletter concerned with numerical taxonomy, "Taxometrics" (write: Mr. L. R. Hill, Progetto Sistematica Actinomiceti, Istituto "P. Stazzi," Via Celoria 10, Milano, Italy), in which descriptions of programs and their availability will be published. In general it has been our experience that programs are not too easily transferred from one computer installation to another; even if two installations have the same computer the machines usually have slightly different specifications. Therefore programs often need to be reworked to a slighter or greater extent to make them compatible. As computers get faster and the so-called automatic coding systems become more flexible and powerful, it is likely that programs for numerical taxonomy will no longer be written in machine language but in one of the automatic coding systems. In the United States FORTRAN, developed by IBM, and in Europe ALGOL seem to be the most widely used languages for addressing a great variety of computers. FORTRAN programs are currently being written for all numerical taxonomy procedures, but these will have to be recompiled at different computation centers in order to adapt them to the specific installations. The average taxonomist has probably never seen a computer and is quite likely to shy away from getting involved in the computing business. We would like to emphasize that learning a language such as FORTRAN is extremely simple and that a little acquaintance with the computational aspects of the work would pay copious dividends. On the other hand, as we have repeatedly emphasized throughout the book, the data can in fact be sent out to a number of installations for processing if the taxonomist is not interested in doing any of the computing himself.

Programs that are to be written for numerical taxonomy should have detailed write-ups to enable machine operators unfamiliar with the computations and taxonomists unfamiliar with computers to do the work with maximum facility. Each program write-up should

1. describe the general idea of what the program will do;
2. describe the maximum capacity of the program—how many OTU's can be processed and how many characters;
3. describe in detail the actual algebra of the program, unless it is a very standard procedure for which reference to a publication would be adequate;

4. give detailed operating instructions of what to do on a given computer to execute this program;

5. specify the exact format in which the data must be presented to the computer;

6. specify in detail the format in which the output of the program will be presented;

7. add time estimates for executing the program on a given computer;

8. provide some examples of prepared data input in order to amplify point 5;

9. provide some examples of the output in order to amplify point 6;

10. provide a small example completely worked out in order to give the worker a test case on which to check the program on his own machine.

Eight different kinds of computer programs for numerical taxonomy are envisaged at present:

Group 1 would be *control programs* for large, powerful machines. These would be master programs which would control the succeeding programs (labeled 2 through 8 here). By this is meant that the master program would call up different subprograms which could coordinate an entire numerical taxonomic study from the initial presentation of the data to the final establishment of a classification, calling on the subsequent subprograms as they are needed and directing the flow of the operations. Such a master program is feasible only on large computers, on which various sections of the program would be stored on magnetic tape units and would be called up as they are needed. On the smaller computers, such as the IBM 650, such a master program is not feasible, and the flow of operations is directed by the operator, who runs the data through repeatedly, using different programs.

Group 2 are *language translation programs*. These programs are still in their infancy. They would take descriptions of characters in words and be programmed in such a way as to convert these into numerical codes in some logical and consistent fashion. Such programs eventually may be able to remove much of the tedium of coding characters from the shoulders of the taxonomist.

Group 3 *processes and converts characters* to prepare them for the calculation of similarity coefficients. These procedures would convert the data to the form necessary for whatever program is to compute the similarity coefficients. Standardization of characters would fall into this category, as would transposition of matrices to change input by rows to input by columns.

Group 4 programs *calculate affinity or similarity coefficients* between pairs of OTU's according to the formulas shown earlier in the book.

Group 5 are *cluster analysis programs*. These take the output of Group 4 programs and make clusters from these data. They often also convert the clusters into dendrograms, printing these in some suitable form.

Group 6 are the *data extraction programs*. These too are only in their infancy. They extract data, answering specific questions which are addressed to the study. So far, work of this sort has usually been done with the printed output, the investigator himself checking into certain situations which seem of interest to him. However, it is quite feasible on larger computers to include such procedures as part of the computer program. Thus any questions such as "What does character 33 in OTU 45 look like?" or "How do OTU's 37 and 89 compare for characters 13 through 35?" can easily be looked up by the machine and the results printed in suitable form for the benefit of the investigator.

Group 7 are *interstudy coordination programs*. Such programs would store and sort previous studies, establish reference taxa and their characters, and correlate different studies. Again such procedures would require large computers and are at present only in their earliest developmental stages.

Group 8 are *publication programs*. These would convert the output into legible and publishable form, such as diagnostic keys with descriptions of characters and organisms.

The above outline is based in part on a memorandum by Sneath and Rohlf in *Taxometrics* 2, December 1962.

# REFERENCES

Abelson, P. H. 1957. Some aspects of paleobiochemistry. *Ann. New York Acad. Sci.*, **69**:276–285.

Adanson, M. 1757. *Histoire naturelle du Sénégal. Coquillages. Avec la relation abrégée d'un voyage fait en ce pays, pendant les années 1749, 50, 51, 52 et 53.* Coquillages, Préface, pp. xi, xx, xxix–lxxxviii. Bauche, Paris. 190 + xcvi + 175 pp.

Adanson, M. 1763. *Familles des plantes*, vol. 1. Préface, pp. cliv et seq., clxiii, clxiv. Vincent, Paris. cccxxv + 190 pp.

Ainsworth, G. C. 1941. A method for characterizing smut fungi exemplified by some British species. *Trans. Brit. Mycol. Soc.*, **25**:141–147.

Ainsworth, G. C. and P. H. A. Sneath (eds.), 1962. The proposal and selection of scientific names for microorganisms. Appendix I, pp. 456–463. In *Microbial Classification*. 12th Symposium of the Society for General Microbiology. Cambridge University Press, Cambridge. 483 pp.

Allison, A. C. and D. C. Burke. 1962. The nucleic acid contents of viruses. *J. Gen. Microbiol.*, **27**:181–194.

Amadon, D. 1949. The seventy-five per cent rule for subspecies. *Condor*, **51**:250–258.

Anderson, E. 1936. Hybridization in American Tradescantias. *Ann. Missouri Botan. Gard.*, **23**:511–525.

Anderson, E. and E. C. Abbe. 1934. A quantitative comparison of specific and generic differences in the Betulaceae. *J. Arnold Arboretum*, **15**:43–49.

Anderson, E. and R. P. Owenbey. 1939. The genetic coefficients of specific difference. *Ann. Missouri Botan. Gard.*, **26**:325–348.

Anderson, E. and T. W. Whitaker. 1934. Speciation in *Uvularia*. *J. Arnold Arboretum*, **15**:28–42.

Andrew, W. 1959. *Textbook of Comparative Histology*. Oxford University Press, Oxford and New York. 652 pp.

Andrewes, C. H. and P. H. A. Sneath. 1958. The species concept among viruses. *Nature*, **182**:12–14.

Anfinsen, C. B. 1959. *The Molecular Basis of Evolution*. Wiley, New York. 228 pp.

Arai, T., S. Kuroda, and M. Ito. 1962. Possible utility of a fluorescent antibody technique in the serological identification of antagonistic *Streptomyces*. *J. Bacteriol.*, **83**:20–26.

Bate-Smith, E. C. 1959. Plant biochemistry. In W. B. Turrill (ed.), *Vistas in Botany, A Volume in Honour of the Bicentenary of the Royal Botanic Gardens, Kew*, pp. 100–123. Pergamon Press, London, New York, Paris, Los Angeles. 547 pp.

Bather, F. A. 1927. Biological classification: past and future. *Quart. J. Geol. Soc. Lond.*, **83**:Proc. lxii–civ.

Beckner, M. 1959. *The Biological Way of Thought*. Columbia University Press, New York. 200 pp.

Beers, R. J., J. Fisher, S. Megraw, and W. R. Lockhart. 1962. A comparison of methods for computer taxonomy. *J. Gen. Microbiol.*, **28**:641–652.

Beers, R. J. and W. R. Lockhart. 1962. Experimental methods in computer taxonomy. *J. Gen. Microbiol.*, **28**:633–640.

Bell, P. R. 1956. A statistical approach to the problem of the phylogeny of a genus of ferns. *Proc. Linnean Soc. Lond.*, 167th session:41–50.

Beyle, H. C. 1931. *Identification and Analysis of Attribute-Cluster-Blocs.* University of Chicago Press, Chicago. 249 pp.

Bielicki, T. 1962. Some possibilities for estimating inter-population relationship on the basis of continuous traits. *Current Anthropology*, 3:3–8, 20–46.

Bigelow, R. S. 1956. Monophyletic classification and evolution. *Systematic Zool.*, 5:145–146.

Bigelow, R. S. 1961. Higher categories and phylogeny. *Systematic Zool.*, 10:86–91.

Birnbaum, A. and A. E. Maxwell. 1961. Classification procedures based on Bayes's Formula. *Appl. Stat.*, 9:152–168.

Blackith, R. E. 1957. Polymorphism in some Australian locusts and grasshoppers. *Biometrics*, 13:183–196.

Blackwelder, R. E. 1962. Animal taxonomy and the New Systematics. *Survey Biol. Progr.*, 4:1–57.

Blackwelder, R. E. and A. Boyden. 1952. The nature of systematics. *Systematic Zool.*, 1:26–33.

Bliss, C. I. and D. W. Calhoun. 1954. *An Outline of Biometry.* Yale Co-op. Corp., New Haven. 272 pp.

Bloch, K. 1956. Zur Theorie der naturwissenschaftlichen Systematik unter besonderer Berücksichtigung der Biologie. *Acta Biotheor.*, 11 (Suppl. 1):138 pp.

Blondeau, H. 1961. *Utilisation des ordinateurs électroniques pour l'étude de l'homogénéité de l'espèce Streptococcus faecalis. Application à la détermination de l'origine de la contamination des semi-conserves de viande.* Maurice Fabre, Lyon. 98 pp.

Boeke, J. E. 1942. On quantitative statistical methods in taxonomy; subdivision of a polymorphous species: *Planchonella sandwicensis* (Gray) Pierre. *Blumea*, 5:47–65.

Bojalil, L. F. and Cerbón, J. 1961. Taxonomic analysis of nonpigmented, rapidly growing mycobacteria. *J. Bacteriol.*, 81:338–345.

Bojalil, L. F., J. Cerbón, and A. Trujillo. 1962. Adansonian classification of mycobacteria. *J. Gen. Microbiol.*, 28:333–345.

Bolton, E. T., C. A. Leone, and A. A. Boyden. 1948. A critical analysis of the performance of the photronreflectometer in the measurement of serological and other turbid systems. *J. Immunol.*, 58:169–181.

Bonner, R. E. 1962. A "logical pattern" recognition program. *IBM J. Res. Develop.*, 6:353–360.

Boyden, A. 1932. Precipitin tests as a basis for quantitative phylogeny. *Proc. Soc. Exp. Biol. Med.*, 29:955–957.

Boyden, A. 1942. Systematic serology: a critical appreciation. *Physiol. Zool.*, 15:109–145.

Boyden, A. 1953. Fifty years of systematic serology. *Systematic Zool.*, 2:19–30.

Boyden, A. 1958. Comparative serology: aims, methods, and results. In W. Cole (ed.), *Serological and Biochemical Comparison of Proteins*, XIV Annual Protein Conference, pp. 3–24. Rutgers University Press, New Brunswick, N. J.

Boyden, A., R. J. DeFalco, and D. Gemeroy. 1951. Parallelism in serological correspondence. *Bull. Serol. Mus.*, 6:6–7.

Boyden, A. and D. Gemeroy. 1950. Relative position of the Cetacea among the orders of Mammalia as indicated by precipitin tests. *Zoologica*, 35:145–151.

Bradley, J. C. 1939. The philosophy of biological nomenclature. *Verhandl. VII. Internat. Kong. Entomol. Berlin, 1938*, 1:531–534.

Brezner, J. and W. R. Enns. 1958. Preliminary studies utilizing paper electrophoresis as a tool in insect systematics. *J. Kansas Entomol. Soc.*, 31:241–246.

Brisbane, P. G. and A. D. Rovira. 1961.

A comparison of methods for classifying rhizosphere bacteria. *J. Gen. Microbiol.*, **26**:379–392.

Buzzati-Traverso, A. A. 1959. Quantitative traits, and polygenic systems in evolution. *Cold Spring Harbor Symp. Quant. Biol.*, **24**:41–46.

Buzzati-Traverso, A. A. 1960. Paper chromatography in relation to genetics and taxonomy. In P. M. B. Walker (ed.), *New Approaches in Cell Biology*, Proceedings of a Symposium held at Imperial College, London, July 1958, pp. 95–123. Academic Press, New York and London.

Cain, A. J. 1956. The genus in evolutionary taxonomy. *Systematic Zool.*, **5**:97–109.

Cain, A. J. 1958. Logic and memory in Linnaeus's system of taxonomy. *Proc. Linn. Soc. Lond.* 169th session, pp. 144–163.

Cain, A. J. 1959a. Deductive and inductive methods in post-Linnaean taxonomy. *Proc. Linn. Soc. Lond.* 170th session, pp. 185–217.

Cain, A. J. 1959b. The post-Linnaean development of taxonomy. *Proc. Linn. Soc. Lond.* 170th session, pp. 234–244.

Cain, A. J. 1959c. Taxonomic concepts. *Ibis*, **101**:302–318.

Cain, A. J. 1962. The evolution of taxonomic principles. In G. C. Ainsworth and P. H. A. Sneath (eds.), *Microbial Classification*, 12th Symposium of the Society for General Microbiology, pp. 1–13. Cambridge University Press, Cambridge. 483 pp.

Cain, A. J. and G. A. Harrison. 1958. An analysis of the taxonomist's judgment of affinity. *Proc. Zool. Soc. Lond.*, **131**:85–98.

Cain, A. J. and G. A. Harrison. 1960a. The phenetic affinity of some hominoid skulls. *Proc. Soc. Study Human Biol.*, 27 May, 1960.

Cain, A. J. and G. A. Harrison. 1960b. Phyletic weighting. *Proc. Zool. Soc. Lond.*, **135**:1–31.

Camp, W. H. 1951. Biosystematy. *Brittonia*, **7**:113–127.

Camp, W. H. and C. L. Gilly. 1943. The structure and origin of species. *Brittonia*, **4**:323–385.

Campbell, B. 1962. The systematics of man. *Nature*, **194**:225–232.

Candolle, A. P. de. 1813. *Théorie élémentaire de la botanique, ou exposition des principes de la classification naturelle et de l'art de décrire et d' étudier les végétaux.* Déterville, Paris. 528 pp.

Cattell, R. B. 1952. *Factor Analysis.* Harper, New York. 462 pp.

Cerbón, J. and L. F. Bojalil. 1961. Physiological relationships of rapidly growing mycobacteria. Adansonian Classification. *J. Gen. Microbiol.*, **25**:7–15.

Challinor, J. 1959. Palaeontology and evolution. In P. R. Bell (ed.), *Darwin's Biological Work*, pp. 50–100. Cambridge University Press, Cambridge. 343 pp.

Cheeseman, G. C. and N. J. Berridge. 1959. The differentiation of bacterial species by paper chromatography. VII. The use of electronic computation for the objective assessment of chromatographic results. *J. Appl. Bacteriol.*, **22**:307–316.

Chenery, E. M. 1960. An introduction to the soils of the Uganda Protectorate. *Mem. Res. Div., Uganda Protectorate Dept. Agr. Ser.* 1, *Soils*, No. 1, 79 pp.

Chester, K. S. 1937. A critique of plant serology. *Quart. Rev. Biol.*, **12**:19–46, 165–190, 294–321.

Chillcott, J. G. 1960. A revision of the nearctic species of Fanniinae. *Canad. Entomol.*, **92** (suppl. 14):1–295.

Chu, C. M., C. H. Andrewes, and A. W. Gledhill. 1950. Influenza in 1948–1949. *Bull. World Hlth. Org.*, **3**:187–214.

Cinader, B. 1957. Antibodies against enzymes. *Ann. Rev. Microbiol.*, **11**:371–390.

Clark, F. H. 1941. Correlation and body proportion in mature mice of the genus *Peromyscus*. *Genetics*, **26**:283–300.

Clark, P. J. 1952. An extension of the coefficient of divergence for use with multiple characters. *Copeia*, **2**:61–64.

Clarke, D. L. 1962. Matrix analysis and archaeology with special reference to British beaker pottery. *Proc. Prehist. Soc. Lond.*, **28**:371–382.

Clay, T. 1949. Some problems in the evolution of a group of ectoparasites. *Evolution*, **3**:279–299.

Clever, U. 1961. Genaktivitäten in den Riesenchromosomen von *Chironomus tentans* und ihre Beziehung zur Entwicklung. I. Genaktivierungen durch Ecdyson. *Chromosome (Berlin)*, **12**:607–675.

Cole, L. C. 1949. The measurement of interspecific association. *Ecology*, **30**:411–424.

Cole, L. C. 1957. The measurement of partial interspecific association. *Ecology*, **38**:226–233.

Colobert, L. and H. Blondeau. 1962. L'espèce *Streptococcus faecalis*. I. Étude de l'homogénéité par la méthode adansonienne. *Ann. Inst. Pasteur*, **103**:345–362.

Colwell, R. R. and J. Liston. 1961a. An electronic computer analysis of some *Xanthomonas* and *Pseudomonas* species. *Bacteriol. Proc.*, **1961**:72.

Colwell, R. R. and J. Liston. 1961b. Taxonomic relationships among the Pseudomonads. *J. Bacteriol.*, **82**:1–14.

Colwell, R. R. and J. Liston. 1961c. Taxonomy of *Xanthomonas* and *Pseudomonas*. *Nature*, **191**:617–619.

Colwell, R. R. and J. Liston. 1961d. Taxonomic analysis with the electronic computer of some *Xanthomonas* and *Pseudomonas* species. *J. Bacteriol.*, **82**:913–919.

Conterio, F. and D. Mainardi. 1959. Analisi elettroforetica dell'emoglobina di Passeracei di diverse famiglie. *La Ricerca Sci.*, **29** (suppl.):1–9.

Core, E. L. 1955. *Plant Taxonomy*. Prentice-Hall, Englewood Cliffs, New Jersey. 459 pp.

Count, E. W. (ed.). 1950. *This Is Race. An Anthology Selected from the International Literature on the Races of Man*. Henry Schuman, New York. 747 pp.

Cowan, S. T. 1955. Introduction: the philosophy of classification. In a symposium on "The principles of microbial classification." *J. Gen. Microbiol.*, **12**:314–319.

Cowan, S. T. 1959. Bacterial classification —problems and developments. In V. Bryson (ed.), *Microbiology, Yesterday and Today*, pp. 54–79. Institute of Microbiology, Rutgers University, New Brunswick, N. J. 122 pp.

Cowan, S. T. and K. J. Steel. 1960. A device for the identification of microorganisms. *Lancet*, 1960 (i): 1172–1173.

Crick, F. H. C. 1958. On protein synthesis. In *The Biological Replication of Macromolecules*, XIIth Symposium of the Society for Experimental Biology, pp. 138–163. Cambridge University Press, London. 255 pp.

Crow, J. F. 1957. Genetics of insecticide resistance to chemicals. *Ann. Rev. Entomol.*, **2**:227–246.

Crowle, A. J. 1960. Interpretation of immunodiffusion tests. *Ann. Rev. Microbiol.*, **14**:161–176.

Cummins, C. S. and H. Harris. 1956. The chemical composition of the cell wall in some Gram-positive bacteria and its possible value as a taxonomic character. *J. Gen. Microbiol.*, **14**:583–600.

Cummins, C. S. and H. Harris. 1958. Studies on the cell-wall composition and taxonomy of Actinomycetales and related groups. *J. Gen. Microbiol.*, **18**:173–189.

Czekanowski, J. 1932. "Coefficient of racial likeness" und "durchschnittliche Differenz." *Anthrop. Anz.*, **9**:227–249.

Dagnelie, P. 1960. Contribution à l'étude des communautés végétales par l'analyse factorielle. *Bull. Serv. Carte Phytogéogr.* (B), **5**:7–71, 93–195.

Daly, H. V. 1961. Phenetic classification and typology. *Systematic Zool.*, **10**:176–179.

Danser, B. H. 1950. A theory of systematics. *Bibl. Biotheor.*, **4**:113–180.

Darwin, C. 1891. *The Origin of Species by Means of Natural Selection, or the Preservation of Favoured Races in the Struggle for Life.* 6th ed. Murray, London. 432 pp.

DeFalco, R. J. 1942. A serological study of some avian relationships. *Biol. Bull.*, **83**:205–218.

Defayolle, M. and L. Colobert. 1962. L'espèce *Streptococcus faecalis*. II. Étude de l'homogénéité par l'analyse factorielle. *Ann. Inst. Pasteur*, **103**:505–522.

Denmark, H. A., H. V. Weems, Jr., and C. Taylor. 1958. Taxonomic codification of biological entities. *Science*, **128**:990–992.

Dice, L. R. 1945. Measures of the amount of ecologic association between species. *Ecology*, **26**:297–302.

Dobzhansky, T. 1959. Evolution of genes and genes in evolution. *Cold Spring Harbor Symp. Quant. Biol.*, **24**:15–27.

Dömök, I., E. Szafir, and E. Farkas. 1954. Laboratory investigations into the influenza epidemics of 1951 and 1952 in Hungary. *Acta Microbiol. Hung.*, **1**:99–110.

Doty, P., J. Marmur, J. Eigner, and C. Schildkraut. 1960. Strand separation and specific recombination in deoxyribonucleic acids: physical chemical studies. *Proc. Nat. Acad. Sci. U.S.A.*, **46**:461–476.

Downs, T. 1961. A study of variation and evolution in miocene *Merychippus*. *Contrib. Sci. Los Angeles County Mus.*, **45**:1–75.

Driver, H. E. 1962. The contribution of A. L. Kroeber to culture area theory and practice. *Intern. J. Am. Linguistics* **28** (Suppl., Memoir No. 18), 28 pp.

Dujarric de la Rivière, R., M. Saint-Paul, and A. Eyquem. 1953. Hémagglutinines végétales, antigènes végétaux et antisérums homologues. *C. R. Acad. Sci. Paris*, **237**:211–213.

DuMas, F. N. 1955. *Manifest Structure Analysis.* Montana State University Press, Missoula, Montana. 193 pp.

DuRietz, G. E. 1930. The fundamental units of biological taxonomy. *Svensk Bot. Tidskr.*, **24**:333–428.

Ehrlich, P. R. 1958. Problems of higher classification. *Systematic Zool.*, **7**:180–184.

Ehrlich, P. R. 1961a. Comparative morphology of the male reproductive system of the butterflies (Lepidoptera: Papilionoidea). 1. Some nearctic species. *Microentomology*, **24**:135–166.

Ehrlich, P. R. 1961b. Systematics in 1970: Some unpopular predictions. *Systematic Zool.*, **10**:157–158.

Ehrlich, P. R. 1961c. Has the biological species concept outlived its usefulness? *Systematic Zool.*, **10**:167–176.

Ehrlich, P. R. and R. W. Holm. 1962. Patterns and populations. *Science*, **137**:652–657.

Elsasser, W. M. 1958. *The Physical Foundation of Biology.* Pergamon Press, London, New York, Paris, Los Angeles. 219 pp.

Erdtman, G. 1943. *An Introduction to Pollen Analysis.* Chronica Botanica, Waltham, Mass. 239 pp.

Erhardt, A. 1931. Die Verwandtschaftsbestimmungen mittels der Immunitätsreaktionen in der Zoologie und ihr Wert für phylogenetische Untersuchungen. *Ergebn. Fortschr. Zool.*, **7**:279–377.

Falconer, D. S. 1960. *Introduction to Quantitative Genetics.* Oliver & Boyd, Edinburgh and London, 365 pp.

Fein, L. 1961. The computer-related sciences (synnoetics) at a university in the year 1975. *Am. Scientist*, **49**:149–168.

Fisher, R. A. 1936. The use of multiple

measurements in taxonomic problems. *Ann. Eugen.*, **7**:179–188.

Floodgate, G. D. 1962. Some remarks on the theoretical aspects of bacterial taxonomy. *Bacteriol. Rev.*, **26**:277–291.

Florkin, M. 1949. *Biochemical Evolution*. Academic Press, New York. 157 pp.

Forbes, W. T. M. 1933. A grouping of the Agrotine genera. *Entomol. Am. N.S.*, **14**:1–40.

Fox, S. W. and P. G. Homeyer. 1955. A statistical evaluation of the kinship of protein molecules. *Am. Naturalist*, **89**:163–168.

Frahm-Leliveld, J. A. 1958. Some considerations on chromosome dynamics in relation to taxonomy of the flowering plants. *Proc. Ned. Akad. Sci. C*, **61**:334–340, 341–352, 353–362.

Frisch-Niggemeyer, W. 1956. Absolute amount of ribonucleic acid in viruses. *Nature*, **178**:307–308.

Frost, F. H. 1930. Specialization in secondary xylem of dicotyledons. I. Origin of vessels. *Botan. Gaz.*, **89**:67–94.

Fruchter, B. 1954. *Introduction to Factor Analysis*. Van Nostrand, New York. 280 pp.

Gay, P. A. 1960. A new method for the comparison of populations that contain hybrids. *New Phytologist*, **59**:218–226.

Gell, P. G. H., J. G. Hawkes, and S. T. C. Wright. 1960. The application of immunological methods to the taxonomy of species within the genus *Solanum*. *Proc. Roy. Soc. London, Ser. B*, **151**:364–383.

George, T. N. 1933. Palingenesis and palaeontology. *Biol. Rev.*, **8**:107–135.

Gilardi, E., L. R. Hill, M. Turri, and L. G. Silvestri. 1960. Quantitative methods in the systematics of Actinomycetales. I. *Giorn. Microbiol.*, **8**:203–218.

Gilmour, J. S. L. 1937. A taxonomic problem. *Nature*, **139**:1040–1042.

Gilmour, J. S. L. 1940. Taxonomy and philosophy. In J. S. Huxley (ed.), *The New Systematics*, pp. 461–474. Clarendon Press, Oxford. 583 pp.

Gilmour, J. S. L. 1951. The development of taxonomic theory since 1851. *Nature*, **168**:400–402.

Gilmour, J. S. L. (rapporteur). 1961a. The mathematical assessment of taxonomic similarity, including the use of computers (by J. Heslop-Harrison, R. R. Sokal, P. H. A. Sneath, A. J. Cain, R. Crawshay-Williams, G. A. Maccacaro, J. A. Barnett, A. F. Parker-Rhodes, R. H. Richens, and S. M. Walters). *Taxon*, **10**:97–101.

Gilmour, J. S. L. 1961b. Taxonomy. In A. M. MacLeod and L. S. Cobley (eds.), *Contemporary Botanical Thought*, pp. 27–45. Oliver & Boyd, Edinburgh, and Quadrangle Books, Chicago. 197 pp.

Gilmour, J. S. L. and J. W. Gregor. 1939. Demes: a suggested new terminology. *Nature*, **144**:333.

Gilmour, J. S. L. and J. Heslop-Harrison. 1954. The deme terminology and the units of micro-evolutionary change. *Genetica*, **27**:147–161.

Good, I. J. 1958. How much science can you have at your fingertips? *IBM J. Res. Develop.*, **2**:282–288. *See also* Speculations concerning information retrieval. International Business Machines Corporation, Research Center; Yorktown Heights, New York, Research Report RC–78 (by the same author).

Goodall, D. W. 1953. Objective methods for the classification of vegetation. I. The use of positive interspecific correlation. *Austral. J. Bot.*, **1**:39–63.

Gould, S. W. 1958. Punched cards, binomial names and numbers. *Am. J. Botany*, **45**:331–339.

Gould, S. W. 1962. *Family Names of the Plant Kingdom*. Vol. I. International Plant Index, New Haven and New York. 111 pp.

Gregg, J. R. 1954. *The Language of Tax-*

*onomy*. Columbia University Press, New York. 71 pp.

Greig-Smith, P. 1957. *Quantitative Plant Ecology*. Butterworth, London, and Academic Press, New York. 198 pp.

Grüneberg, H. 1938. An analysis of the "pleiotropic" effects of a new lethal mutation in the rat (*Mus norvegicus*). *Proc. Roy. Soc. London, Ser. B*, **125**:123–144.

Grüneberg, H. 1958. Genetical studies on the skeleton of the mouse. XXII. The development of Danforth's short-tail. *J. Embryol. Exp. Morphol.*, **6**:124–148.

Guilford, J. P. 1942. *Fundamental Statistics in Psychology and Education*. McGraw-Hill, New York. 333 pp.

Haas, O. and G. G. Simpson. 1946. Analysis of some phylogenetic terms, with attempts at redefinition. *Proc. Am. Philos. Soc.*, **90**:319–349.

Haldane, J. B. S. 1949. Suggestions as to quantitative measurement of rates of evolution. *Evolution*, **3**:51–56.

Haltenorth, T. 1937. Die verwandtschaftliche Stellung der Grosskatzen zueinander. *Z. Säugetierkunde*, **12**:97–240.

Hamann, U. 1961. Merkmalsbestand und Verwandtschaftsbeziehungen der Farinosae. Ein Beitrag zum System der Monokotyledonen. *Willdenowia*, **2**:639–768.

Hammond, W. H. 1957. The constancy of physical types as determined by factorial analysis. *Human Biol.*, **29**:40–61.

Harberd, D. J. 1960. Association-analysis in plant communities. *Nature*, **185**:53–54.

Harland, S. C. 1936. The genetical conception of the species. *Biol. Rev.*, **11**:83–112.

Harman, H. H. 1960. *Modern Factor Analysis*. University of Chicago Press, Chicago. 469 pp.

Hayata, B. 1921. In *Icones Plantarum Formosanarum* **10**:75–95, 97–234. Government of Formosa, Taihoku.

Hayata, B. 1931. Le système dynamique

des plantes fondé sur la théorie de la participation. *C. R. Acad. Sci. Paris*, **192**: 1286–1288.

Heincke, F. 1898. Naturgeschichte des Herings. I. Die Lokalformen und die Wanderungen des Herings in den europäischen Meeren. *Abh. Deutsch. Seefischerei-Vereins*, **2**:i–cxxxvi, 1–223.

Hennig, W. 1950. *Grundzüge einer Theorie der phylogenetischen Systematik*. Deutsch. Zentralverl., Berlin. 370 pp.

Hennig, W. 1957. Systematik und Phylogenese. *Ber. Hundertjahrfeier Deutsch. Entomol. Ges.*, pp. 50–70. Berlin.

Heslop-Harrison, J. 1962. Purposes and procedures in the taxonomic treatment of higher organisms. In G. C. Ainsworth and P. H. A. Sneath (eds.), *Microbial Classification*, 12th Symposium of the Society for General Microbiology, pp. 14–36. Cambridge University Press, Cambridge. 483 pp.

Hill, L. R. 1959. The Adansonian classification of staphylococci. *J. Gen. Microbiol.*, **20**:277–283.

Hill, L. R. and L. Silvestri. 1962. Quantitative methods in the systematics of Actinomycetales. III. The taxonomic significance of physiological-biochemical characters and the construction of a diagnostic key. *Giorn. Microbiol.*, **10**: 1–28.

Hill, L. R., M. Turri, E. Gilardi, and L. G. Silvestri. 1961. Quantitative methods in the systematics of Actinomycetales. II. *Giorn. Microbiol.*, **9**:56–72.

Hole, F. D. and M. Hironaka. 1960. An experiment in ordination of some soil profiles. *Proc. Soil Sci. Soc. Am.*, **24**:309–312.

Holttum, R. E. 1949. The classification of ferns. *Biol. Rev.*, **24**:267–296.

Holzinger, K. J. and H. H. Harman. 1941. *Factor Analysis*. University of Chicago Press, Chicago. 417 pp.

Hudson, G. E., P. J. Lanzillotti, and G. D. Edwards. 1959. Muscles of the pelvic limb in galliform birds. *Am. Midland Naturalist*, **61**:1–67.

Hughes, R. E. and D. V. Lindley. 1955. Application of biometric methods to problems of classification in ecology. *Nature*, **175**:806–807.

Hutchinson, G. E. 1957. Concluding remarks. *Cold Spring Harbor Symp. Quant. Biol.*, **22**:415–427.

Huxley, J. S. 1932. *Problems of Relative Growth*. Methuen, London. 276 pp.

Huxley, J. S. (ed.), 1940. *The New Systematics*. Clarendon Press, Oxford. 583 pp.

Huxley, J. S. 1943. *Evolution: The Modern Synthesis*. Harper, New York and London. 645 pp.

Huxley, J. S. 1957. The three types of evolutionary process. *Nature*, **180**:454–455.

Huxley, J. S. 1958. Evolutionary processes and taxonomy with special reference to grades. *Uppsala Univ. Arssks.*, **1958**: 21–39.

Huxley, T. H. 1869. *An Introduction to the Classification of Animals*. Churchill, London. 147 pp.

IBM. 1959. The IBM taxonomy application—an experimental procedure for classification and prediction purposes. Parts I and II. IBM 704 Program IB CLF. Mathematics and Applications Department, Data Systems Division, International Business Machines Corporation, New York.

Inger, R. F. 1958. Comments on the definition of genera. *Evolution*, **12**:370–384.

International Code of Botanical Nomenclature, adopted by the Ninth International Botanical Congress, Montreal, August 1959. 1961 International Bureau for Plant Taxonomy and Nomenclature, Utrecht (*Regnum Vegetabile*, No. 23, 372 pp.)

International Code of Nomenclature for Cultivated Plants. 1961. International Bureau for Plant Taxonomy and No-

menclature, Utrecht (*Regnum Vegetabile*, No. 22, 30 pp.).

International Code of Nomenclature of Bacteria and Viruses. 1958. Iowa State University Press, Ames, Iowa; reprinted with corrections, 1959. 156 pp.

International Code of Zoological Nomenclature, adopted by the XV International Congress for Zoology, London, July 1958. London: International Trust for Zoological Nomenclature. 19 Belgrave Square, London S.W. 1, 1961. 176 pp.

Irwin, M. R. 1959. Interrelationships of genetic characters which differentiate species of doves (*Streptopelia*). *Systematic Zool.*, **8**:48–57.

Jaccard, P. 1908. Nouvelles recherches sur la distribution florale. *Bull. Soc. Vaud. Sci. Nat.*, **44**:223–270.

Jacob, F. and E. L. Wollman. 1958. Genetic and physical determinations of chromosomal segments in *Escherichia coli*. In *The Biological Replication of Macromolecules*, XIIth Symposium of the Society for Experimental Biology, pp. 75–92. Cambridge University Press, London. 255 pp.

Jacob, F. and E. L. Wollman. 1959. The relationship between the prophage and the bacterial chromosome in lysogenic bacteria. In *Recent Progress in Microbiology*, Symposia held at the VIIth International Congress of Microbiology, pp. 15–30. Almqvist & Wiksell, Stockholm.

Jahn, T. L. 1961. Man versus machine: a future problem in protozoan taxonomy. *Systematic Zool.*, **10**:179–192.

Jahn, T. L. 1962. The use of computers in systematics. *J. Parasitol.*, **48**:656–663.

James, M. T. 1953. An objective aid in determining generic limits. *Systematic Zool.*, **2**:136–137.

Jevons, W. S. 1877. *The Principles of Science: a Treatise on Logic and Scientific*

*Method.* 2nd ed., rev., Macmillan, London and New York. 786 pp.

Jolicoeur, P. 1959. Multivariate geographical variation in the wolf *Canis lupus* L. *Evolution*, **13**:283–299.

Joysey, K. A. 1956. The nomenclature and comparison of fossil communities. In P. C. Sylvester-Bradley (ed.), *The Species Concept in Palaeontology*, pp. 83–94. Systematics Association Publication No. 2, London. 145 pp.

Joysey, K. A. 1959. The evolution of the liassic oysters *Ostrea-Gryphaea. Biol. Rev.*, **34**:297–332.

Kelus, A. and J. Lukaszewicz. 1953. Taksonomia wroclawska w zastosowaniu do zagadnien seroantropologii. *Archiwum Immunol. Terap. Doswiadczalnej*, **1**:245–254.

Kiriakoff, S. G. 1959. Phylogenetic systematics versus typology. *Systematic Zool.*, **8**:117–118.

Kiriakoff, S. G. 1962. On the neo-Adansonian school. *Systematic Zool.*, **11**:180–185.

Kraus, B. S. and S. C. Choi. 1958. A factorial analysis of the prenatal growth of the human skeleton. *Growth*, **22**:231–242.

Kulczynski, S. 1927. Die Pflanzenassoziationen der Pieninen. [In Polish, German summary.] *Bull. Intern. Acad. Pol. Sci. Lett. Cl. Sci. Math. Nat., B (Sci. Nat.)*, 1927 (Suppl. 2):57–203.

Kurtén, B. 1958. A differentiation index, and a new measure of evolutionary rates. *Evolution*, **12**:146–157.

Kurtén, B. 1959. Rates of evolution in fossil mammals. *Cold Spring Harbor Symp. Quant. Biol.*, **24**:205–215.

Lack, D. 1947. *Darwin's Finches, an Essay on the General Biological Theory of Evolution.* Cambridge University Press, Cambridge. (Reprinted, 1961, Harper, New York. 204 pp.)

Lam, H. J. 1959. Taxonomy. General principles and angiosperms. In W. B. Turrill (ed.), *Vistas in Botany. A Volume in Honour of the Bicentenary of the Royal Botanic Gardens, Kew*, pp. 3–75. Pergamon Press, London, New York, Paris, Los Angeles. 547 pp.

Lambert, J. M. and J. N. Jennings. 1951. Alluvial stratigraphy and vegetational succession in the region of the Bure valley broads. II. Detailed vegetational-stratigraphical relationships. *J. Ecol.*, **39**:120–148.

Lanjouw, J. (ed.). 1950. *Synopsis of Proposals Concerning the International Rules of Botanical Nomenclature, Submitted to the Seventh International Botanical Congress, Stockholm, 1950.* Intern. Comm. Taxonomy, IUBS, Utrecht, and Chronica Botanica, Waltham, Mass. 255 pp.

Lanyon, W. E. 1960. The ontogeny of vocalization in birds. In W. E. Lanyon and W. N. Tavolga (eds.), *Animal Sounds and Communication*, pp. 321–347. Am. Inst. Biol. Sci. Publ. 7, Washington, D. C.

Lawrence, G. H. M. 1951. *Taxonomy of Vascular Plants.* Macmillan, New York. 823 pp.

Lawrence, G. H. M. 1955. *An Introduction to Plant Taxonomy.* Macmillan, New York. 179 pp.

Leach, E. R. 1962. Classification in social anthropology. *Aslib. Proc.*, **14**:239–242.

Lederberg, E. M. 1960. Genetic and functional aspects of galactose metabolism in *Escherichia coli* K-12. In W. Hayes and R. C. Clowes (eds.), *Microbial Genetics*, Xth Symposium of the Society for General Microbiology, pp. 115–131. Cambridge University Press, Cambridge. 300 pp.

Ledley, R. S. and L. B. Lusted. 1959a. Reasoning foundations of medical diagnosis. *Science*, **130**:9–21.

Ledley, R. S. and L. B. Lusted. 1959b. The use of electronic computers to aid in medical diagnosis. *Proc. Inst. Radio Eng.*, **47**:1970–1977.

Lee, K. Y., R. Wahl, and E. Barbu. 1956. Contenu en bases purique et pyrimidiques des acides désoxyribonucléiques des bactéries. *Ann. Inst. Pasteur*, **91**: 212–224.

Leeper, G. W. 1954. The classification of soils—an Australian approach. *Trans. V. Internat. Cong. Soil Sci.*, **4**:217–226.

Leone, C. A. 1947. Systematic serology among certain insect species. *Biol. Bull.*, **93**:64–71.

Leone, C. A. (ed.). 1963. *Taxonomic Biochemistry, Physiology and Serology*. Ronald Press, New York (in press).

Lerner, I. M. 1958. *The Genetic Basis of Selection*. Wiley, New York. 298 pp.

Lipkin, M., R. L. Engle, Jr., B. J. Davis, V. K. Zworykin, R. Ebald, M. Sendrow, and C. Berkley. 1961. Digital computer as aid to differential diagnosis. *Arch. Intern. Med.*, **108**:56–72.

Lipkin, M. and J. D. Hardy. 1957. Differential diagnosis of hematologic diseases aided by mechanical correlation of data. *Science*, **125**:551–552.

Liston, J. 1960. Some results of a computer analysis of strains of *Pseudomonas* and *Achromobacter*, and other organisms. *J. Appl. Bacteriol.*, **23**:391–394.

Liston, J. and R. R. Colwell. 1960. Taxonomic relationships among the pseudomonads. *Bacteriol. Proc.*, **1960**:78–79.

Little, F. J., Jr. 1963. An experimental or tentative revision of the genus *Cliona* utilizing the principles of numerical taxonomy. Unpublished Ph.D. thesis. University of Texas. 255 pp.

Lockhart, W. R. and P. A. Hartman. 1963. Formation of monothetic groups in quantitative bacterial taxonomy. *J. Bacteriol.* **85**:68–77.

Löve, A. and D. Löve. 1961. Chromosome numbers of central and northwest European plant species. *Opera Botan. Soc. Botan. Lund*, **5**:1–581.

Lowe, J. 1961. The phylogeny of monocotyledons. *New Phytologist*, **60**:355–387.

Lusted, L. B. 1960. Logical analysis in Roentgen diagnosis. *Radiology*, **74**:178–193.

Lysenko, O. 1961. *Pseudomonas*—an attempt at a general classification. *J. Gen. Microbiol.*, **25**:379–408.

Lysenko, O. and P. H. A. Sneath. 1959. The use of models in bacterial classification. *J. Gen. Microbiol.*, **20**:284–290.

Maccacaro, G. A. 1958. La misura delle informazione contenuta nei criteri di classificazione. *Ann. Microbiol. Enzimol.*, **8**:231–239.

Mahalanobis, P. C. 1936. On the generalized distance in statistics. *Proc. Nat. Inst. Sci. India*, **2**:49–55.

Mainardi, D. 1958a. La filogenesi nei Fringillidi basata sui rapporti immunologici. *R. C. Ist. Lombard Sci. B.*, **92**:336–356.

Mainardi, D. 1958b. Immunology and chromatography in taxonomic studies on gallinaceous birds. *Nature*, **182**:1388–1389.

Mainardi, D. 1959a. Un nuovo metodo di immunologia comparata a scopo sistematico basato sulla sommazione degli antigeni comuni. *R. C. Ist. Lombard. Sci. B*, **93**:91–96.

Mainardi, D. 1959b. Immunological distances among some gallinaceous birds. *Nature*, **184**:913–914.

Mainardi, D. 1959c. Le parentele tra sette specie di galliformi definite dall' analisi immunologica degli antigeni eritrocitari. *Boll. Zool.*, **26**:207–211.

Manil, G. 1959. General considerations on the problem of soil classification. *J. Soil Sci.*, **10**:5–13.

Mattick, A. T. R., G. C. Cheeseman, N. J. Berridge, and V. Bottazzi. 1956. The differentiation of species of lactobacilli and streptococci by means of paper partition chromatography. *J. Appl. Bacteriol.*, **19**:310–321.

Mayr, E. 1942. *Systematics and the Origin of Species*. Columbia University Press, New York. 334 pp.

Mayr, E. 1959. Trends in avian systematics. *Ibis*, **101**:293–302.

Mayr, E., E. G. Linsley and R. L. Usinger. 1953. *Methods and Principles of Systematic Zoology*. McGraw-Hill, New York. 328 pp.

Medawar, P. B. 1945. Size, shape, and age. In W. E. LeGros Clark and P. B. Medawar (eds.), *Essays on Growth and Form Presented to D'Arcy Wentworth Thompson*, pp. 157–187. Clarendon Press, Oxford. 408 pp.

Metcalf, Z. P. 1954. The construction of keys. *Systematic Zool.*, **3**:38–45.

Mez, C. and H. Ziegenspeck. 1926. Der Königsberger serodiagnostische Stammbaum. *Bot. Arch.*, **13**:483–486.

Michener, C. D. 1949. Parallelisms in the evolution of the saturniid moths. *Evolution*, **3**:129–141.

Michener, C. D. 1953. Life-history studies in insect systematics. *Systematic Zool.*, **2**:112–118.

Michener, C. D. 1957. Some bases for higher categories in classification. *Systematic Zool.*, **6**:160–173.

Michener, C. D. and R. R. Sokal. 1957. A quantitative approach to a problem in classification. *Evolution*, **11**:130–162.

Michener, C. D. and R. R. Sokal. 1963. Two tests of the hypothesis of nonspecificity in the *Hoplitis* complex (in preparation).

Micks, D. W. and A. A. Benedict, 1953. Infrared spectrophotometry as a means for identification of mosquitoes. *Proc. Soc. Exp. Biol. Med.*, **84**:12–14.

Micks, D. W. and J. P. Ellis. 1952. Free amino acids in the developmental stages of the mosquito. *Proc. Soc. Exp. Biol. Med.*, **79**:191–193.

Moll, J. W. 1934. *Phytography as a Fine Art, Comprising Linnean Description, Micrography and Penportraits*. Brill, Leyden. 534 pp.

Möller, F. 1962. Quantitative methods in the systematics of Actinomycetales. IV. The theory and application of a probabilistic identification key. *Giorn. Microbiol.*, **10**:29–47.

Morant, G. M. 1936. A contribution to the physical anthropology of the Swat and Hunza valleys based on records collected by Sir Aurel Stein. *J. Roy. Anthrop. Inst.*, **66**:19–42.

Morishima, H. and H. Oka. 1960. The pattern of interspecific variation in the genus *Oryza*: its quantitative representation by statistical methods. *Evolution*, **14**:153–165.

Morse, M. L., E. M. Lederberg, and J. Lederberg. 1956. Transductional heterogenotes in *Escherichia coli*. *Genetics*, **41**:758–779.

Mullins, L. J. and W. J. Nickerson. 1951. A proposal for serial number identification of biological species. *Chron. Botan.*, **12**:211–215.

Myers, G. S. 1960. The endemic fish fauna of Lake Lanao, and the evolution of higher taxonomic categories. *Evolution*, **14**:323–333.

Naef, A. 1919. *Idealistische Morphologie und Phylogenetik*. Gustav Fischer, Jena. 77 pp.

Nash, F. A. 1954. Differential diagnosis. An apparatus to assist the logical faculties. *Lancet*, 1954 (i):874–875.

Nash, F. A. 1960. Diagnostic reasoning and the logoscope. *Lancet*, 1960 (ii): 1442–1446.

Norris, K. P. 1959. Infra-red spectroscopy and its application to microbiology. *J. Hyg.*, **57**:326–345.

Nuttall, G. H. F. 1901. The new biological test for blood in relation to zoological classification. *Proc. Roy. Soc. Lond. Ser. B*, **69**:150–153.

Nuttall, G. H. F. 1904. *Blood Immunity and*

*Blood Relationship; a Demonstration of Certain Blood-relationships amongst Animals by Means of the Precipitin Test for Blood.* Cambridge University Press, Cambridge. 444 pp.

Ochiai, A. 1957. Zoogeographic studies on the soleoid fishes found in Japan and its neighbouring regions. [In Japanese, English summary.] *Bull. Jap. Soc. Sci. Fish.*, **22**:526–530.

Ogur, M., R. O. Erickson, G. U. Rosen, K. B. Sax, and C. Holden. 1951. Nucleic acids in relation to cell division in *Lilium longiflorum. Exper. Cell. Res.*, **2**:73–89.

Olson, E. C. 1959. The evolution of mammalian characters. *Evolution*, **13**:344–353.

Olson, E. C. and R. L. Miller. 1958. *Morphological Integration.* University of Chicago Press, Chicago. 317 pp.

Ornstein, L. 1960. Pattern recognition, morphology, and the generation of hypotheses. (Lecture presented at the meeting of the Am. Assn. Adv. Sci., New York, December 1960.)

Ouchterlony, Ö. 1958. Diffusion-in-gel methods for immunological analysis. *Progress in Allergy*, **5**:1–78. (Karger, Basel, and New York).

Ouchterlony, Ö. 1962. Diffusion-in-gel methods for immunological analysis. II. *Progress in Allergy*, **6**:30–154. (Karger, Basel, and New York).

Parker-Rhodes, A. F. 1961. *Contributions to the Theory of Clumps.* Cambridge Language Res. Unit, 20 Millington Rd., Cambridge. 34 pp.

Pearson, E. S. and H. O. Hartley (eds.). 1958. *Biometrika Tables for Statisticians.* Vol. I. Cambridge University Press, Cambridge. 240 pp.

Pearson, K. 1926. On the coefficient of racial likeness. *Biometrika*, **18**:105–117.

Pecket, R. C. 1959. The constituents of leaf extracts in the genus *Lathyrus* and their bearing on taxonomy. *New Phytologist*, **58**:182–187.

Penrose, L. S. 1954. Distance, size, and shape. *Ann. Eugenics*, **18**:337–343.

Perlman, F. 1961. Insect allergens: their interrelationship and differences. *J. Allergy*, **32**:93–101.

Perlmann, P. 1953. Soluble antigens in sea urchin gametes and developmental stages. *Exp. Cell. Res.*, **5**:394–399.

Pichi-Sermolli, R. E. G. 1959. Pteridophyta. In W. B. Turrill (ed.), *Vistas in Botany. A Volume in Honour of the Bicentenary of the Royal Botanic Gardens, Kew,* pp. 421–493. Pergamon Press, London, New York, Paris, Los Angeles. 547 pp.

Pimentel, R. A. 1958. Taxonomic methods, their bearing on subspeciation. *Systematic Zool.*, **7**:139–156.

Pimentel, R. A. 1959. Mendelian infraspecific divergence levels and their analysis. *Systematic Zool.*, **8**:139–159.

Pirie, N. W. 1962. Prerequisites for virus classification. In G. C. Ainsworth and P. H. A. Sneath (eds.) *Microbial Classification*, 12th Symposium of the Society for General Microbiology, pp. 374–393. Cambridge University Press, Cambridge. 483 pp.

Pohja, M. S. 1960. Micrococci in fermented meat products. Classification and description of 171 different strains. *Suomen Maataloust. Seur. Julkais. (Acta agralia fenn.)* Bull. 96. 80 pp.

Pontecorvo, G. 1956. The parasexual cycle in fungi. *Ann. Rev. Microbiol.*, **10**:393–400.

Pontecorvo, G. and J. A. Roper. 1956. Resolving power of genetic analysis. *Nature*, **178**:83–84.

Proom, H. and A. J. Woiwod. 1949. The examination, by partition paper chromatography, of the nitrogen metabolism of bacteria. *J. Gen. Microbiol.*, **3**:319–327.

Race, R. R. and R. Sanger. 1950. *Blood Groups in Man.* 1st ed. Blackwell, Oxford. 290 pp.

Randall, H. M., D. W. Smith, A. C. Colm, and W. J. Nungester. 1951. Correlation of biologic properties of strains of *Mycobacterium* with infra-red spectrums. I. Reproducibility of extracts of *M. tuberculosis* as determined by infra-red spectroscopy. *Am. Rev. Tuberc.*, **63**:373–380.

Rao, C. R. 1948. The utilization of multiple measurements in problems of biological classification. *J. Roy. Stat. Soc., Ser. B*, **10**:159–193.

Raup, D. M. 1961. The geometry of coiling in gastropods. *Proc. Nat. Acad. Sci. U.S.A.*, **47**:602–609.

Reed, C. A. 1960. Polyphyletic or monophyletic ancestry of mammals, or: What is a class? *Evolution*, **14**:314–322.

Remane, A. 1956. *Die Grundlagen des natürlichen Systems, der vergleichenden Anatomie und der Phylogenetik. Theoretische Morphologie und Systematik. I.* 2nd ed. Akademische Verlagsges. Geest und Portig, Leipzig. 364 pp.

Renkonen, O. 1938. Statistische-ökologische Untersuchungen über die terrestrische Käferwelt der finnischen Bruchmoore. *Ann. Zool. Soc. Vanamo*, **6**:1–231.

Rensch, B. 1947. *Neuere Probleme der Abstammungslehre.* Ferdinand Enke, Stuttgart. 401 pp.

Rescigno, A. and G. A. Maccacaro. 1960. The information content of biological classifications. In C. Cherry, (ed.), *Information Theory—A Symposium Held at the Royal Institution, London, August 29th–September 2nd 1960*, pp. 437–446. Butterworth, London, 476 pp.

Rhodes, M. E. 1961. The characterization of *Pseudomonas fluorescens* with the aid of an electronic computer. *J. Gen. Microbiol.*, **25**:331–345.

Rice, S. A. 1927. The identification of blocs in small political bodies. *Am. Polit. Sci. Rev.*, **21**:619–627.

Rickett, H. W. 1958. So what is a taxon? *Taxon*, **7**:37–38.

Robinson, W. S. 1951. A method for chronologically ordering archaeological deposits. *Am. Antiquity*, **16**:293–301.

Rogers, D. J. 1961. Recent endeavors with computers in taxonomy. *Garden J.*, **1961**: 201–204.

Rogers, D. J. and T. T. Tanimoto. 1960. A computer program for classifying plants. *Science*, **132**:1115–1118.

Rogoff, M. 1957. Automatic analysis of infrared spectra. *Ann. New York Acad. Sci.*, **69**:27–37.

Rohlf, F. J. 1962. A numerical taxonomic study of the genus *Aedes* (Diptera: Culicidae) with emphasis on the congruence of larval and adult classifications. Unpublished Ph.D. thesis. University of Kansas. 98 pp.

Rohlf, F. J. and R. R. Sokal. 1962. The description of taxonomic relationships by factor analysis. *Systematic Zool.*, **11**: 1–16.

Rohlf, F. J. and R. R. Sokal. 1963. Coefficients of correlation and distance in numerical taxonomy. *Univ. Kansas Sci. Bull.* (in press).

Ross, A. S. C. 1950. Philological probability problems. *J. Roy. Stat. Soc., Ser. B.*, **12**:19–41.

Russell, N. H. 1961. The development of an operational approach in plant taxonomy. *Systematic Zool.*, **10**:159–167.

Russell, P. F. and T. R. Rao. 1940. On habitat and association of species of anopheline larvae in south-eastern Madras. *J. Malar. Inst. India*, **3**:153–178.

Ruud, J. T. 1954. Vertebrates without erythrocytes and blood pigment. *Nature*, **173**:848–850.

Sandnes, G. C. 1957. Fertility and viability in intergeneric pheasant hybrids. *Evolution*, **11**:426–444.

Schenk, E. T. and J. H. McMasters. 1956.

*Procedure in Taxonomy*. 3rd ed. rev. by A. M. Keene and S. W. Muller. Stanford University Press, Stanford, Calif., and Oxford University Press, London. 119 pp.

Schilder, F. A. and M. Schilder, 1951. *Anleitung zu biostatistischen Untersuchungen*. Max Niemeyer, Halle (Saale), Germany. 111 pp.

Schildkraut, C. L., J. Marmur, and P. Doty. 1961. The formation of hybrid DNA molecules and their use in studies of DNA homologies. *J. Molec. Biol.*, 3:595–617.

Schmalhausen, I. I. 1949. *Factors of Evolution; the Theory of Stabilizing Selection*. Blakiston, Philadelphia. 327 pp.

Schopf, J. M. 1960. Emphasis on holotype? *Science*, 131:1043.

Seitner, P. G. 1960. *Biology Code of the Chemical-Biological Coordination Center*. Publ. 790, Nat. Acad. Sci., Nat. Res. Council, Washington, D. C. 222 pp.

Seitner, P. G., G. A. Livingston, and A. S. Williams. 1960. *Key to the Biological Code of the Chemical-Biological Coordination Center*. Publ. 790K, Nat. Acad. Sci., Nat. Res. Council, Washington, D. C. 210 pp.

Sheppard, P. M. 1959. Blood groups and natural selection. *Brit. Med. Bull.*, 15:134–139.

Shewan, J. M., G. Hobbs, and W. Hodgkiss. 1960. A determinative scheme for the identification of certain genera of Gram-negative bacteria, with special reference to the Pseudomonadaceae. *J. Appl. Bacteriol.*, 23:379–390.

Sibley, C. G. 1960. The electrophoretic patterns of avian egg-white proteins as taxonomic characters. *Ibis*, 102:215–284.

Silvestri, L. 1960. Vantaggi e problemi di una sistematica adansoniana dei microorganismi. *Nuov. Ann. d'Ig. Microbiol.*, 11:1–12.

Silvestri, L. G. 1962. Computer correlations of microorganisms. *Giorn. Microbiol.* (in press).

Silvestri, L., M. Turri, L. R. Hill, and E. Gilardi. 1962. A quantitative approach to the systematics of actinomycetes based on overall similarity. In G. C. Ainsworth and P. H. A. Sneath (eds.), *Microbial Classification*, 12th Symposium of the Society for General Microbiology, pp. 333–360. Cambridge University Press, Cambridge. 483 pp.

Simpson, G. G. 1940. Types in modern taxonomy. *Am. J. Sci.*, 238:413–431.

Simpson, G. G. 1944. *Tempo and Mode in Evolution*. Columbia University Press, New York. 237 pp.

Simpson, G. G. 1945. The principles of classification and a classification of mammals. *Bull. Am. Mus. Nat. Hist.*, 85:1–350.

Simpson, G. G. 1951. *Horses: the Story of the Horse Family in the Modern World and Through Sixty Million Years of History*. Oxford University Press, Oxford. (Republished, 1961, Doubleday, Garden City, New York. 323 pp.)

Simpson, G. G. 1953. *The Major Features of Evolution*. Columbia University Press, New York. 434 pp.

Simpson, G. G. 1959. Mesozoic mammals and the polyphyletic origin of mammals. *Evolution*, 13:405–414.

Simpson, G. G. 1960. Diagnosis of the classes Reptilia and Mammalia. *Evolution*, 14:388–392.

Simpson, G. G. 1961. *Principles of Animal Taxonomy*. Columbia University Press, New York. 247 pp.

Simpson, G. G., A. Roe, and R. C. Lewontin. 1960. *Quantitative Zoology*. Harcourt, Brace, New York. 440 pp.

Singer, C. 1959. *A History of Biology*. 3rd ed. Abelard-Schuman, London. 579 pp.

Smirnov, E. 1925. The theory of type and the natural system. *Z. Indukt. Abstamm. Vererbungsl.*, 37:28–66.

Smirnov, E. 1927. Mathematische Studien

über individuelle und Kongregationen-variabilität. *Verh. 5. Intern. Kong. Vererbungswiss.*, **2**:1373–1392.

Smirnov, E. S. 1960. Taxonomic analysis of a genus. [In Russian, English summary.] *Zhurnal Obshenye Biologii*, **21**:89–103.

Sneath, P. H. A. 1957a. Some thoughts on bacterial classification. *J. Gen. Microbiol.*, **17**:184–200.

Sneath, P. H. A. 1957b. The application of computers to taxonomy. *J. Gen. Microbiol.*, **17**:201–226.

Sneath, P. H. A. 1958. Some aspects of Adansonian classification and of the taxonomic theory of correlated features. *Ann. Microbiol. Enzimol.* **8**:261–268.

Sneath, P. H. A. 1960. A study of the bacterial genus *Chromobacterium*. *Iowa State Coll. J. Sci.*, **34**:243–500.

Sneath, P. H. A. 1961. Recent developments in theoretical and quantitative taxonomy. *Systematic Zool.*, **10**:118–139.

Sneath, P. H. A. 1962. The construction of taxonomic groups. In G. C. Ainsworth and P. H. A. Sneath (eds.), *Microbial Classification*, 12th Symposium of the Society for General Microbiology, pp. 289–332. Cambridge University Press, Cambridge. 483 pp.

Sneath, P. H. A. 1964. Comparative biochemical genetics in bacterial taxonomy. In C. A. Leone (ed.), *Taxonomic Biochemistry and Serology*, pp. 565–583. Ronald Press, New York. 728 pp.

Sneath, P. H. A. and F. E. Buckland. 1959. The serology and pathogenicity of the genus *Chromobacterium*. *J. Gen. Microbiol.*, **20**:414–425.

Sneath, P. H. A. and S. T. Cowan. 1958. An electro-taxonomic survey of bacteria. *J. Gen. Microbiol.*, **19**:551–565.

Sneath, P. H. A. and R. R. Sokal. 1962. Numerical taxonomy. *Nature*, **193**:855–860.

Sokal, R. R. 1952. Variation in a local population of *Pemphigus. Evolution*, **6**:296–315.

Sokal, R. R. 1958. Quantification of systematic relationships and of phylogenetic trends. *Proc. Xth Intern. Cong. Entomol.*, **1**:409–415.

Sokal, R. R. 1959. Comments on quantitative systematics. *Evolution*, **13**:420–423.

Sokal, R. R. 1960. Die Grundlagen der numerischen Taxonomie. *Verhandl. XI Internat. Kong. Entomol.*, **1**:7–12.

Sokal, R. R. 1961. Distance as a measure of taxonomic similarity. *Systematic Zool.*, **10**:70–79.

Sokal, R. R. 1962a. Variation and covariation of characters of alate *Pemphigus populi-transversus* in eastern North America. *Evolution*, **16**:227–245.

Sokal, R. R. 1962b. Typology and empiricism in taxonomy. *J. Theor. Biol.*, **3**:230–267.

Sokal, R. R. 1964. The future systematics. In C. A. Leone (ed.), *Taxonomic Biochemistry and Serology*, pp. 33–48. Ronald Press, New York. 728 pp.

Sokal, R. R. and P. E. Hunter. 1955. A morphometric analysis of DDT-resistant and non-resistant house fly strains. *Ann. Entomol. Soc. Am.*, **48**:499–507.

Sokal, R. R. and C. D. Michener. 1958. A statistical method for evaluating systematic relationships. *Univ. Kansas Sci. Bull.*, **38**:1409–1438.

Sokal, R. R. and R. C. Rinkel. 1963. Geographic variation of alate *Pemphigus populi-transversus* in eastern North America. *Univ. Kansas Sci. Bull.* (in press).

Sokal, R. R. and F. J. Rohlf. 1962. The comparison of dendrograms by objective methods. *Taxon*, **11**:33–40.

Sokal, R. R. and P. A. Thomas. 1963. Geographic variation of *Pemphigus populi-transversus* in Eastern North America: Stem mothers and new data on alates. *Univ. Kansas Sci. Bull.* (in press).

Sonneborn, T. M. 1957. Breeding systems,

reproductive methods, and species problems in protozoa. In E. Mayr (ed.), *The Species Problem*, pp. 155–324. Am. Assn. Adv. Sci. Publ. No. 50. 395 pp.

Sørensen, T. 1948. A method of establishing groups of equal amplitude in plant sociology based on similarity of species content and its application to analyses of the vegetation on Danish commons. *Biol. Skr.*, **5** (4):1–34.

Soria, V. J. and C. B. Heiser, Jr. 1961. A statistical study of relationships of certain species of the *Solanum nigrum* complex. *Econ. Botany*, **15**:245–255.

Spearman, C. 1913. Correlations of sums and differences. *Brit. J. Psychol.*, **5**:417–426.

Spiegel, M. 1960. Protein changes in development. *Biol. Bull.*, **118**:451–462.

Sporne, K. R. 1948. Correlation and classification in dicotyledons. *Proc. Linn. Soc. Lond.*, 160th session:40–47.

Sporne, K. R. 1956. The phylogenetic classification of the angiosperms. *Biol. Rev.*, **31**:1–29.

Stallings, D. B. and J. R. Turner. 1957. A review of the Megathymidae of Mexico, with a synopsis of the classification of the family. *Lepidopterists' News*, **11**:113–137.

Stearn, W. T. 1956. Keys, botanical, and how to use them. In P. M. Synge (ed.), *Supplement to the Dictionary of Gardening, a Practical and Scientific Encyclopaedia of Horticulture*, pp. 251–253. Clarendon Press, Oxford. 334 pp.

Stearn, W. T. 1961. Botanical gardens and botanical literature in the eighteenth century. In *Catalogue of Botanical Books in the Collection of R. M. M. Hunt*, vol. 2, pp. xli–cxl. Hunt Foundation, Pittsburgh.

Stearns, S. D. 1960. A method for the design of pattern recognition logic. *Inst. Radio Eng. Trans. Electr. Comp.*, March (1960):48–53.

Stebbins, G. L., Jr. 1950. *Variation and Evolution in Plants*. Columbia University Press, New York. 643 pp.

Steel, R. G. D. and J. H. Torrie. 1960. *Principles and Procedures of Statistics*. McGraw-Hill, New York. 481 pp.

Stephenson, W. 1936. The inverted factor technique. *Brit. J. Psychol.*, **26**:344–361.

Stevenson, H. J. R. and O. E. A. Bolduan. 1952. Infrared spectrophotometry as a means for identification of bacteria. *Science*, **116**:111–113.

Stresemann, E. 1959. The status of avian systematics and its unsolved problems. *Auk*, **76**:269–280.

Stroud, C. P. 1953. An application of factor analysis to the systematics of *Kalotermes*. *Systematic Zool.*, **2**:76–92.

Sturtevant, A. H. 1939. On the subdivision of the genus *Drosophila*. *Proc. Nat. Acad. Sci. U.S.A.*, **25**:137–141.

Sturtevant, A. H. 1942. The classification of the genus *Drosophila*, with descriptions of nine new species. *Univ. Texas Publ.* **4213**. 51 pp.

Sueoka, N. 1961. Variation and heterogeneity of base composition of deoxyribonucleic acids: a compilation of old and new data. *J. Molec. Biol.*, **3**:31–40.

Swinnerton, H. H. 1932. Unit characters in fossils. *Biol. Rev.*, **7**:321–335.

Talbot, J. M. and P. H. A. Sneath. 1960. A taxonomic study of *Pasteurella septica*, especially of strains isolated from human sources. *J. Gen. Microbiol.*, **22**:303–311.

Telfer, W. H. and C. M. Williams. 1953. Immunological studies of insect metamorphosis. I. Qualitative and quantitative description of the blood antigens of the *Cecropia* silkworm. *J. Gen. Physiol.*, **36**:389–413.

Thienemann, A. 1924. Über die Chironomidengattung *Lundströmia* nebst einer Bestimmungstabelle für die Larven und Puppen der Sectio *Tanytarsus genuinus*. *Zool. Anz.*, **58**:331–345.

Thienemann, A. 1936. Die Orthocladiinen-Gattungen *Eucricotopus, Trichocladius, Rheorthocladius. Festschr. 60. Geburtst. E. Strand.*, **1**:531–553.

Thienemann, A. and F. Krüger. 1937. "*Orthocladius*" *abiskoensis* Edwards und *rubicundus* (Mg.), zwei "Puppen-Spezies" der Chironomiden. *Zool. Anz.*, **117**:257–267.

Thompson, D. W. 1917. *Growth and Form.* Cambridge University Press, Cambridge. 793 pp.

Thompson, H. R. 1956. Distribution of distance to $n$th neighbour in a population of randomly distributed individuals. *Ecology*, **37**:391–394.

Thompson, J. F., S. I. Honda, G. E. Hunt, R. M. Krupka, C. J. Morris, L. E. Powell, O. O. Silberstein, G. H. N. Towers, and R. M. Zacharius. 1959. Partition chromatography and its use in the plant sciences. *Botan. Rev.*, **25**:1–263.

Thompson, W. R. 1952. The philosophical foundations of systematics. *Canad. Entomol.*, **84**:1–16.

Thomson, G. H. 1951. *The Factorial Analysis of Human Ability.* Houghton Mifflin, Boston, and Riverside Press, Cambridge. 383 pp.

Thornley, M. J. 1960. Computation of similarities between strains of *Pseudomonas* and *Achromobacter* isolated from chicken meat. *J. Appl. Bact.*, **23**:395–397.

Thurstone, L. L. 1947. *Multiple-factor Analysis.* University of Chicago Press, Chicago. 535 pp.

Tolles, W. E., C. A. Steinberg, W. J. Carbery, and A. H. Freiman. 1961. Experimental techniques and results of a study using a computer as a diagnostic aid. *Trans. New York Acad. Sci., Ser. 2*, **23**:246–258.

Treloar, A. E. 1942. *Correlation Analysis.* Burgess, Minneapolis. 64 pp.

Trueman, A. E. 1930. Results of some recent statistical investigations of invertebrate fossils. *Biol. Rev.*, **5**:296–308.

Truman, D. B. 1959. *The Congressional Party: A Case Study.* Wiley, New York. 336 pp.

Tschulok, S. 1922. *Deszendenzlehre.* Gustav Fischer, Jena. 324 pp.

Turner, B. L. and R. Alston. 1959. Segregation and recombination of chemical constituents in a hybrid swarm of *Baptisia laevicaulis* × *B. viridis* and their taxonomic implications. *Am. J. Bot.*, **46**:678–686.

Turrill, W. B. 1950. Character combinations and distribution in the genus *Fritillaria* and allied genera. *Evolution*, **4**:1–6.

Unger, S. H. 1959. Pattern detection and recognition. *Proc. Inst. Radio Eng.*, **47**:1737–1752.

van Sande, M. and D. Karcher. 1960. Species differentiation of insects by hemolymph electrophoresis. *Science*, **131**:1103–1104.

Van Valen, L. 1960. Therapsids as mammals. *Evolution*, **14**:304–313.

Verheyen, R. 1960. Outline of procedure in basic avian systematics. *Gerfaut*, **1960**:223–230.

Vicq-d'Azyr, F. 1792. Quadrupèdes. Discours préliminaire. In *Encylopédie méthodique*, vol. 2, pp. i–cliv. Panckoucke, Paris. clxiv + 632 pp.

Vithayathil, A. J., F. Buck, M. Bier, and F. F. Nord. 1961. On the mechanism of enzyme action. LXXII. Comparative studies on trypsins of various origins. *Arch. Biochem.*, **92**:532–540.

Voss, E. G. 1952. The history of keys and phylogenetic trees in systematic biology. *J. Sci. Lab. Denison Univ.*, **43**:1–25.

Waddington, C. H. 1957. *The Strategy of the Genes.* Allen & Unwin, London. 262 pp.

Walters, S. M. 1954. The distribution

maps scheme. *Proc. Botan. Soc. Brit. Is.*, 1954(1):121–130.

Walters, S. M. 1961. The shaping of angiosperm taxonomy. *New Phytologist*, 60:74–84.

Wanke, A. 1953. Metoda badán częstósci występowania zespołow cach czyli metoda stochastycznej korelacji wielorakiej. *Przeglad antropologiczny*, 19:106–147.

Westoll, T. S. 1949. On the evolution of the Dipnoi. In G. L. Jepsen, E. Mayr, G. G. Simpson (eds.), *Genetics, Paleontology, and Evolution*, pp. 121–184. Princeton University Press, Princeton, N. J. 474 pp.

Whewell, W. 1840. *The Philosophy of the Inductive Sciences, Founded upon their History*. 2 vols. Parker, London and Deighton, Cambridge. (Cited material in vol. I, pp. 449–523.)

Whitehead, F. H. 1954. An example of taxonomic discrimination by biometric methods. *New Phytologist*, 53:496–510.

Whittaker, R. H. 1953. A consideration of climax theory: the climax as a population and pattern. *Ecol. Monogr.*, 23:41–78.

Whitten, E. H. T. 1961a. Quantitative areal modal analysis of granitic complexes. *Bull. Geol. Soc. Am.*, 72:1331–1360.

Whitten, E. H. T. 1961b. Systematic quantitative areal variation in five granitic massifs from India, Canada, and Great Britain. *J. Geol.*, 69:619–646.

Wierciński, A. 1962. The racial analysis of human populations in relation to their ethnogenesis. *Current Anthropol.*, 3:2, 9–46.

Wilhelmi, R. W. 1940. Serological reactions and species specificity of some helminths. *Biol. Bull.*, 79:64–90.

Williams, W. T. and J. M. Lambert. 1959. Multivariate methods in plant ecology. I. Association-analysis in plant communities. *J. Ecol.*, 47:83–101.

Williams, W. T. and J. M. Lambert. 1961a. Multivariate methods in plant ecology. III. Inverse association-analysis. *J. Ecol.*, 49:717–729.

Williams, W. T. and J. M. Lambert. 1961b. Nodal analysis of associated populations. *Nature*, 191:202.

Williams, W. T. and J. M. Lambert. 1961c. Multivariate methods in taxonomy. (Report of Systematics Association Meeting, papers by P. Slater, M. J. R. Healy, F. H. Whitehead, W. T. Williams, A. Pettet, J. G. Manners, R. C. Jancey, M. H. Williamson, P. H. A. Sneath, and J. M. Lambert). *Taxon*, 10:205–211.

Williams, W. T. and J. M. Lambert. 1962. Multivariate methods in plant ecology, IV. Nodal analysis. *J. Ecol.*, 50:775–802.

Williamson, M. H. 1961. An ecological survey of a Scottish herring fishery. IV. Changes in the plankton during the period 1949 to 1959. *Bull. Marine Ecol.*, 5 (48):207–229.

Willis, J. C. 1922. *Age and Area. A Study in Geographical Distribution and Origin of Species*. Cambridge University Press, Cambridge. 259 pp.

Willis, J. C. and G. U. Yule. 1922. Some statistics of evolution and geographical distribution in plants and animals, and their significance. *Nature*, 109:177–179.

Wilson, E. O. and W. L. Brown, Jr. 1953. The subspecies concept and its taxonomic application. *Systematic Zool.*, 2:97–111.

Woodger, J. H. 1937. *The Axiomatic Method in Biology*. Cambridge University Press, Cambridge. 174 pp.

Woodger, J. H. 1945. On biological transformations. In W. E. LeGros Clark and P. B. Medawar (eds.), *Essays on Growth and Form Presented to D'Arcy Wentworth Thompson*, pp. 94–120. Clarendon Press, Oxford. 408 pp.

Woodger, J. H. 1951. Science without

properties. *Brit. J. Philos. Sci.*, **2**:193–216.

Woodger, J. H. 1952. From biology to mathematics. *Brit. J. Philos. Sci.*, **3**:1–21.

Wright, C. A. 1959. The application of paper chromatography to a taxonomic study in the molluscan genus *Lymnaea*. *J. Linn. Soc. Lond. Zool.*, **44**:222–237.

Wright, S. 1941. The "age and area" concept extended. *Ecology*, **22**:345–347.

Yule, G. U. 1924. A mathematical theory of evolution, based on the conclusions of Dr. J. C. Willis, F. R. S. *Philos. Trans. Roy. Soc. Lond. Ser. B*, **213**:21–87.

Yule, G. U. and M. G. Kendall. 1950. *An Introduction to the Theory of Statistics*. 14th ed. Hafner, New York. 701 pp.

Zangerl, R. 1948. The methods of comparative anatomy and its contribution to the study of evolution. *Evolution*, **2**:351–374.

Zarapkin, S. R. 1934. Zur Phänoanalyse von geographischen Rassen und Arten. *Arch. Naturgesch. N.F.*, **3**:161–186.

Zarapkin, S. R. 1939. Das Divergenzprinzip in der Bestimmung kleiner systematischer Kategorien. *Verhandl. VII. Intern. Kong. Entomol.*, **1**:494–518.

Zarapkin, S. R. 1943. Die Hand des Menschen und der Menschenaffen. *Z. Menschl. Vererb. Konstitutionsl.*, **27**:390–414.

Zubin, T. 1938. A technique for measuring like-mindedness. *J. Abnorm. Soc. Psychol.*, **33**:508–516.

# AUTHOR INDEX

# SUBJECT INDEX

*Boldface numbers indicate definitions, descriptions, or important sections; italic numbers indicate Figures.*

*a* (constant in allometry formula), 80
$a_{jk}$ (number of characters applicable to two OTU's), 165
Aberrant organisms: occurrence of, 68, 247; recognition of, 61, 160; systematic position of, 13, 188, 259
Acanthaceae, 23
Actinomycetes, Actinomycetales, 170, 260, 261, 263
Adansonian classification: axioms of, 50; in bacteriology, 39; equal weighting in, 51, 267
Adaptive characters, 35
Additional data, incorporation of, **210–215**
Additive coding, 76
Adult and larval stages (*see also* Congruence), 87–90, 166
*Aedes:* congruence in, 90; effect of standardizing characters, 142; numerical taxonomy of, 166, 259; serology of species, 285; undescribed characters from, 269
*Aeromonas*, 261
Affinitätsrechnung, 38
Affinity (*see also* Similarity, Resemblance): in Adansonian classification, 21, 50; Adanson's views on, 17; based on few characters, 22; cladistic, 27, **220;** in defining convergence and parallelism, 106–109; different kinds of distribution of, 171, *172;* early methods for computing, 38; effect of evolution theory on, 20; estimation of, 50, 123 *et seq.;* incorporating new data, 211; patristic, 28, **220;** phenetic or static, 3, 55, 123; relation to "family resemblance," 14; relation to phylogenetic relationship, **22** *et seq.;* relation to size and shape factors, 152; serological, 40; use in grouping OTU's, 169; used interchangeably with "similarity" and "resemblance," 3, 123
Affinity index of Brisbane and Rovira, 133
Age and area hypothesis, 232

Age of organisms, 79, 247
Albinos, 8, 68
Albumens, 239
Algae, 23
ALGOL, 317
Allergic reactions, 45
Allometry: discussion, **79;** formulas, 80, 238; growth gradients, 241; need in paleontology, 247
Allopolyploidy, 31, 99, 224
All-or-none characters, *see* Two-state characters
Alpines, 19
*Ambystoma mexicanum*, 81
Amino-acid sequence, 41, 64, 73
Ammonites, 108
Amphibian larvae, 81
*Amphiuma*, 64
Analogy (*see also* Homology), 22, 71
Analytic methods of rotation to simple structure, 195
Ancestors: inclusion in phenetic classification, **232;** most probable, criteria for, 56, 57; proteins of, 239
Ancestral characters (*see also* Primitive organisms, Primitive characters): of common ancestor, 160, *225*, 227; estimates from living forms, **221–225**
Ancestry, relationship by, *see* Phylogenetic relationship
*Anemia*, 289
Angles, correlations between taxa as, 203
Annelid worms, 23, 244
*Anthocopa, 199*
Anthropoids, 161
Anthropology: cultural, review of methods, 285, 286; indices used in, 146; physical, 282; variation in characters, 157
Antibiotics, 170, 260, 263
Antibodies, 40
Anti-evolutionists, 56

345

**Bristol**
Polytechnic    ASHLEY DOWN

Author:    ATKINS

Title:    Highway materials ...

UWE BRISTOL
WITHDRAWN
LIBRARY SERVICES

This book should be returned by the last
date stamped below. The period of loan
may be extended if no other reader wishes
to use the book.

| | | | |
|---|---|---|---|
| 14. DEC. 1983 | | R, 11. MAR. 199 | 4. NOV 1996 |
| | 20. OCT. 1986 | | |
| 24. MAY 1984 | -5. NOV. 1987 | AD-6. MAY 1992 | 16. OCT 1998 |
| 29. JUN. 1984 | | | 12. OCT 199 |
| 17. OCT. 1984 | 26. NOV. 1987 | CL-1 DEC 1992 | |
| | 17. DEC. 1987 | | |
| -7. JAN. 1985 | | | |
| | 10. MAR. 1988 | CL-3 FEB. 1993 | 24. MAR 2000 |
| 20. FEB. 1985 | | | |
| 29. MAY 1985 | 25. APR. 1988 | 11. MAR. 1994 | 23. JUN 2000 |
| -9. OCT. 1985 | 22. JUN. 1988 | CL 15. DEC. 1994 | 07. OCT 2002 |
| 26. NOV. 1985 | I.L.L. | | |
| | d.6. 3.10. 88 | CL-1. MAR 1995 | 23. FEB. 2004 |
| 27. JAN. 1986 | renewed 3/11 | | 4. JAN 2009 |
| -5. JUN. 1986 | AD-4. MAR 199 | 22. MAR 1995 | |
| | | 30. JAN 1996 | |

JCA 5/71    7229